When water chokes you, what are you to drink to wash it down?

Aristotle

How many times it
thundered before
Franklin took the
hint! How many apples
fell on Newton's head
before he took the
hint! Nature is always
hinting at us. It hints
over and over again.
And suddenly we
take the hint.

Robert Frost

An Introduction to
Environmental Sciences

An Introduction to Environmental Sciences

JOSEPH M. MORAN

MICHAEL D. MORGAN

JAMES H. WIERSMA

UNIVERSITY OF WISCONSIN, GREEN BAY

LITTLE, BROWN AND COMPANY   BOSTON

LIBRARY OF CONGRESS CATALOG CARD NO. 72-9414

FIRST PRINTING

Published simultaneously in Canada by Little, Brown & Company (Canada) Limited

PRINTED IN THE UNITED STATES OF AMERICA

Cover photographs:
Front cover — *David W. Corson from A. Devaney, N.Y.* Back cover, top to bottom — *NASA; Environmental Protection Agency; Richard F. Conrat, Photofind, S.F.; Hugh Rogers from Monkmeyer.*

Chapter opening photographs:
Facing page 1 — *NASA.* Page 6 — top left: *USDA from Monkmeyer;* top right: *British Columbia Forest Service;* center left: *U.S. Department of the Interior;* center right: *USDA-Soil Conservation Service;* bottom: *Leonard Rue from Monkmeyer.* Page 28 — top: *Sam Falk from Monkmeyer;* center left: *Monkmeyer;* center right: *Wilford L. Miller from National Audubon Society;* bottom: *Copyright © Gordon S. Smith.* Page 48 — top: *Copyright © Gordon S. Smith;* center left: *Ed Cooper, Photofind, S.F.;* center right: *NOAA;* bottom: *USDA-Soil Conservation Service.* Page 70 — top: *David Stanley from Monkmeyer;* center left: *USDA-Soil Conservation Service;* center right: *U.S. Coast Guard photograph;* bottom: *Copyright © M. P. Kahl from Black Star.* Page 92 — *Environmental Protection Agency.* Page 126 — *NOAA.* Page 146 — *Air Pollution Control District, County of Los Angeles.* Page 172 — *U.S. Department of the Interior, National Park Service photograph.* Page 196 — Milwaukee Journal *(photograph by Clarence Schmidt).* Page 232 — *Union Pacific Railroad photograph.* Page 256 — top: *Richard F. Conrat, Photofind, S.F.;* bottom: *U.S. Department of the Interior, National Park Service photograph.* Page 298 — top: *Dominique Roger from UNESCO;* bottom: *USDA-Soil Conservation Service.* Page 324 — top: *Godsey from Monkmeyer;* bottom: *New England Electric.* Page 344 — *Wide World Photos.* Page 356 — *Union Pacific Railroad photograph; Grant Heilman, Littitz, Pa.; Air Pollution Control District, County of Los Angeles.*
The photograph on page 363 is Copyright © Gordon S. Smith.

This book is printed on recycled paper.

To our wives and children:

Janet

Gloria and Michelle

Nancy, Dale, and David

Preface

One consequence of the current awareness of the problems of pollution and population has been the student demand for environmentally oriented courses. Such courses are now recognized as an important part of a college curriculum. As a result many books have appeared that contain topical environmental subjects. Many of these, however, are collections of articles that do not provide a sufficient scientific foundation for a meaningful understanding of the functioning of the environment. These anthologies and recent texts that utilize a "systematic" approach have also failed to integrate successfully the contributions of the sciences. Students are thus deprived of a sound understanding of the causes, ramifications, and alternatives to environmental problems. The purpose of this book is to provide an integrated understanding.

Our integrated approach provides a framework for an interdisciplinary analysis of environmental problems. We have attempted to present a balance of contributions from the several physical and biological disciplines. The text presents fundamental principles to the degree necessary for a basic understanding of environmental problems. Illustrative examples of problems are drawn from around the globe, but the fundamentals presented permit the student to apply his understanding to his local environment.

The ecosystem is first examined as a whole and then subdivided into its constituent parts. Finally the parts are reunited in a "wholistic" view. The interrelations of the processes and components within ecosystems demonstrate our absolute dependence upon the environment, which allows us to evaluate our capabilities and limitations in attaining a quality environment.

We are especially indebted to Professor John F. Reed for his initial and continuous encouragement. We are grateful to our other colleagues at the University of Wisconsin, Green Bay — especially to Professors

J. Herbert Huddleston, Jon R. Maki, Charles R. Rhyner, Ronald H. Starkey, and Paul E. Sager — for their valuable contributions. To the students of Environmental Sciences 102, we are thankful for critiques of the course and the preliminary edition. We extend a special thanks to Mary Castonia for her enthusiastic, prompt, and accurate typing of the manuscript's numerous drafts. We also appreciate the helpful reviews of the preliminary edition by Professors John R. Holum, Thomas S. Helget, Andrew C. Kowalik, Wayne M. Wendland, and Jon Rosenthal, and by our students, John Pischner and Patrick Canney.

To Jane Aaron, Barbara Levitt, and Ann Lightbown of Little, Brown and Company, we are grateful for their tireless efforts in translating ideas into reality. And to Thomas Sears, our editor, many thanks for his faith in us, his continual encouragement, and his constant zing that kept our enthusiasm high.

Finally, we are grateful to the University of Wisconsin, Green Bay, for providing the environment in which a book such as this is possible.

J.M.M.
M.D.M.
J.H.W.

Contents

X CONTENTS

An Introduction to
Environmental Sciences

Prologue

The Earth is one of nine known planets that together with a multitude of smaller bodies (including asteroids, comets, moons, and meteors) orbit the sun — one of some 100 billion stars that make up the Milky Way Galaxy. At least 10 billion other galaxies similar to our own are within range of sophisticated telescopes.

Photographs taken from the moon during the manned Apollo VIII expedition dramatically illustrate the insignificance of the Earth in relation to the vast realm of space. Even within our solar system, magnitudes of distances are staggering when compared to those we encounter in everyday experience (Figure P.1). For example, our nearest neighbor, Venus, is 25 million miles (40 million kilometers) away at its closest. Traveling at current spaceship speed, it would take more than four months to reach Venus.

Even if man finally reaches Venus, however, he will find a surface temperature of nearly 750°F (400°C), an atmosphere of approximately 94 percent carbon dioxide, and very little water and oxygen. To survive would require a very elaborate life support system involving importation of Earth resources. The other planets of our solar system are farther away and have even less hospitable environments for human life.

It may be that planets in other star systems are capable of supporting human life, but journeys to such planets would probably take hundreds of years — assuming that a wholly self-sufficient spaceship could be built for the voyage.

The inescapable conclusion, verified by recent space ventures, is that 99.99 percent or more of us are bound to the Earth. It is our only home; we were born here and we will die here.

Just as the Earth is finite, so also are its food, land, water, and air. The Earth is like the spaceship journeying to Venus with a limited

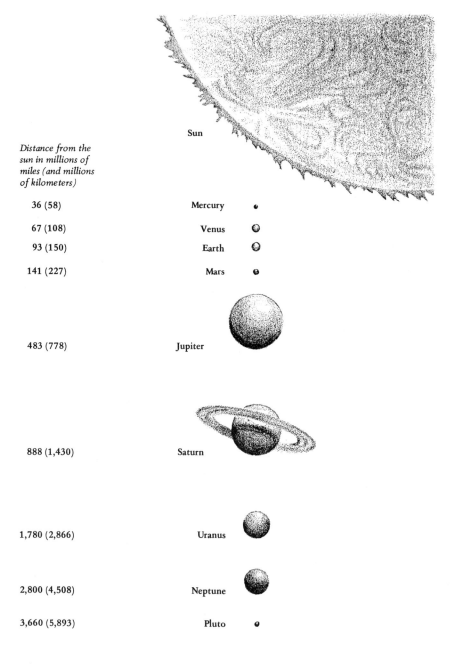

Distance from the sun in millions of miles (and millions of kilometers)

Sun

36 (58)	Mercury
67 (108)	Venus
93 (150)	Earth
141 (227)	Mars
483 (778)	Jupiter
888 (1,430)	Saturn
1,780 (2,866)	Uranus
2,800 (4,508)	Neptune
3,660 (5,893)	Pluto

Figure P.1
Relative sizes of the planets in the solar system and their distances from the sun.

supply of life-supporting resources. In the interest of our own survival and that of our offspring, we must exercise a wise stewardship over its resources.

Events of recent years have made us increasingly aware of this very fundamental obligation and of how it is ignored. The terms "environment" and "ecology" are now commonplace in television, radio, and newspaper reports. Daily we are told that the environment is being polluted with pesticides, phosphates, mercury, lead, excess heat, radioactive materials, sulfur dioxide, and carbon monoxide. In the Southeast and the West, huge areas are being destroyed by strip mining (Figure P.2) to provide coal for power plants that degrade the air (Figure P.3). The proposed Alaskan pipeline may disrupt the migration patterns and habitats of tundra animals. In portions of Vietnam, vegetation has been devastated by herbicides (Figure P.4) and the landscape pockmarked by bomb craters. Cities burn their solid wastes and foul the

Figure P.2
Strip-mining operations, such as this one for coal in Belmont County, Ohio, ravage thousands of acres yearly. *(Rotkin, Photography for Industry.)*

Figure P.3
Belching incinerator smoke is an important contributor to urban air pollution. *(Rotkin, Photography for Industry.)*

Figure P.4
Rubber trees in Cambodia have been defoliated by aerial spraying of herbicides in the Vietnam war. According to the United States Department of State, the chemicals were blown over the border from South Vietnam. *(Courtesy of* Environment *magazine.)*

air or dump them in landfill sites and imperil wildlife (Figure P.5). Seminatural and wilderness areas are lost to urban and suburban expansion. Power plants endanger aquatic life with discharges of excess heat. Water pollution is accelerating the aging process of the Great Lakes (Figure P.6). Our ever-increasing population threatens to over-

Figure P.5
Tons of solid waste, much of it potentially reusable, is abandoned daily in this garbage dump in New Jersey. *(Hugh Rogers from Monkmeyer.)*

Figure P.6
Summer bathers find their favorite swimming spots increasingly spoiled by water pollution. This beach is on the southern end of Lake Michigan. *(Environmental Protection Agency.)*

whelm the capacity of the planet to adequately provide for us. The problems of the environment are as diverse and multifaceted as its components.

Since most of us acknowledge the hazards of present conditions, the chief question to be answered is that of priority. How does the gravity of environmental pollution rank with that of war, racial unrest, poverty, crime, or drugs? In light of our total dependence upon the environment, safeguarding it ought to be given major consideration. All our food ultimately comes from other organisms; if they die, we die, either from the pollutants that killed them or from starvation. In addition, we require clean air and water. We breathe to obtain oxygen, but we also inhale whatever else is present in the air. Polluted air now appears to be a central factor in the sharply rising incidence of lung cancer and emphysema.

A sound environment is also essential to our economic well-being. Not only is the farmer dependent on the land, but so too are the wholesaler, grocery store owner, and all their employees. Workers in the paper industry, whether in the mill or in the office, are just as reliant upon the forest as the lumberjack is. Add to this chain the printer, the publisher, the news agent, and the banker who finances their businesses and lends them money to build homes, and it becomes clear how thoroughly we are indebted to a viable environment for our livelihoods. Degradation of the environment can lead only to the degradation of our economic base.

Polluting the environment is costly in many ways. Air pollution in the United States is estimated to cause $16 billion annual damage to buildings, clothing, and crops. Then there is the human toll. As rising numbers of people become ill from pollution-aggravated diseases, health insurance rates increase. Workers subjected to excessive noise levels are less efficient and hence less productive; the result is a higher cost per product that is passed on to the consumer. And the newly expanding service industries, tourism for example, are equally dependent upon a robust environment. If a resort area becomes overcrowded, unsightly, or polluted, people look elsewhere for a place to spend their vacation. These are but a few of the many economic ties that man has with the environment.

The above examples illustrate the significance of the environment for us and some of the consequences of our damaging the environment. Although the concern of the general public for the environment will most likely decline as some new cause becomes popular, the importance of the problems for man will always remain. And these are complex, long-term problems that will not be remedied quickly.

Each of us can contribute to solutions. Some will work directly in the environmental sciences, but all of us are in a position to help make the decisions that will determine the future. As voters, we can make choices about sewage treatment plants, recycling centers, and local air and water quality standards. As workers, we can influence the corporate structure regarding the environmental effects of its activities. As members of civic or service groups, we can devise and promote solutions to neighborhood and local problems. To make the proper choices, we need a basic but integrated understanding of the environment that draws on contributions from many scientific disciplines. This is the basic purpose of this book.

chapter

1

The Structure and Function of Ecosystems

Environmental problems can be more readily understood in terms of the unit comprising what is called the *ecosystem*. Accordingly, the ecosystem will be a central focus for organizing our knowledge of the environment.

STRUCTURE

Components

An ecosystem can be defined as the basic functional unit of nature, including both *biotic* (living) and *abiotic* (nonliving) constituents. A walk in the countryside puts us in contact with many of the abiotic and biotic members of the environment. Surrounded by air, we climb over rocks and slosh through streams. Air, rock, and water are the basic components of the abiotic environment.

Biotic components are classified according to the function of the particular organism. There are three groups: producers, consumers, and decomposers. The *producers* — the green plants such as grasses and trees — are so called because they are capable of producing their own food from materials of the abiotic environment. *Consumers* are organisms that are incapable of producing their own food and that must use (consume) other organisms for their food; all animals fall into this category. There are three types of consumers: *herbivores*, which eat plants (producers); *carnivores*, which eat animals — either herbivores or other carnivores; and *omnivores*, which are both herbivorous and carnivorous. A pheasant feeding on corn is a herbivore. A fox making a meal of the pheasant is a carnivore. Man, who eats both corn and pheasant, is an omnivore. *Decomposers*, also called microconsumers, include bacteria, fungi, and some of the small invertebrates (animals without backbones). Like consumers, these organisms cannot produce their own food; but unlike consumers, they obtain their food energy by breaking down dead plants and animals to their basic components, thereby releasing these substances back into the abiotic portions of the environment.

Types of Ecosystems

Any area that contains the three abiotic and the three biotic components is said to be an ecosystem. Classification of ecosystems may be based on the type of biotic components present. There are, for example, forest ecosystems, grassland ecosystems, tundra ecosystems, or desert ecosystems (see Figures 1.1–1.5). Sometimes ecosystems are classified according to abiotic components — the freshwater or saltwater (marine) ecosystem, for example.

Figure 1.1
A deciduous forest ecosystem in New York State. *(USDA from Monkmeyer.)*

Figure 1.2

Figure 1.3

Figure 1.2
A coniferous forest ecosystem in British Columbia, Canada. *(British Columbia Forest Service.)*

Figure 1.3
A grassland ecosystem in Adams County, Washington. *(USDA–Soil Conservation Service.)*

Figure 1.4
A desert ecosystem in the American Southwest. *(U.S. Department of the Interior.)*

Figure 1.5
A North American tundra ecosystem. *(Leonard Rue from Monkmeyer.)*

Figure 1.4

Figure 1.5

It should not be thought that the ecosystem concept applies only to natural areas. A cornfield is also an ecosystem. The corn is the major producer organism, but weeds likely to be present are also producers. Herbivorous insects eat portions of the corn plants, and birds and carnivorous insects feed upon corn-eating insects. And bacteria and other microconsumers exist within the soil. Even a city can be considered an ecosystem, though a highly modified one. Disregarding pigeons and rats, man is the major consumer in urban areas. There are few food plants growing in the city, and the decomposer component is also small. Food is brought into the urban ecosystem, and wastes (garbage) are usually taken out for action by decomposers.

Concept of Spheres

Instead of subdividing the planet into ecosystems, we can view the Earth as one large ecosystem composed of four spheres: The air comprises the *atmosphere*; soil and rocks, the *lithosphere*; water, the *hydrosphere*; and living organisms, the *biosphere*. Each sphere is a reservoir for, or is located within, another sphere. For example, fish (members of the biosphere) live in the water (hydrosphere), yet their bodies also contain a high percentage of water. Thus, the biosphere serves as a reservoir of the hydrosphere. Similarly, the soil (lithosphere) contains many pore spaces; some contain air (reservoir of atmosphere), others contain water (reservoir of hydrosphere). In addition, many types of organisms (bacteria, fungi, earthworms, etc.) live entirely in the soil, where plant roots are also present (reservoir of biosphere). Thus, it can be seen that the four spheres are so interconnected that the study of one requires the study of all.

Any ecosystem contains portions of the four spheres (Figure 1.6). For example, the air component of an ecosystem consists of that portion of the atmosphere above it. The biotic component is made up of plants and animals, and animals may migrate from one ecosystem to another. Air and water, being fluids, can also move and transport materials between ecosystems. It is important to realize that except when we consider the entire planet as a single ecosystem, we view each ecosystem as exchanging with and thus influencing other ecosystems.

Our environmental analysis involves a consideration of the properties of each of the spheres and its interrelations. Although the planet Earth can be regarded as one unit, we study many of the problems at the ecosystem level.

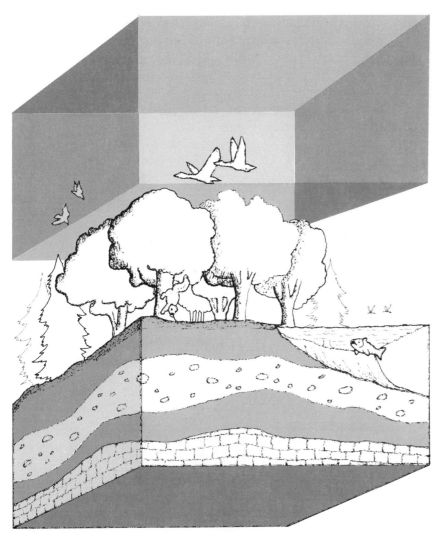

Figure 1.6
Schematic representation of the four spheres of an ecosystem. *(Illustration courtesy of Beckman Instruments, Inc.)*

A basic function of ecosystems is that of energy movement. Energy moves through biotic portions of ecosystems in characteristic patterns called *food chains*. These chains are important because they represent man's only source of food energy.

ENERGY
MOVEMENT

Role of Producers

The sun is the ultimate source of more than 99 percent of the energy available at the Earth's surface. Some of this energy is transformed by green plants into chemical energy (food energy) by the process of *photosynthesis*. The plants in a clover field, for example, use light energy to combine low-energy substances from the environment (carbon dioxide from the atmosphere and water from the soil) to produce food of high energy content (Figure 1.7).

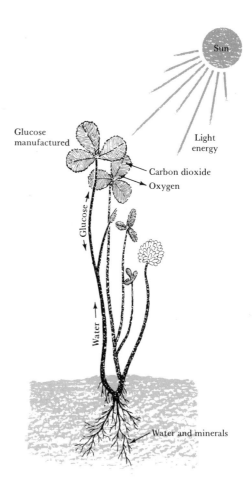

Figure 1.7
The sources of raw materials and the products of photosynthesis are shown in this drawing of a clover plant. Sugars can be sent upward through the stem for growth or storage in seeds, or can be sent downward for storage or root growth.

Equation for photosynthesis:

$$6CO_2 + 6H_2O + \text{light energy} \rightarrow C_6H_{12}O_6 + 6O_2$$

| carbon dioxide | water | | sugar (high chemical energy) | oxygen |

The food produced by photosynthesis is a sugar known as glucose. The clover plant can change glucose (a carbohydrate) into other types of food, including proteins, fats, and other carbohydrates such as starch. These foods are a stable form of chemical energy; i.e., they don't spontaneously burn and lose their energy. From the equation it can be seen that the carbon (C) formerly present in the carbon dioxide is now part of the sugar. All biotic materials contain carbon and are called organic, and thus all foods (proteins, fats, and carbohydrates) are organic substances. The other product of photosynthesis is oxygen, which is usually released into the surroundings.

Some of the food produced by photosynthesis is used as an energy source to "run the machinery" of the clover "plant." The plant requires energy to grow, develop, and reproduce. Because foods are stable, they undergo a series of changes before the clover plant can use the energy. These changes are collectively known as *respiration*, which occurs continuously in all living organisms. By this process, oxygen from the atmosphere is combined with food. The result is the transfer of chemical energy from the sugar to a new substance called *adenosine triphosphate* (ATP). Adenosine triphosphate is an unstable form of chemical energy that cannot be stored but can be immediately used to build or repair cells, the basic structural units of all organisms.

Equation for respiration:

$$C_6H_{12}O_6 + 6O_2 \rightarrow 38ATP + 6CO_2 + 6H_2O + \text{heat energy}$$

| sugar (high chemical energy) | oxygen | (high chemical energy) | carbon dioxide | water |

Two other products of respiration are carbon dioxide and water, which may be released to the environment. Respiration is an inefficient process so not all the chemical energy present in the food is transferred to ATP. Some is transformed into heat energy, which is lost. Normally, the amount of energy fixed by photosynthesis exceeds that lost by respiration. The excess food is used for growth or is stored, usually in roots, seeds, or fruits; it is termed net production and represents the total energy available for consumption by plant eaters, or herbivores.

Role of Consumers

In a clover field, mice feed upon the leaves of the plants. Some of the consumed plant material is used as an energy source. As in plants, the stable food must go through the respiration process whereby chemical energy is continuously transferred to ATP and used to provide energy for movement, to build new cells, or to repair old ones. Respiration in mice is also inefficient and produces heat energy as a by-product. The mouse, a warm-blooded animal, uses some of this energy to maintain a constant body temperature but eventually loses some to its surroundings. The energy difference between what is consumed and what is lost in respiration results in bigger and/or more mice. This difference, as in plants, is termed net production.

Net production of mice (herbivores) represents the amount of energy that is available to the carnivores. In the clover field, there is also a weasel that feeds upon mice. Again, respiration occurs with some loss of heat energy, and the food not respired goes into the maintenance and production of weasels.

Significance of Food Chains

The above sequence is called a food chain or, more precisely, a grazing food chain (Figure 1.8). It is important to note that the energy movement through food chains is in one direction only. There is never energy movement from herbivores to producers. Each link is dependent upon the links immediately below it for energy. Although man can function as either a herbivore or a carnivore, the fact that he ultimately cannot obtain food energy directly from the sun makes him dependent upon plants for food energy. Human cells are capable only of transforming light energy into heat energy — a form of energy that cannot be used as fuel to run the machinery of an organism.

Not only can energy movement be considered a one-way street, but with respect to usable chemical energy it is also a downhill street. We have seen that at each link in the food chain, some usable chemical energy is converted to unusable heat energy that is eventually lost from the system. Within ecosystems, this necessitates a continual

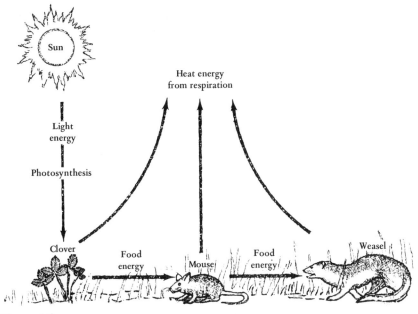

Figure 1.8
A food chain — one means of energy movement in an ecosystem.

input of energy if the ecosystem is not to collapse. An interesting application of this principle is the city, whose trees and lawns do not serve as a food source for man — the major consumer component of the urban ecosystem. Thus, to meet the food energy requirement of the urbanite and the suburbanite, food must be imported from other ecosystems, such as agricultural ecosystems. Our increasingly urbanized and surburbanized society demands a healthy rural ecosystem to maintain it. Food energy must be fixed somewhere, for a system deprived of an energy source for any extended time is doomed.

The second major function of ecosystems is the cycling of materials among the four spheres. These materials include carbon, oxygen, nitrogen, and water, among many other components of the environment. Cycles in the ecosystem are seldom simple, and the complex set of interacting subcycles forming the carbon cycle exemplifies the significance of cycles within ecosystems.

CYCLES OF MATERIALS

Atmosphere-
Biosphere
Subcycle of the
Carbon Cycle

A major subcycle of the carbon cycle is that of the interaction between atmosphere and biosphere (Figure 1.9). Having seen that carbon is present in the atmosphere in the form of carbon dioxide, it is clear that green plants (producers) remove carbon dioxide from the atmosphere and, by the process of photosynthesis, incorporate carbon into such food substances as sugars, fats, and proteins. In the process some carbon is tied up in the biosphere; a portion of the fixed carbon is transformed back to carbon dioxide as a product of respiration by producers and consumers. Carbon dioxide then moves from these organisms back into the atmosphere. The carbon that is tied up in dead

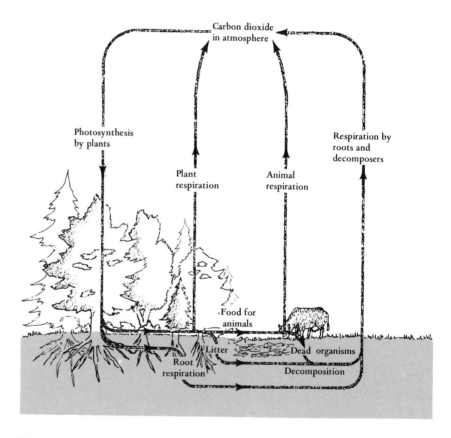

Figure 1.9
The biosphere-atmosphere subcycle of the carbon cycle. *(Redrawn with permission from Bert Bolin, "The Carbon Cycle," Scientific American [September 1970], p. 126. Copyright © 1970 by Scientific American, Inc. All rights reserved.)*

plants and animals is also eventually returned to the atmosphere by the respiration of decomposers (microconsumers). The subcycle tends to remain in equilibrium; i.e., about as much carbon is fixed by photosynthesis of the producers as is released by respiration of all the inhabitants of the biosphere.

During the Carboniferous Period, 280–345 million years ago (see Appendix I), large amounts of plant and animal material became buried before they could be broken down by decomposers (Figure 1.10). In subsequent eons of compression and heat, plant and animal remains were transformed into *fossil fuels* — coal, oil, natural gas. By

Figure 1.10
Carboniferous swamp forests, such as the one shown by this model, existed 280 to 345 million years ago. *(Field Museum of Natural History, Chicago.)*

burning these fuels to obtain energy, carbon dioxide is added to the atmosphere just as it is by respiration in living organisms. This sort of combustion differs little from the "burning" of food by organisms to obtain usable chemical energy: In both processes oxygen is combined with the energy source to produce carbon dioxide. The major difference is the temperature at which the two processes occur. Burning fossil fuels takes place at temperatures that are thousands of degrees higher than the body temperatures of living organisms. To compensate for the lower operating temperatures of all organisms, special proteins called *enzymes* are present that speed up the process of respiration. In fact, enzymes speed up all chemical changes (metabolic processes) within an organism. Without enzymes, organisms would cease to function.

Other Subcycles
of the Carbon Cycle

Another important subcycle is that between the atmosphere and hydrosphere (Figure 1.11). Large amounts of carbon dioxide are exchanged between the atmosphere and the upper layers of the ocean

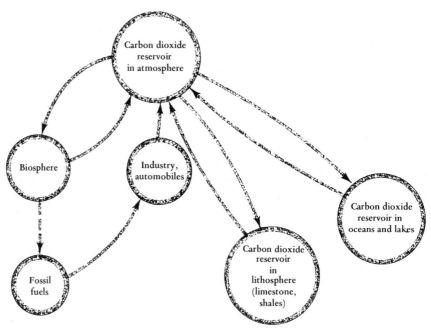

Figure 1.11
The three major subcycles of the carbon cycle.

waters by winds and waves. The exchange occurs in both directions through the surface of the water, about as much carbon dioxide moving from the surface water to the lower atmosphere as in the opposite direction. This interaction is important because an increase in atmospheric carbon dioxide tends to be balanced by an increased absorption of carbon dioxide by the oceans, which helps maintain equilibrium in the carbon dioxide content of the environment.

A third subcycle is the formation of limestones, dolomite, and carbonaceous shales (Figure 1.12). By several different rock-forming processes, carbon becomes incorporated into these components of the lithosphere. These may be subsequently broken down, releasing carbon dioxide to the atmosphere. Although they have little significance for us in the immediate future, processes of formation and degradation (cycling) of lithospheric components are important in balancing conditions over periods of hundreds of thousands of years.

Figure 1.12
The White Cliffs of Dover, England, are the result of the accumulation of carbonaceous shells of aquatic plants over a period of millions of years. *(British Tourist Authority.)*

Pollution: Change in Transfer Rates

Rates of transfer among reservoirs that have been established over the past several thousand years are now being disturbed by human activity. The developed nations' tremendous consumption of fossil fuels has greatly increased the transfer of carbon from the lithosphere into the atmosphere. Some of the increase has subsequently been transferred to the oceans, and some perhaps has been taken up by the biosphere. These two subcycles, however, have not been able to offset the input from man's activities. Approximately one-third of the carbon resulting from burning fossil fuels stays in the atmosphere. This has increased the carbon dioxide content of the atmosphere by about 10 percent during the last century (Figure 1.13). Scientists know too little at present to fully comprehend and assess the consequences of this increase. One thing we can be sure of: If man continues his accelerating consumption of fossil fuels, the carbon dioxide content of the atmosphere will continue to increase, perhaps another 25 percent by the year 2000, and it will increase despite compensating transfers of it into the oceans and organisms.

Most materials in the ecosystem are exchanged among the reservoirs comprising the four spheres by mechanisms analogous to those already discussed. There are, of course, some differences in the routing that depend upon the material involved. It should be pointed out that man's synthetic compounds such as pesticides, plastics, and radioactive wastes are also being exchanged among the four reservoirs — with what consequences we are yet to know fully.

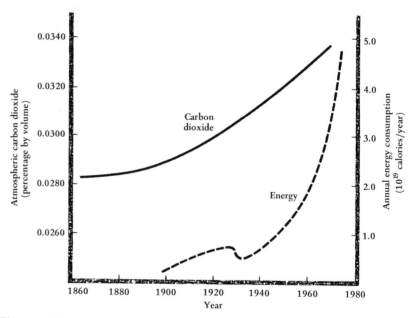

Figure 1.13
Atmospheric carbon dioxide levels and annual energy consumption. *(Carbon dioxide curve after Gilbert Plass, "Carbon Dioxide and Climate," Scientific American, 201 [July 1959], p. 43; data from G. S. Callendar. Energy consumption curve adapted and redrawn with permission of Holt, Rinehart and Winston, Inc., from John Harte and Robert H. Socolow, Patient Earth, p. 285. Copyright © 1971 by Holt, Rinehart and Winston, Inc.)*

The rate of transfer between reservoirs depends primarily upon the characteristics of the materials involved. For any particular material and set of reservoirs, there is usually a "normal" rate that may vary but within certain limits. We define any rate of transfer that departs from "normal" as *pollution*. For example, man is polluting the air by increasing the rate of transfer of carbon dioxide into the atmosphere. Through much of geological time, carbon dioxide has been in the atmosphere, but only now is it a pollutant because there is more of it present than normally was present in the recent past.

Increased rates of transfer do not always imply human activity. In 1815, the volcano Tambora in Indonesia spewed millions of tons of volcanic ash into the air, thus cooling the atmosphere. The following year became known as the "year without a summer" when New England experienced snows in June, light frost in July and August, and severe frost in September. The effects of sporadic nonhuman pollution are usually short-term, however, lasting a matter of days or perhaps a few years. The continual impact of human activity may well have effects of great duration. When transfer rates of material between reservoirs begin to depart from the normal, adjustments are made by the other components of the environment, but in the biosphere, organisms may not be able to adapt to the changing environment quickly enough to maintain the necessary equilibrium.

LIMITING FACTORS

Optima and Tolerance Limits

Almost all the problems associated with changes in transfer rates are products of readjustments made by members of the biosphere. The naturally following question as to why organisms are affected by pollution can be answered by considering a basic principle that governs the functioning of the biosphere, i.e., the principle of *limiting factors*. Most scientists would agree that an excessive discharge of phosphates is polluting our waterways because they increase the population of tiny, green aquatic plants called algae. This problem is better illustrated by the schematic representation of the principle of limiting factors in Figure 1.14. A minimum concentration of phosphates in the water is needed before the algae will grow. As the concentration of phosphates increases, larger algal populations can be supported. Eventually, a phosphate concentration is reached that is optimal for algal growth, and an increase beyond this becomes toxic to some members

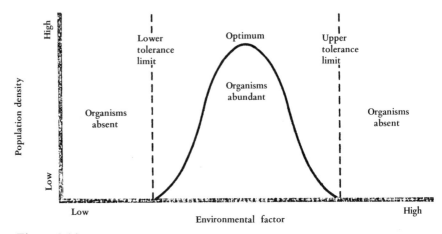

Figure 1.14
A schematic representation of the principle of limiting factors. A species has lower and upper limits of tolerance for an environmental factor. There is also a level of the factor that is optimal for the species.

of the algal population. Finally, a concentration is reached that will be lethal to all the algae. The three critical points on the curve are the lower tolerance limit, the optimum concentration, and the upper tolerance limit: This is termed a *limiting factor curve*.

Each plant and animal species has a characteristic limiting factor curve for each environmental factor, such as temperature, oxygen, food energy, nutrients, and resistance to disease. The tolerance limits and optimum for each factor are determined by the information contained within the *chromosomes* (genetic make-up) of individual organisms (Figure 1.15). The information is passed on from one generation to another by means of the sex cells (sperms and eggs).

Changes in Limiting Factor Curves: Mutations

A change in genetic information is called a *mutation*. Mutations are random events that sometimes result in an organism's becoming less adapted to the environment. This point can be better understood by comparing this sort of mutation with a random change in the gearwork of a Swiss watch. A watch contains a complex set of parts that are finely tuned to function together smoothly and accurately. An amateur handyman's attempts to adjust the watch's gearwork would likely result in its running worse. In fact, the watch may stop running altogether.

Figure 1.15
Photomicrograph of the 23 pairs of chromosomes in human cells. *(Courtesy of Carolina Biological Supply Company.)*

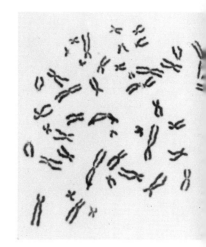

So it is with an organism. A product of long and complex evolution, every living organism is a finely tuned, intricately complex mechanism. The information contained within the chromosomes is the result of selection for the characteristics that make that organism best adapted to its environment. Obviously, a random change in its chromosomes could make it less adaptable, perhaps to the point of inducing extinction.

When mutations occur in the sex cells of an individual, there is a fair chance that the mutation will be passed on to the next generation. Some mutations, though, cause sterility, thereby precluding transmission to further generations.

Our concern with mutations in this text is that certain pollutants are known to or thought to cause mutations. The radioisotopes associated with the processes of nuclear fission and fusion, if present in sufficient amounts, are known to cause serious mutations. There are also indications that some of our pesticides may cause mutations, but the evidence is as yet inconclusive. And certain drugs, such as LSD, are thought to cause chromosome breakage — a type of mutation.

Even though the environment may be optimum for all factors except one, if that factor is essential and does not lie within the tolerance limits of the organism, the organism either dies, migrates, or modifies its environment. Winters in the northern United States can be severe, with low temperatures and little food for animals. Some wildlife, such as many species of birds, migrate south for the winter and thus unknowingly avoid an environment that is outside their tolerance limits. Primitive man also migrated with the seasons, but the advent of technology allowed his modern counterpart to modify greatly the immediate environment, for example by building houses and heating them and by wearing clothes.

If an organism cannot migrate or modify its environment to avoid stress conditions, then it will die. Many types of vegetation have been killed by exposure to excessive concentrations of air pollutants such as sulfur dioxide and ozone. There are many cases of fish kills resulting

Consequences of Limiting Factors

from pollutants. In fact, most pollution-related deaths are a consequence of pollutants' exceeding the tolerance limits of organisms.

Complicating
Aspects of Limiting
Factors

Although the concept of limiting factors appears simple, it has many complicating aspects. For one thing, it varies with the age of the individual. A small child requires four times more protein per unit of body weight than a mature adult. The tolerance limits for the young are also narrower. A diet deficient in protein may cause mental retardation in a child, whereas an adult would probably not suffer retardation because his brain is already fully developed. The extent of results is, naturally, a function of the severity and length of the diet deficiency.

Another complication is that of factor interaction. Good nutrition, for example, builds up resistance to disease so diet will affect the limiting factor curve for resistance.

A special type of factor interaction is *synergism*. The interaction of two factors is said to be synergistic if the total effect is greater than the sum of the two effects evaluated independently. In other words, zero plus zero does not always equal zero. This concept is illustrated by a simple experiment. If mice are exposed to a type of lung virus, their resistance keeps them healthy. If the mice are then exposed to smog, there are again no ill effects. If, however, the mice are exposed to the lung virus and the smog simultaneously, they will develop lung cancer. If the effects were simply additive, the mice would be expected to show no ill effects.

The concept of limiting factors would be simple enough to deal with if we could isolate one species and one factor at a time. But an ecosystem is composed of hundreds of species, each with its own set of interacting curves that are in turn affected both by abiotic factors and by other species as well. In addition, the abiotic components (temperature, precipitation, etc.) are constantly changing on daily and seasonal bases.

We can now begin to appreciate why it is so difficult to predict changes in the biosphere resulting from man's manipulation of the environment; few simple cause-and-effect relations can be proven. Unfortunately, many of us use the lack of absolute proof as justification for doing nothing. We say, "Prove that my using DDT is killing wildlife" or "Prove that my car is polluting the air and killing trees." Nineteenth-century societies did not require absolute proof that garbage and wastes contained disease-causing bacteria before they prohibited dumping in the streets.

One aspect of limiting factors of special impact is the toxicity of certain substances for man. Toxicity is a measure of how much of a chemical substance (e.g., mercury) or physical agent (e.g., radiation) is required to cause discomfort, illness, or death. There has been considerable controversy recently over the effects of food additives such as cyclamates or of medical preparations such as hexachlorophene. There is disagreement over how much of a pollutant such as DDT or mercury can be in our diet without causing harmful effects. We can gain a better insight into why these controversies occur by looking more closely at the properties of the upper tolerance limit and the concept of toxicity.

Toxicity is often expressed as LD_{50}, the single-dose quantity of a substance that will kill 50 percent of the test population. It is usually given in the units of milligrams of poison per kilogram of animal body weight.* For example, the chemical that causes food poisoning (botulism) has an LD_{50} of 0.0014. Hence if we feed the poison to ten men each weighing 220 pounds (100 kilograms), a dose of 0.000049 ounces (0.0014 milligrams) would kill five of them.

The values for LD_{50} are affected by several factors. One variable is the means whereby the chemical enters the body. For example, the LD_{50} for DDT in man is 113 if the DDT is taken orally but 2510 (22 times less toxic) if it enters through the skin. A complication that we would expect from our prior discussion of limiting factors is that the LD_{50} often varies with age and sex.

It should be remembered that LD_{50} values are based upon a single dosage, not on cumulative effects. Many potentially lethal substances can accumulate in certain body tissues — for example, lead in the liver.

Finally, it is very difficult to take the results from one species and apply them to another. Many of the LD_{50} data are based upon experiments with laboratory animals such as white rats and guinea pigs. In the absence of tests on humans, it is difficult to know exactly where to set the safe exposure level to any chemical.

From the above discussion, we can begin to understand why there are differences of opinion, even among experts, over the levels of

Toxicity

* See inside back cover for conversion tables to weight.

environmental pollution to which we or any other organism can be safely exposed. Given the likelihood of error, it would seem to make sense to be on the safe side by setting our standards too high rather than find out after it is too late that we have allowed ourselves to be exposed to a dangerous level of pollutants.

KEY WORDS
AND SUMMARY
STATEMENTS

ecosystem	atmosphere	enzymes
biotic	lithosphere	pollution
abiotic	hydrosphere	limiting factors
producers	biosphere	limiting factor curve
consumers	food chains	chromosomes
decomposers	photosynthesis	mutation
herbivores	respiration	synergism
carnivores	adenosine triphosphate	LD_{50}
omnivores	fossil fuels	

A basic unit for studying the environment is the ecosystem, which is composed of two basic components: the abiotic, or nonliving, portion and the biotic, or living, portion. Organisms are subdivided into the producers (green plants), consumers (animals), and the decomposers, or microconsumers (some bacteria, fungi, and invertebrates).

Examples of ecosystems include grasslands, forests, deserts, and cornfields. Although highly modified, cities can also be considered ecosystems.

The Earth can be thought of as an ecosystem consisting of four complexly interrelated spheres: atmosphere (air), the hydrosphere (water), lithosphere (rocks and soil), and biosphere (organisms).

A major function of ecosystems is energy movement. Light energy is absorbed by green plants and transformed into chemical energy by photosynthesis. Plants use this energy for growth and maintenance. Plants are eaten by consumers called herbivores, which can be subsequently eaten by other consumers called carnivores. In each case the consumer obtains some of the energy originally fixed by the plants. This sequence is called a food chain.

Energy movement through food chains is always in one direction only — from producer to consumer. Because a large amount of chemical energy is lost as heat energy at each link in the food chain, energy must continually be supplied to ecosystems.

A second major function of ecosystems is the cycling of material among the four spheres. All materials present on Earth are cycled. Cycles consist of complex sets of interacting subcycles.

For any particular material and reservoir, there is usually a normal rate of transfer that varies within certain limits. Pollution is defined as any departure from the "normal" rate of transfer. Pollution can be either man-induced or "natural."

Limiting factor curves illustrate an organism's lower and upper tolerance limits and also its optimum level of an environmental factor.

Limiting factor curves are determined by the genetic make-up (chromosomes) of an organism. A change in the chromosomes is known as a mutation.

If an environment is not within the tolerance limits of an organism, the organism will either modify its present habitat, migrate to a more suitable one, or die.

Limiting factor curves vary with species, age, and factor interaction.

1. Why can't man obtain food energy directly from sunlight as plants do?

2. What happens to heat energy after it is lost from living organisms?

3. What ecosystems other than agricultural (farm) provide food energy for the urbanite?

4. Although farmers are a minority group in the United States, it is in the self-interest of all citizens to be concerned about the economic welfare of farmers. Why?

5. At what temperatures do enzymes usually function in the human body? What ultimately happens to the enzymes and the individual 'if body temperature rises as a result of disease or infection?

6. In terms of limiting factors for humans, what are several examples of factor interactions that affect man's well-being?

7. Before such drugs as those used for birth control are allowed on the market, they must undergo extensive testing. Although initial tests are done on laboratory animals, people of varied ages, races, and economic backgrounds are also tested. In light of the concept of limiting factors, why is the latter step necessary?

QUESTIONS AND PROJECTS

The following give a fundamental introduction to the structure and functions of ecosystems:

SELECTED READINGS

The Biosphere. San Francisco: Freeman, 1970.

Boughey, Arthur S. *Fundamental Ecology.* Scranton, Pa.: Intext Educational Publishers, 1971.

Kormondy, E. J. *Concepts of Ecology.* Englewood Cliffs, N.J.: Prentice-Hall, Inc., 1969.

Odum, E. P. *Ecology.* New York: Holt, Rinehart and Winston, 1966.

chapter

2

Energy and Energy Transformation

In recent years questions concerning *energy* have arisen with great frequency. During peak periods of energy demand (summer) East Coast metropolitan area residents have been asked to limit the use of electrical appliances to prevent brownouts. Hearings and court cases contesting the location and environmental effects of electric power plants are much more common than in the past. Oil spills resulting from offshore drilling (Santa Barbara) and transportaiton *(Torrey Canyon)* have had major impact. The location of the Alaskan oil pipeline not only involves environmental effects but also has diplomatic ramifications involving our relations with Canada.

Why the numerous struggles over energy? Insight may be gained by tracing the historical development of man's energy requirements. The caveman's primary energy requirement was his approximately 2,400 kilocalories of food consumed per day. Although modern Western man's food requirements have changed little since then, his higher standard of living has expanded his total energy demand to about 200,000 kilocalories per day — a hundred-fold increase. We burn fossil fuels to heat our homes and to generate the electrical energy we use to light out cities, power our industry, and run our appliances. Transportation requires energy. Use of fossil fuels in agriculture has greatly increased farm production.

Not only is energy vital to our society, it is also essential to maintain the interactions within and among the hydrosphere, lithosphere, atmosphere, and biosphere. Energy erodes rock and drives winds and waves; it pervades all activities of living organisms. A prerequisite to the discussion of environmental processes and problems is thus an understanding of the concept of energy.

KINETIC AND POTENTIAL ENERGY

The two major classifications of energy are *potential energy* and *kinetic energy*. Potential energy can be thought of as stored energy, i.e., in reserve for future use. Kinetic energy is what a body possesses because of its motion (Figure 2.1). Water behind a dam represents potential energy that can be converted into kinetic energy if the water

Potential energy

Kinetic energy

Figure 2.1
The difference between potential (stored) and kinetic (moving) energy.

is released and allowed to flow. Fossil fuels also contain potential energy that, upon combustion, is converted to kinetic energy. Kinetic energy from either or both of these two sources may be harnessed to turn generators to produce electrical energy. The atmosphere offers awesome examples of kinetic energy in the form of hurricanes and tornadoes.

Kinetic and potential energy are manifested in many different forms: thermal, mechanical, light, sound, chemical, electrical, and nuclear. *Thermal* (heat) *energy* is a form of kinetic energy present in the minute particles (atoms or molecules) that make up all substances. Because kinetic energy is that of motion, increased thermal energy can be thought of as an increase in the motion of the particles that comprise an object. Water illustrates the concept very well. The solid state, ice, contains energy sufficient only to allow molecules to vibrate within fixed positions; the liquid state represents an energy level high enough for the molecules to move about with considerably more freedom; and the gaseous state contains enough energy for the molecules to move with essentially complete freedom (Figure 2.2).

A measure of the intensity of molecular motion is temperature; the greater the motion, the higher the temperature. Two different objects at the same temperature, however, do not necessarily possess the same amount of energy. The amount of kinetic molecular energy that a substance contains is measured in calories. The *calorie* is defined as the amount of energy required to raise the temperature of one gram of water one Celsius degree. The definition specifies the substance (water), the mass of water (1 gram), and the temperature change (one Celsius degree). Not all substances, however, require the same number of calories to increase the temperature of the same quantity of material one Celsius degree. The amount of heat required to raise the temperature of one gram of a substance one Celsius degree is called its *specific heat*. The specific heat of all substances is measured relative to the specific heat of water, which has a value of 1.00 calories per gram (Table 2.1). Sand, for example, has a specific heat of 0.20 calories per gram, which means that it takes only one-fifth as much energy to raise the temperature of sand as it does to bring about an equivalent temperature rise in water.

Potential energy within materials such as coal and food is also

THERMAL ENERGY

Temperature and Heat Content

Table 2.1
Specific heat of selected substances.

Substance	Specific heat
Water	1.00
Ice	0.478
Aluminum	0.214
Sand	0.188
Granite	0.192
Sugar	0.274
Wood	0.42
Gold	0.031

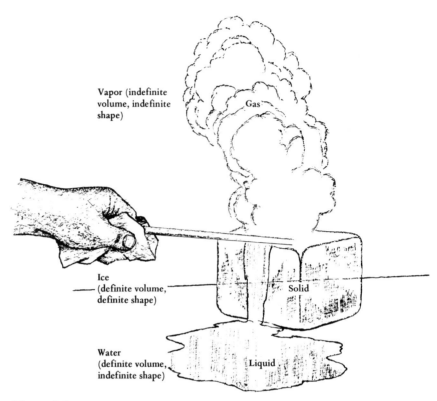

Vapor (indefinite
volume, indefinite
shape)

Gas

Ice
(definite volume,
definite shape)

Solid

Water
(definite volume,
indefinite shape)

Liquid

Figure 2.2
The three states of matter — gas, liquid, and solid — are all present when a piece of
ice acquires energy from a heated rod.

measured in calories. The potential caloric yield of materials refers to
the quantity of energy that would be released upon burning the material. A high-grade coal, for example, releases 7,600 calories per gram
of coal burned. (The reader is cautioned that the "calorie" used in
measuring the energy content of food is actually 1,000 calories, or one
kilocalorie.)

Temperature Scales

Two commonly used measures of molecular activity are the Fahrenheit and the Celsius temperature scales. Fahrenheit temperatures are
used in weather measurements and for body temperatures, whereas the
Celsius scale is used in most other scientific studies. If each of the two
types of thermometers is immersed into a glass of ice and water, the

Fahrenheit scale will read 32 degrees while the Celsius scale will read 0 degrees. In boiling water, the readings will be 212 degrees Fahrenheit and 100 degrees Celsius. The Celsius scale has the mathematical convenience of a 100-degree interval between the boiling and freezing points of water.

We have indicated that colder substances have less molecular motion than hot substances. There is, theoretically, a temperature at which molecular motion ceases; it is called *absolute zero,* or zero degrees Kelvin, and corresponds to −273.15 degrees Celsius and −459.6 degrees Fahrenheit. The Kelvin scale simply indicates temperature by the number of degrees a substance is above absolute zero. A one-degree interval on the Kelvin scale corresponds precisely to a one-degree change on the Celsius scale. (The three scales are contrasted in Figure 2.3.)

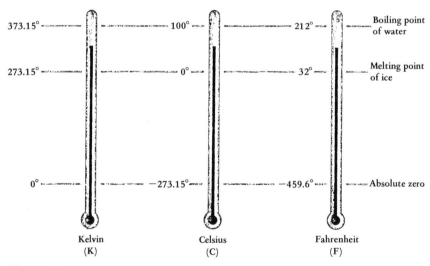

Figure 2.3
A comparison of the three most common temperature scales.

Mechanical energy, the most familiar form of energy, is what initiates movement of a body, changes its velocity if it is already in motion, or alters its shape. Industries use great quantities of mechanical energy to produce and distribute goods. Much of it is expended in overcoming the frictional resistance resulting from cutting, bending, grinding, fas-

MECHANICAL ENERGY

tening, and polishing. And every machine that has moving parts expends some of its energy in counteracting internal losses to friction. This energy is not actually lost but is manifested as useless heat.

Work and Power

To carry out mechanical operations requires mechanical energy, or *work*. In fact, scientists often define energy as the ability to do work. The amount of energy or work required to perform a task is calculated by multiplying the force by the distance over which the force is applied:

$$\text{work} = \text{force} \times \text{distance.}$$

In Figure 2.4 we see a workman lifting a 110-pound cornerstone a distance of five feet. The amount of work exerted by the worker is

$$110 \text{ pounds} \times 5 \text{ feet} = 550 \text{ foot-pounds.}$$

We can convert foot-pounds of work to calories by multiplying by the conversion factor, 0.324 calories per foot-pound. The result is that the man has used up 178 calories of energy to set the cornerstone. The major point is that to perform work, energy must be expended.

A concept not to be confused with work is that of *power*. Power is the rate at which work is performed:

$$\text{power} = \frac{\text{work}}{\text{time}}.$$

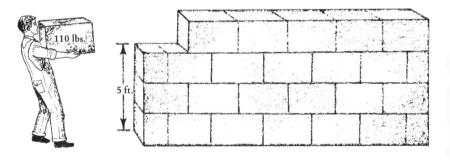

Figure 2.4
A worker raising a 110-pound cornerstone 5 feet does 550 foot-pounds of work (110 lbs. × 5 ft.), which requires 178 calories.

The amount of work an electric power generating plant, an automobile engine, or any motor can do is called its power rating. One familiar power rating is horsepower. A one-horsepower rating means that 550 foot-pounds of energy are expended in one second. Thus if our worker in Figure 2.4 lifted the stone in one second, he would have generated the equivalent of one horsepower. If, however, it took him four seconds to lift the stone, he would be generating only one-fourth horsepower. A highly trained athlete can perform work at the rate of one horsepower, but only over short periods of time.

We are familiar with the fact that water is used to generate electric power. Every cubic foot of water (62.4 pounds in weight) is capable of doing 62.4 foot-pounds of work for each one foot of distance it falls (Figure 2.5). This power-producing capacity has been one of the major

Figure 2.5
Fast moving water in a rapids gives an idea of the work water can perform. *(Ed Cooper, Photofind, S.F.)*

reasons used to justify the damming of many of our rivers for the building of hydroelectric plants. For example, the Moses-Saunders power dam near Niagara Falls diverts about 56,000 cubic feet (1,600 cubic meters) of water every second. This is 25–50 percent of the flow of the St. Lawrence River. Falling approximately 150 feet and moving through this hydroelectric complex, the water generates an average of 1,137,000 horsepower or 850,000 kilowatts of power. (See Figure 2.6.)

Figure 2.6
Aerial view of the Moses-Saunders hydroelectric complex on the St. Lawrence River near Niagara Falls. *(Power Authority of the State of New York.)*

ELECTRO-MAGNETIC ENERGY

Although we may not realize it, we are familiar with the many forms of electromagnetic energy, such as visible light, television and radio waves, and X-rays. Visible light is the most familiar to us and will be used to illustrate the characteristics common to all forms of electromagnetic energy. Light comes to us in the form of waves traveling at a speed of 186,000 miles (299,800 kilometers) per second.* The length of a wave, or *wavelength,* is the distance between successive wave crests or troughs (Figure 2.7). Waves are also identified by their *frequency,* which is defined as the number of complete wavelengths that pass a fixed point in one second, i.e., the number of times per second a wave oscillates up and down. Waves introduced into a rope (Figure 2.8) aid

* See inside back cover for conversion tables to length.

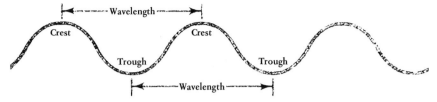

Figure 2.7
Wavelength is the distance between successive crests or troughs of a wave.

in clarifying the concept. The frequency of the rope is equal to the number of up-down motions made by the hand in one second. The relation between wavelength and frequency is inverse, i.e., the higher the frequency, the shorter the wavelength. Both parameters are used to describe electromagnetic energy.

Examination of white light reveals that it is actually composed of waves, which vary in frequency and length. As white light passes through a prism it is broken up into a spectrum of colors, with violet and red light at the visible limits (Figure 2.9). The violet component, which has the greatest frequency, is bent (refracted) the most; the less energetic red light is bent the least.

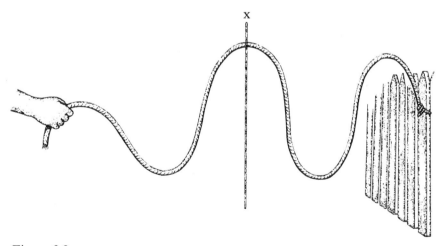

Figure 2.8
The number of up-down motions of the hand per second determines the number of waves per second of the rope that will pass point X. If the hand oscillates faster, higher frequencies and shorter wavelengths result.

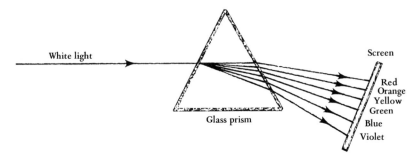

Figure 2.9
As white light passes through a solid glass prism, it is dispersed into a spectrum of colors. Violet light is bent the most; red light is bent only slightly.

The Electromagnetic Spectrum

Visible light, ranging in wavelength from 4×10^{-5} to 8×10^{-5} centimeters,* is essential to many processes in the environment. (English units are seldom used in discussion of electromagnetic energy and thus are not included.) For photosynthesis, plants absorb chiefly blue (4.5×10^{-5} cm) and red (6.5×10^{-5} cm) light. Although visible wavelengths make up only a small band of the *electromagnetic spectrum* (Figure 2.10), as much as 49 percent of the energy that reaches the Earth's surface lies within the visible band.

Ultraviolet light is sufficiently more energetic than visible light to cause eye damage, even blindness, so it is important never to look directly at the sun, even during periods of eclipse. Hospitals use this destructive character of ultraviolet light to prevent bacterial contamination of medical instruments.

X-rays and gamma rays are even more energetic than ultraviolet waves, so energetic they can pass directly through the human body. Because bone stops more X-rays than surrounding tissue, developed X-ray film, called simply an X-ray, can reveal skeletal features. Even though most of the X-rays pass through an individual, some interact with body tissue and can cause damage to cells and tissues, possibly cancer, sterilization, or genetic mutations. Gamma rays are the products of changes that take place within the nucleus of atoms; they are similar to X-rays except that they are even more energetic.

The portion of the electromagnetic spectrum adjacent to red light is called the infrared region. Our eyes are not sensitive to infrared waves, but our skin is. A glowing ember in a campfire or fireplace

* Readers unfamiliar with numbers expressed as powers of ten are referred to Appendix II.

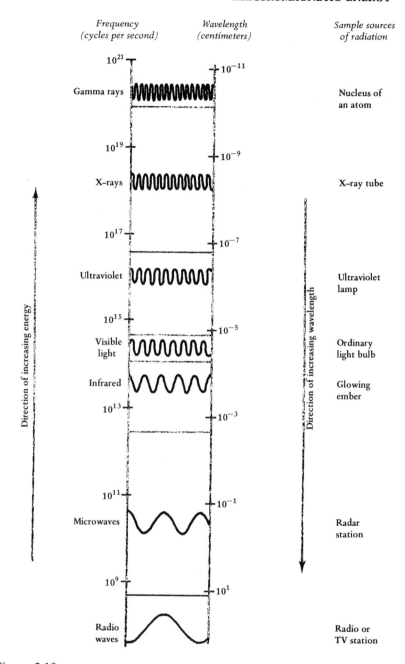

Figure 2.10
The electromagnetic spectrum consists of a continuous range of radiation that differs in wavelength and frequency.

emits infrared waves that are absorbed by the skin and felt as heat. Wavelengths longer than the infrared region characterize microwaves and radar, radio, and television waves. These low-energy waves have lengths that range from a fraction of an inch to over a mile. The standard AM radio, for example, receives waves between 200 and 520 meters in length.

The means by which electromagnetic waves are emitted and transferred is called *radiation,* a unique process in that it requires no transfer medium; i.e., it can travel through a vacuum. All forms of radiant energy travel at their maximum velocity through a vacuum and slow down when passing through a substance. However, waves of different lengths do not travel through a substance at the same rate (Figure 2.9). In this case, the violet portion of the visible spectrum has the greatest interaction with the object and is slowed and bent the most.

SOUND ENERGY

Sound energy continually bombards us, emanating from such diverse things as jet aircraft, amplified music, machinery, lawn mowers, snowmobiles, and motorcycles. Sound energy also travels as waves but differs from light waves in that the waves require a medium for transport. Sound energy travels through gases, liquids, and solids, but not through a vacuum; and the medium it travels through experiences "push-pull" compressional motions. A vibrating string on a guitar causes the air in the region of the string to experience alternate compressions (push) and decompressions (pull). The number of compressions per second (i.e., the frequency, or pitch) determines the number received by the ear. High-pitched sounds come from sources that vibrate at high rates; low-pitched sounds result from slowly vibrating objects.

The actual amount of energy involved in sound waves is very small. It has been estimated that the sound energy produced by 10 million people talking at the same time, roughly that of 10 jet aircraft, is only enough to operate an ordinary light bulb. But because of the extremely sensitive nature of the ear, results of excessive amounts of sound energy can range from psychological tension to permanent hearing loss. This is why people working near jet aircraft wear earmuffs.

Sound intensity is measured in units called *decibels.* In Table 2.2 the noise level produced by some common sources and human thresholds of response to them are listed. The decibel scale is not the type of scale we ordinarily encounter. Going from 50 to 60 decibels, for example,

Table 2.2
Decibel ratings of selected sounds.

Sound intensity in arbitrary units	Decibels	Response	Examples
1,000,000,000,000,000	150 ↑	Eardrum ruptures	Jet takeoff close by
100,000,000,000,000	140		Aircraft carrier deck
10,000,000,000,000	130		Upper limit of speech with amplifier
1,000,000,000,000	120 ←Very painful→		Jet takeoff (200 feet); discotheque
100,000,000,000	110		Auto horn (3 feet)
10,000,000,000	100	Deafening	Shout (half a foot); N.Y. subway station
1,000,000,000	90	Very annoying	Hearing damage (8 hours); pneumatic drill (50 feet)
100,000,000	80	Annoying; very loud; must shout to be heard	Freight train (50 feet)
10,000,000	70	Intrusive	Freeway traffic (50 feet)
1,000,000	60	Loud	Vacuum cleaner
100,000	50	Moderately quiet	Conversation in restaurant
10,000	40	Quiet	Conversation in living room
1,000	30	Very quiet	Whisper (15 feet); broadcasting studio
100	20	Faint	Whisper (5 feet)
10	10	Very faint	Rustling leaves
1	0	Barely audible	Soft breathing

Source: John R. Holum and Richard A. Boolootian, *Topics and Terms of Environmental Sciences* (Boston: Little, Brown and Co., 1973).

represents an increase in noise level by a factor of 10; i.e., every 10-decibel increase corresponds to a ten-fold increase in noise level.

CHEMICAL ENERGY

Chemical energy is a special form of potential energy. Useful chemical energy may result from changes in arrangement of the atoms that make up a substance. Food and oxygen or coal and oxygen represent potential chemical energy. When coal is burned, the carbon atoms of the coal unite with oxygen from the air and form carbon dioxide. If this process is carried out in a closed system, where no heat or matter is introduced or lost, we would find that the product — carbon dioxide — contains considerable amounts of kinetic molecular energy, as evidenced by high temperatures. This heat energy was formerly present as potential chemical energy in the coal. The kinetic energy produced by burning coal to run energy-demanding machines is analogous to that of burning food (respiration) by organisms to provide energy for biological functions.

NUCLEAR ENERGY

Nuclear energy has come into use only during the past three decades. Initially developed for military weapons, nuclear energy is now being put to peaceful uses such as the production of electrical power, the treatment of disease, and the preservation of food. The nuclei of certain atoms are sources of energy that hold promise of meeting our energy demands of the future. Because of the complicated means whereby energy is released from the nucleus of an atom, we will defer dealing with it to the fuller discussion in Chapter 3.

ENERGY TRANS-FORMATION

Prior discussions of energy have illustrated that energy can be transformed from one form into another. All the devices we use in our everyday experience are energy converters. One that has important

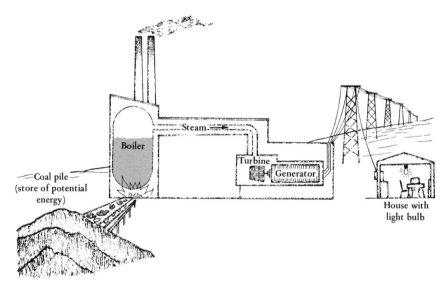

Figure 2.11
Some examples of energy transformations that take place in the production and use of electricity.

environmental effects is the electric generating plant shown in Figure 2.11. Next to the plant are huge piles of coal containing potential chemical energy. The coal is taken into the plant and burned, thereby releasing thermal energy. This energy is then used to convert water to the pressurized steam that upon release causes a turbine to rotate — a conversion of heat energy into mechanical energy. The turbine is connected to an electric generator that causes mechanical energy to be transformed to electrical energy. The electrical energy is then transmitted through wires to homes and industries. Indeed, the ease with which electrical energy can be transported and then converted to various forms has been one of the main contributing factors to our increased energy demands. However, it is important to keep in mind that the original source of this energy, coal, is a nonrenewable resource.

ENERGY LAWS

First Law of Thermodynamics

All changes in energy follow two fundamental laws. The first is the law of conservation of energy, or *First Law of Thermodynamics,* which states that energy may be changed from one form to another but cannot be created or destroyed. No component of the ecosystem can create its own energy supply. It can only fulfill its energy demands by relying upon energy transformations among the energy reservoirs within either its own ecosystem or adjacent ones. Ultimately, our energy supply is fixed and finite.

Applying the First Law of Thermodynamics to an electric generating plant, we find that only about 35 percent of the thermal energy released by burning coal is transformed to electrical energy for useful distribution. The remaining 65 percent is accounted for by the plant's discharge of heated water and hot gases into nearby waterways and the atmosphere. Thus, we see that all the energy is accounted for, though not all of it is usable. (The environmental consequences of thermal alteration of lakes and streams will be discussed in Chapter 9.)

Second Law of Thermodynamics

The *Second Law of Thermodynamics* cannot be stated as simply as the first. One way of putting it is that heat never flows spontaneously from a cold body to a hot one. We wouldn't expect to get warmed up by sitting on a block of ice. Another way of putting it is that systems tend toward disorder; order is restored only by the expenditure of energy. One implication of the second law is that energy must be expended if we are to recover and recycle pollutants. At first glance, living organisms would seem to be an exception to this tendency toward disorganization, but we have already seen that respiration is needed to provide the energy that maintains living organisms.

The second law places even more subtle limitations on man's machines. The efficiency of machines such as automobile engines and steam turbines increases as their internal temperatures increase. Automobile efficiency could be increased if engine temperature after combustion were higher, but the materials the engine is made of are temperature-limited. Typically, an automobile engine operates 45 to 50 percent efficiently, whereas a steam engine achieves 35 percent efficiency. The practical significance of the second law is that a major portion of the energy content within fuels ends up as wasted heat. As previously stated, obtaining heat from work is simple, but the converse has limitations.

Restating an example from the biosphere, energy that enters food chains is lost as heat because of inefficient transformations in respiration and other metabolic processes. The efficiency of energy transformation varies greatly depending upon the characteristics of the system and the type of transformation.

To summarize, the first law tells us that all energy within a system must be accounted for; the second law tells us why the total energy within a system is divided. All systems adhere to both energy laws.

ENERGY TRANSFER PROCESSES

Basically, there are three mechanisms whereby energy is transferred from place to place: *radiation, conduction,* and *convection.* The fastest is radiation, the means by which the sun's energy reaches our planet at 186,000 miles per second. The second is conduction. Conduction within a body or between two bodies in contact involves the direct transfer of energy from molecule to molecule. For example, when a metal spoon is placed in a steaming cup of coffee, the handle warms as a result of the transfer of thermal energy from particle to particle. Substances vary in their ability to conduct heat, but metals are generally better conductors than rock, which in turn is a better conductor than woody vegetation. The third means of energy transfer is convection, the movement of matter from a region of higher energy to one of lower energy. For example, cool air moving over a warm surface is heated from below, and it expands and rises. This is called a convection current.

Energy is the essential factor for the operation of the environment. Further appreciation of the consequences of the interrelations of the various energy forms and matter will develop as we continue our study of the environment.

potential energy	electromagnetic energy	First Law of Thermo-dynamics
kinetic energy	electromagnetic spectrum	Second Law of Thermo-dynamics
thermal energy	radiation (specific waves)	radiation (as means of energy transfer)
calorie	sound energy	conduction
specific heat	decibels	convection
mechanical energy	chemical energy	
work	nuclear energy	
power		
frequency		

Although energy exists in many different forms (thermal, mechanical, light, sound, chemical, electrical, and nuclear), all can be classified as either kinetic or potential.

Temperature is a measure of the intensity of molecular motion. Adding heat or thermal energy to a substance increases its molecular motion.

Potential and kinetic energy are both measured in calories, i.e., the amount of heat required to raise the temperature of one gram of water one Celsius degree.

Mechanical energy is usually measured in terms of work. Power is the rate at which work is performed, i.e., the amount of energy expended per unit of time.

Electromagnetic energy is transmitted in the form of waves. The electromagnetic spectrum spans a wide range of wavelengths (or frequencies) from the highly energetic gamma rays to radio waves. Our eyes are sensitive to only a small portion of this spectrum, which is called the visible region.

Electromagnetic waves in the ultraviolet, X-ray, and gamma ray bands are particularly hazardous to living organisms.

Sound energy travels as waves and at high decibel levels can cause tension or hearing damage.

Chemical energy results from the combination or recombination of atoms that make up substances.

All forms of energy can be changed from one form into another by various processes, e.g., in an electric power generating plant.

Energy is conserved (the First Law of Thermodynamics).

The Second Law of Thermodynamics indicates why there are limitations and inefficiencies in energy transformation.

Energy is transferred from place to place by three processes: conduction, convection, and radiation; but only radiation requires no material medium.

Energy in its many forms is essential for the functioning of the processes within and among the biosphere, hydrosphere, lithosphere, and atmosphere.

QUESTIONS AND PROJECTS

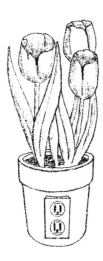

1. During the summer months the greatest amount of thermal energy is present, yet man's highest electrical energy demands occur at this time. Why?

2. Make a list of some possible uses of the 65 percent wasted energy from electric generating plants.

3. We have classified energy into seven categories: mechanical, thermal, light, sound, chemical, electrical, and nuclear. Name an appliance, machine, or device that uses or produces each form of energy.

4. What is the difference between noise and music?

5. Name some ways other than ear damage in which noise may affect people.

6. Explain why on a beach on a hot sunny day, dry sand is hot and wet sand is much cooler.

7. Evaluate the device shown on the left as a means of power production.

8. If energy is conserved, what happened to the kinetic energy of the boulder in Figure 2.1?

9. How many times more intense is the sound from an 80-decibel source than that from a 40-decibel source?

10. Trace the energy transformations in filling a bucket of water from a well by hand, by windmill, and by electric pump.

11. Comment on the definition of pollution as "energy out of place."

SELECTED READINGS

Booth, V. H. *Elements of Physical Science: The Nature of Matter and Energy.* New York: Macmillan, 1970. Chapters 7, 8, and 10 include further discussions of energy-related topics.

Hewitt, P. G. *Conceptual Physics.* Boston: Little, Brown and Co., 1971. A descriptive physics text written for nonscience students. Chapters 6, 14–18, and 25–27 are most relevant.

Ward, C. R. *This Blue Planet*. Boston: Little, Brown and Co., 1972. Chapters 3 and 5 expand upon energy, the laws of thermodynamics, and the electromagnetic spectrum at the level of the nonscience student.

chapter

3

Matter: Structure and Properties

All substances are said to be composed of matter; it is the fundamental component of the lithosphere, hydrosphere, atmosphere, and biosphere. The interactions between matter and energy are the basis for the functioning of the environment. Matter is a reservoir for energy, but the amount of energy determines the state in which matter exists. Consider an ice cube, the solid state of water. As long as the temperature is above absolute zero, it possesses energy. As additional energy is supplied, the water passes to the liquid and gaseous states of matter in sequence.

Categorizing matter as solids, liquids, or gases is useful but does not provide a complete description of the composition of matter. It must be added that tiny particles called *atoms* make up all matter. Atoms are the ultimate units of matter that upon division lose their identity. They are the fundamental building blocks of all substances.

Atoms can combine with other atoms to form more complex units called molecules, which in turn are the building blocks of the abiotic (rock and water) and biotic (cells that compose organisms) components of the environment. Many processes that occur in the environment can be understood only by grasping the functioning of ecosystems at the atomic or molecular level.

STRUCTURE OF MATTER

49

Atoms

DESCRIPTION

Scientific experiments around the turn of the century led to the discovery of the structure of the atom. From them scientists concluded that the atom is composed of an extremely tiny dense center, called a nucleus, with particles orbiting it. We now know that the diameter of an atom's nucleus is on the order of 10^{-12} to 10^{-13} centimeters and that the diameter of the atom itself (defined by the outer orbiting particles) is approximately 2×10^{-8} centimeters, about 100,000 times that of the nucleus; thus the atom is mostly empty space.

FUNDAMENTAL
PARTICLES

Atoms are made up of three fundamental particles: *electrons, protons,* and *neutrons.* (Hydrogen is an exception in that it has no neutrons.) Protons and neutrons are found in the nucleus of an atom and make up virtually its entire mass. Electrons are particles that orbit the nucleus and define the atom's outer diameter. The properties of these three fundamental particles, the building materials of atoms, are summarized in Table 3.1.

Table 3.1
The fundamental particles.

	Charge	*Mass (atomic mass units)*[a]
Electron	−1	0.00055
Proton	+1	1.00728
Neutron	0	1.00867

[a] One atomic mass unit (amu) equals 1/12th the weight of one carbon-12 atom.

Electrons and protons are the charged particles of an atom. An electron carries a negative charge, a proton a positive charge. Like charges repel each other and unlike charges attract. Charges within atoms are balanced so that the negative electrons are kept in orbit around the positive nucleus. Any change within matter involves an alteration of the electron or proton balance or arrangement, so all changes in the environment can be seen as electrical in nature.

ATOMIC NUMBER

The simplest atom consists of one proton and one orbiting electron. All atoms of this structure are called atoms of the element hydrogen. The next simplest element is helium, which contains two protons and two neutrons in its nucleus and has two orbiting electrons (Figure 3.1).

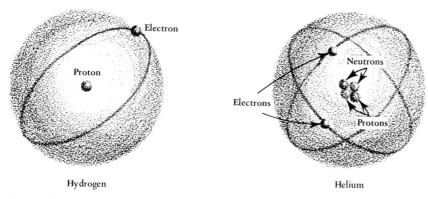

Hydrogen   Helium

Figure 3.1
The electrons of an atom orbit a tiny nucleus. The nucleus of a hydrogen atom has only one proton, whereas the helium nucleus has two protons and two neutrons. The nucleus comprises virtually the entire mass of an atom.

The number of protons in the nucleus distinguishes one *element* from another; it is called the *atomic number* of that element. Arranged in order of atomic number, each element has one more proton than does its predecessor. Eighty-eight elements have been found to occur naturally in the environment, and an additional seventeen have been made in the laboratory for a total of one hundred and five (complete list in Appendix III).

Atomic mass is approximately equal to the total number of protons and neutrons in the atom's nucleus. A shorthand notation (Figure 3.2) is used to designate an element, its atomic mass, and its atomic number. $^{16}_{8}O$, for example, denotes oxygen, which has the atomic

ATOMIC MASS

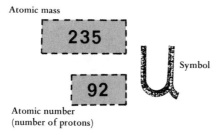

Figure 3.2
Shorthand notation indicating the characteristics of an element.

number 8 and a mass of 16 atomic mass units (amu). This notation is especially useful when dealing with atoms of the same element that have different atomic masses; these are called *isotopes*. Uranium atoms found in the lithosphere include $^{235}_{92}U$ and $^{238}_{92}U$. Both of these atoms have 92 protons but 143 and 146 neutrons, respectively. Although the word "isotope" is commonly associated with radioactive material, most isotopes in the environment are not radioactive.

REASONS FOR STABILITY
OF NUCLEUS

In the atom's nucleus, positive protons are crammed into an extremely small space, an apparently unstable arrangement in view of the fact that particles having the same charge repel one another. A complete explanation cannot yet be given of this puzzling situation, but two factors that tend to stabilize the nucleus are known. First, the nucleus of each atom appears to require a certain number of neutrons to maintain stability. And as the number of protons in the nucleus increases, the number of neutrons per proton also increases (Figure 3.3). For lighter elements the number of neutrons is approximately equal to the number of protons, but heavier elements require about 1.5

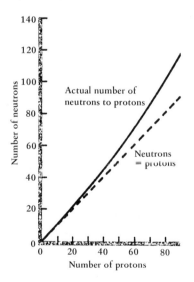

Figure 3.3
Heavier elements contain more neutrons per proton as indicated by the deviation of the solid line from the dashed line, which represents a constant ratio of one neutron per proton.

neutrons per proton to maintain nuclear stability. Heavier elements, with more protons in their nuclei, apparently require more neutrons to shield the positive charges.

Second, nuclear stability involves the conversion of matter to energy. The simplest example of this is that of the helium nucleus, which contains two protons and two neutrons. Because the mass of the proton is 1.00728 amu and the mass of the neutron is 1.00867 amu (Table 3.1), the calculated mass for the helium nucleus is:

$$2 \times 1.00728 + 2 \times 1.00867 = 4.03190 \text{ amu}.$$

However, precise experiments have shown the mass of the helium nucleus to be 4.0015 amu, an apparent loss of 0.0304 amu. Scientists believe that the reason for this discrepancy is that a small amount of mass is converted into energy. The amount of energy is calculated using Einstein's famous equation, $E = mc^2$, where E is the energy, where m is the mass converted to energy, and where c is the velocity of light (2.99×10^5 km/sec). The result is that 1.1×10^{-12} calories of energy are used in holding one helium nucleus together. The amount of energy involved in nuclear changes is more easily comprehended if we convert one gram (0.0022 pounds) of matter to energy: One gram of matter completely converted to energy is equivalent to the energy released by 20,000 tons of TNT. All nuclei are thought to be stabilized by the energy that has resulted from the conversion of mass into energy and also by the interactions between neutrons and protons.

ELECTRON ARRANGEMENT

Electrons orbit the atom's nucleus within certain confined regions called *shells*, which are numbered in order of their nearness to the nucleus (Figure 3.4). Electrons in the first shell require the most energy to be removed because of their proximity to the positive nucleus. Each shell successively farther from the nucleus requires less energy for electrons to be removed. But less energy is released when an outer shell gains an electron than when an inner shell does.

Each shell has a limited capacity for electrons. The first shell accommodates two electrons, the second shell eight, the third eighteen, and

Figure 3.4
The electron shell structure of an atom. *(After L. Don Leet and Sheldon Judson, Physical Geology, 4th ed. [Englewood Cliffs, N.J.: Prentice-Hall, 1971], p. 16.)*

the fourth thirty-two. By these rules, an element's electron arrangement can be predicted. For example, sodium has atomic number 11 and therefore has 11 electrons. (To be electrically neutral an atom must have as many electrons as it has protons.) These electrons occupy the 11 lowest possible energy levels; two in the first shell, 8 in the second, one in the third.

A compilation of electron arrangements (Table 3.2) for various elements reveals a repeating pattern. The elements helium, neon, and argon are all chemically nonreactive gases; all have completely filled shells and, consequently, they have similar chemical properties. They do not participate in any chemical reactions in the environment. Lithium, sodium, and potassium all have only one electron in their outermost shell. As this is not as stable an electron arrangement as a completely filled shell, these elements are very reactive. Sodium and potassium react violently when placed into water, so the natural existence of each is not as an element but rather as an ion, which will be

Table 3.2
Electron arrangement of the first nineteen elements.

Element	Symbol	Atomic number	Shell 1	Shell 2	Shell 3	Shell 4
Hydrogen	H	1	1			
Helium	He	2	2			
Lithium	Li	3	2	1		
Beryllium	Be	4	2	2		
Boron	B	5	2	3		
Carbon	C	6	2	4		
Nitrogen	N	7	2	5		
Oxygen	O	8	2	6		
Fluorine	F	9	2	7		
Neon	Ne	10	2	8		
Sodium	Na	11	2	8	1	
Magnesium	Mg	12	2	8	2	
Aluminum	Al	13	2	8	3	
Silicon	Si	14	2	8	4	
Phosphorus	P	15	2	8	5	
Sulfur	S	16	2	8	6	
Chlorine	Cl	17	2	8	7	
Argon	Ar	18	2	8	8	
Potassium[a]	K	19	2	8	8	1

[a] Beyond argon the order of electron filling is more complex than that for the first eighteen elements.

discussed shortly. It is important, however, to remember that the chemical and physical properties of all elements are determined by their electron arrangement.

Most elements appear in the environment not as individual atoms but as more complicated units called molecules or ions. A *molecule* is composed of two or more atoms that are joined together. It is a unit with properties quite distinct from those of the atoms that comprise the molecule. Molecules of the same substance always behave in the same way, as do atoms of the same element.

Molecules range in complexity, but the simpler ones are fairly familiar. An oxygen molecule in the air consists of two oxygen atoms held together as one unit, and a carbon dioxide molecule (Figure 3.5) consists of two oxygen atoms bonded to a carbon atom to form a linear molecule ($O = C = O$). Complex molecules often require long names in order to keep track of the number, type, and exact position of each

Molecules and
Ionic Substances

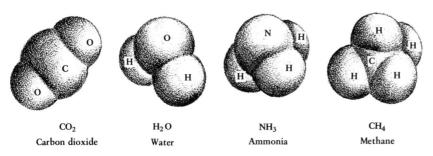

| CO_2 | H_2O | NH_3 | CH_4 |
| Carbon dioxide | Water | Ammonia | Methane |

Figure 3.5
The electron cloud of a molecule defines its size and shape and determines a molecule's chemical properties.

atom in the molecule. For example, 1,1,1,-trichloro-2,2-bis(p-chlorophenyl)-ethane would overwhelm anyone seeing it for the first time. But just imagine someone trying to describe the molecule shown in Figure 3.6: "Starting at the top there is a chlorine atom that is connected to a carbon atom that in turn is connected to two other chlorine atoms . . . ," etc. We immediately see that the chemist's seemingly long name for a molecule is actually a shorthand description. When a particular chemical substance is used commonly, it acquires an abbreviated name. Thus 1,1,1,-trichloro-2,2-bis(p-chlorophenyl)-ethane

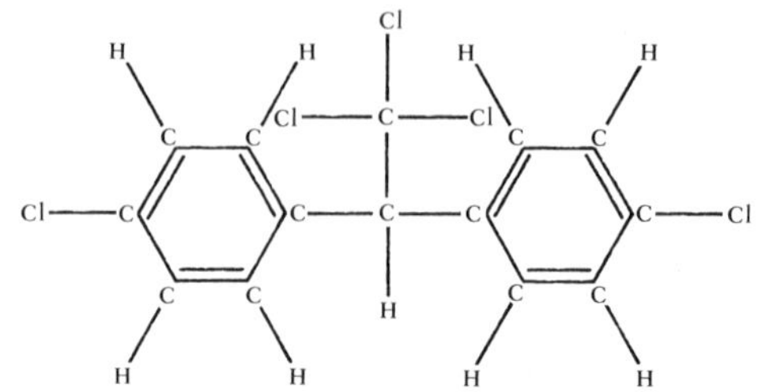

Figure 3.6
This molecule, containing only carbon, chlorine, and hydrogen atoms, is called DDT.

is known simply as DDT. Other examples are 2,4,6-trinitrotoluene (TNT), and acetylsalycylic acid (aspirin).

Though there are literally millions of different molecules, we can see the general principle that when two atoms are brought in the vicinity of one another, their electron interaction may produce a re-arrangement of electrons about the two atoms and that if the new arrangement is stable, the two atoms will remain joined together and behave as a molecule.

IONIC BONDS

One possible rearrangement of electrons involves the complete transfer of an electron from one atom to another (Figure 3.7). For example, when an atom of chlorine and an atom of sodium are brought together they interact so that sodium loses one of its electrons to the chlorine atom. The sodium atom is now positively charged because it has one more proton than electrons. The chlorine atom with an extra electron is negatively charged. Any atom or combination of atoms that is not electrically balanced, i.e., having either a net positive or negative charge, is called an *ion*. Substances held together by the attraction of oppositely charged ions are called ionic substances, and the attraction is called an *ionic bond*. Both ions have filled outer shells – a stable configuration. The sodium and chloride ions together form the com-pound sodium chloride, ordinary table salt. The salt crystals are the result of an ordered stacking of chloride and sodium ions (Fig-ure 3.8).

Other ions are more complex in that several atoms together form an ion. The carbonate ion, CO_3^{2-}, is a unit made up of one carbon atom and three oxygen atoms; it has two more electrons associated with it than protons and therefore carries two units of negative charge. Car-

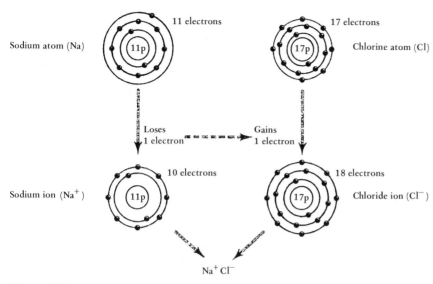

Figure 3.7
The complete transfer of an electron from one atom to another results in the formation of a positive ion and a negative ion.

bonate ions are found both in limestone (calcium carbonate) and in baking soda (sodium bicarbonate). Some of the other important ions in the environment are sulfate SO_4^{2-}; nitrate, NO_3^-; phosphate, PO_4^{3-}; silicate, SiO_4^{4-}; and hydroxide, OH^-.

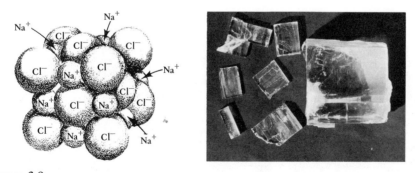

Figure 3.8
Sodium chloride (NaCl) is an ordered solid composed of ions stacked in a specific three-dimensional arrangement. Atomic structure (left) and cleaved crystals (right). *(Photograph by the Field Museum of Natural History, Chicago.)*

COVALENT BONDS

A second rearrangement of electrons involves the sharing between atoms. For example, when two oxygen atoms are brought near each other, they are held together by sharing a pair of electrons and are thus said to be *covalently bonded.* Because the electrons are rapidly circling the two nuclei of the oxygen atoms, their exact position is not known, so the position of the electrons is envisioned as an electron cloud. Most bonds in organic molecules are covalent bonds.

METAL BONDS

An understanding of the forces that bond atoms is not complete without an explanation of how metallic atoms are held together. Metals are composed of individual atoms, not molecules, held together in the solid state by the sharing of electrons. The electrons are free to migrate throughout the entire mass of metal. This ease of electron movement explains why many metals are good conductors of electricity.

CHANGES IN MATTER

Physical Change

Changes that matter undergoes are divided into three processes: physical, chemical, and nuclear. Changes in shape, luster, density, and hardness are examples of *physical changes,* those which do not alter the arrangement of atoms making up the molecules of a substance. In breaking a substance (a physical change, in shape), neighboring molecules are torn apart, but individual molecules remain intact (Figure 3.9).

A change in the physical state involves energy (Figure 3.10). A relatively small amount of energy is required to heat up a chunk of

Figure 3.9
Snowflakes result when water changes physically from the gaseous state to the solid state. *(NOAA.)*

ice, 0.5 calories per gram for each Celsius degree (0.5 cal/gm/°C). Adding 20 calories of energy to one gram of ice would warm it from −40 degrees Celsius to 0 degrees Celsius. Once 0 degrees Celsius is reached, an addition of 80 calories of energy is required to break the forces that hold one gram of ice molecules together, but the temperature of water and ice remains at 0 degrees Celsius until all the ice is melted. From this point it takes 1.0 calorie of heat energy to warm one gram of water one Celsius degree (the definition of a calorie); warming it to 100 degrees Celsius requires an addition of 100 calories. Once the boiling point of water is reached (100 degrees Celsius) the water temperature again remains constant until all the water is vaporized. This change of phase requires 540 calories per gram of water. If the sequence

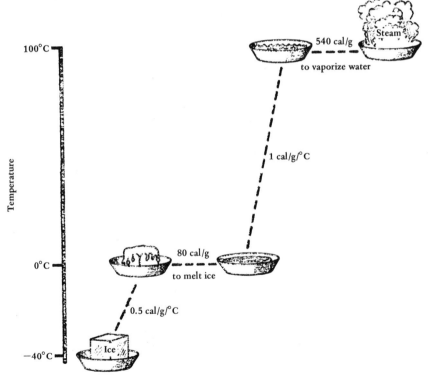

Figure 3.10
Energy requirements to change temperature (specific heat) and physical states (heat of fusion and heat of vaporization) of water.

is reversed, equivalent amounts of heat energy are released. The energies required to cause a phase change from the solid to the liquid and from liquid to vapor are called the *heat of fusion* and *heat of vaporization* respectively. (It will be recalled that the amount of heat energy required to warm a unit mass of a substance when a phase change is not taking place is called its specific heat.)

Chemical Change

Chemical changes are formations of new distinct molecules by means of a rearrangement of atoms, termed a chemical reaction. For instance, charcoal is composed of carbon atoms. If the temperature of charcoal is high enough (Figure 3.11), carbon atoms combine with oxygen molecules (O_2) in the air to form carbon dioxide (CO_2). If the supply of oxygen is limited, however, some carbon monoxide (CO) results.

This reaction of oxygen with carbon initially requires energy to break the covalent bonds that hold the oxygen molecules together. However, subsequent formation of covalent bonds between the carbon

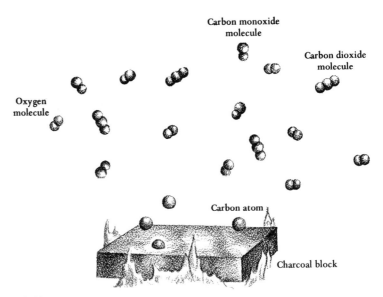

Figure 3.11
The burning of a charcoal block (carbon) in air results in a rearrangement of atoms and the formation of the new molecules carbon dioxide and carbon monoxide.

atom and the oxygen atom(s) releases heat and light energy. This heat production is utilized by industry. Unfortunately, coal contains the element sulfur, which undergoes a similar reaction with oxygen to form sulfur dioxide (SO_2). Burning sulfur releases energy, which of course is desired by industry, but sulfur dioxide molecules discharged into the atmosphere interact detrimentally with organisms and structures.

Chemical reactions between substances are usually written in a shorthand notation called a chemical equation. The reactions discussed above are written as:

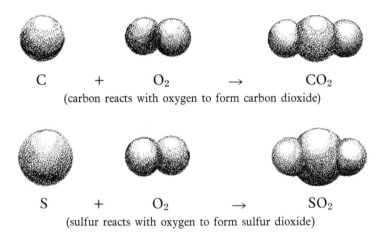

C   + O_2 $\rightarrow$ CO_2
(carbon reacts with oxygen to form carbon dioxide)

S   + O_2 $\rightarrow$ SO_2
(sulfur reacts with oxygen to form sulfur dioxide)

These equations show the molecules (atoms) involved before reaction (reactants) on the left side of the equation and the resulting new molecules (products) on the right. Note that there are the same number and type of atoms on both sides of the equation in accordance with the conservation of matter.

Nuclear Changes

PARTICLE EMISSION

Nuclear changes are those that occur within atomic nuclei. One type of nuclear change involves the stabilization of isotopes. Although most naturally occurring elements in the environment are composed of stable isotopes, some are not. Unstable isotopes tend to stabilize by spontaneously emitting from the nucleus particles called gamma, beta, and alpha rays (Table 3.3) and are said to be radioactive. The particles

Table 3.3
The radioactive rays.

Name	Charge	Approx. mass, amu	Penetrating power
Alpha	+2	4	Weak, produces many ions
Beta	−1	0.00055	About 100 times that of alpha rays, produces fewer ions
Gamma	0	0	Very penetrating, produces only a few ions

release a small portion of the tremendous store of energy within the nucleus.

A shift toward a more stable arrangement of neutrons and protons within nuclei may produce energy in the form of *gamma rays* (high energy electromagnetic radiation). The penetrating power of gamma rays allows them to pass directly through substances with little interaction. This does not mean, however, that organisms are not affected by exposure to gamma particles. Exposure to gamma rays results in whole body exposure. The high energy of gamma rays can seriously disrupt the molecular architecture of an organism. Chemical bonds are broken to form radicals (uncharged chemical species having an unshared electron) and ions. These radicals and ions are very reactive and result in the alteration of the molecular structure of cells. Such changes in genetic material are called mutations.

Emission of *beta particles* requires that a neutron within the nucleus be converted to a proton and an electron. The electron is ejected at a high speed and is known as a beta ray. It has less penetrating power than a gamma ray, but it produces a greater number of ions over a shorter distance as it passes through matter. Thus exposure to beta particles results in more localized damage to organisms.

An *alpha particle* consists of a helium nucleus — two protons and two neutrons — moving at a speed of about 10,000 miles (16,000 km) per second. Alpha particles (or rays) are emitted from the nucleus of many of the heavier isotopes such as polonium. They have a low penetrating power but are more efficient ion producers than beta and gamma rays. Again, exposure to alpha rays results in localized damage.

NUCLEAR FISSION

Nuclear fission involves the splitting of the nucleus into fragments. For example, when the U-235 atom captures a slow-moving neutron,

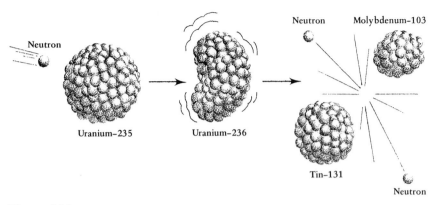

Figure 3.12
A nuclear fission reaction of U-235.

the extra neutron creates an unstable nucleus that subsequently undergoes fission (Figure 3.12). Fission produces two isotopes of different
elements and an average of 2.5 neutrons. If these neutrons are captured
by other U-235 atoms they too undergo fission, thus sustaining a chain
reaction.

The U-235 atom undergoes fission in more than 30 different ways,
which result in over 200 different isotopes. Two examples of U-235
fission are:

$$\,_{0}^{1}n \;+\; \,_{92}^{235}U \;\rightarrow\; \,_{42}^{103}Mo \;+\; \,_{50}^{131}Sn \;+\; 2\,_{0}^{1}n \;+\; energy;$$

neutron uranium molybdenum   tin   neutron

and

$$\,_{0}^{1}n \;+\; \,_{92}^{235}U \;\rightarrow\; \,_{56}^{139}Ba \;+\; \,_{36}^{94}Kr \;+\; 3\,_{0}^{1}n \;+\; energy.$$

neutron uranium   barium   krypton neutron

Notice that the mass and charge of the particles on the left side are
equal to those on the right.

The unstable isotopes that result from fission emit radioactive
particles at various rates until a stable form is reestablished. The unit
of measure of this rate is the *half-life* — the time it takes half the nuclei
of a radioactive isotope to decay (Figure 3.13). For example, the half-
life of strontium-90 is 28 years. If we start with one gram of Sr-90,

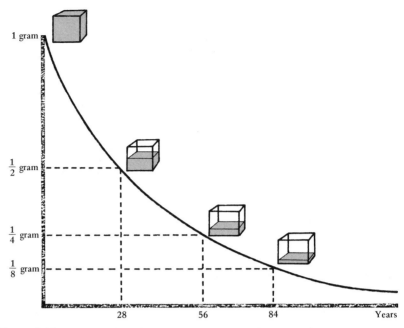

Figure 3.13
The amount of radioactivity from a strontium-90 source decreases by half every 28 years. *(After Paul G. Hewitt,* Conceptual Physics: A New Introduction to Your Environment *[Boston: Little, Brown and Company, 1971], p. 496.)*

0.5 grams remain after 28 years. After another 28 years, 0.25 grams remain. After 10 half-lives, all isotopes emit so little radioactivity that they are essentially decayed.

Nuclear fission reactions release tremendous amounts of energy through the conversion of a small amount of matter into energy ($E = mc^2$). Nuclear fission reactions can be carried out continuously in devices called nuclear reactors. At present the only isotope that is used as a nuclear energy source is U-235. However, naturally occurring uranium deposits contain so little U-235 that the U-235 must be concentrated to about 3 percent of its original amount before it is capable of sustaining a chain reaction within the reactor.

NUCLEAR FUSION   The nuclei of atoms can undergo a change essentially the opposite of nuclear fission called *nuclear fusion.* At temperatures near 100,000,-000°C, nuclei of hydrogen and other light elements can fuse together to form heavier nuclei. This process also involves the conversion of mass to energy. Some of the energy is used to bind the nucleus together, and the remainder is given off as excess energy. Scientists currently believe that the sun acts as a gigantic fusion reactor in which hydrogen nuclei are fused to form a helium nucleus. The excess energy in this process is emitted from the sun in the form of electromagnetic radiation. In the future fusion reactions may serve as a source of energy for man if these reactions can be controlled.

The discovery of these fundamental principles of chemistry and atomic physics has been instrumental in the development of our modern technological society. By various chemical reactions, industry has been able to manufacture countless products from the inorganic and organic materials that exist in the lithosphere, biosphere, hydrosphere, and atmosphere (Table 3.4). Too often, though, we have lacked adequate concern for the environmental consequences of their production, usage, and disposal (Figure 3.14). The complex collection of chemical

USES OF MATTER

Figure 3.14
An aerial view of an industrial complex in Cleveland, Ohio, that manufactures many primary products. *(Rotkin, Photography for Industry.)*

Table 3.4
Usage of chemically processed materials in the United States, 1969 (1 pound = 0.454 kilograms).

	Pounds per person per year	Total
Polymers		
Synthetic fibers	30	
Plastics	80	
Synthetic rubber	20	130
Paper products		
Paper	240	
Paperboard	260	
Other fibers	10	510
Metals		
Steel	1,400	
Aluminum	40	
Copper	20	
Lead	10	
Zinc	10	1,480
Cleaning agents		
Detergents	25	
Soaps	5	30
Fertilizers		
Nitrogen as N	70	
Phosphorus as P_2O_5	40	
Potassium as K_2O	40	150
Pesticides		
Insecticides	2	
Herbicides	2	
Fungicides	1	5
Medicinal chemicals	150	
Glass	130	
Building materials		
Cement	900	
Plaster	100	1,000

Source: Adapted with permission from G. Barrow, *General Chemistry* (Belmont, Cal.: Wadsworth Publishing Co., 1972), p. 621.

reactions carried out by living organisms and abiotic processes must function properly if ecosystems are to survive. Foreign substances that disturb the biotic and abiotic chemical machinery will cause an ecosystem to function at less than optimal conditions, perhaps even cause its expiration.

			KEY WORDS
atoms	isotopes	chemical changes	AND SUMMARY
electrons	molecule	nuclear changes	STATEMENTS
protons	ion	gamma rays	
neutrons	ionic bond	beta particle	
nucleus	covalently bonded	alpha particle	
element	physical changes	nuclear fission	
atomic number	heat of fusion	half-life	
atomic mass	heat of vaporization	nuclear fusion	

All matter is composed of atoms.

Energy is contained in matter and is required for interactions to occur in matter.

Protons and neutrons reside within the tiny dense nucleus of an atom; electrons orbit the nucleus.

Atoms are described by atomic numbers and atomic masses. Isotopes of an element have the same atomic number but different atomic masses.

The nuclei of atoms are thought to be stabilized by neutron shielding and by the conversion of a small amount of matter to energy that is expended in holding the nucleus together.

Electrons orbiting atoms are arranged in a shell structure. The capacities of the shells are as follows: first shell 2, second shell 8, third shell 18, fourth shell 32. Filled shells are stable electron arrangements.

Atoms join together to form ionic and covalent compounds. Ionic substances are bonded by attraction of oppositely charged ions. Covalent bonds result from the sharing of electrons between atoms.

Changes in matter are classified as physical, chemical, and nuclear. Physical changes involve the separation of molecules but not an alteration of arrangement of atoms within the molecules. Chemical changes involve changes in the arrangement of atoms within or between molecules. Nuclear changes are the result of reorganizations within the nuclei of atoms. All changes involve energy.

Matter is conserved.

Unstable nuclei tend toward a more stabilized condition by emitting alpha, beta, or gamma particles or by undergoing fission.

1. The alchemist thought the elements were earth, air, fire, and water. How would you classify these "substances" today?

2. If a spaceship can escape the Earth's gravity by virtue of its speed, what can be concluded about the speed of gaseous molecules in the atmosphere?

3. In the study of environmental science, why is it important to have at least a general understanding of the composition of matter?

QUESTIONS AND
PROJECTS

4. Comment on the definition of pollution as "matter out of place."

5. Smell is an example of the sensing of the presence of certain molecules. Cite examples of how this process is used by man to protect himself. Is smell always a reliable means of protection against toxic gases?

6. Why is it important to distinguish between physical, chemical, and nuclear changes?

7. Trace the production of a basic material needed for our society such as steel. Indicate points or processes that especially disrupt ecosystems.

8. What parts of the body would be most affected if *(a)* air, *(b)* food, or *(c)* your surroundings were contaminated by the emission of alpha and beta particles? Gamma rays?

SELECTED READINGS

The following are physical science texts that give a historical background and further depth to the concepts of chemistry and atomic physics for the nonscience student:

Booth, V. H. *Elements of Physical Science: The Nature of Matter and Energy.* New York: Macmillan, 1970. Chapter 13, 20, 22, 23, 25, 28.

Miles, V. W. *College Physical Science.* New York: Harper and Row, 1964. Chapters 12, 13, 16.

Ward, C. R. *This Blue Planet.* Boston: Little, Brown and Co., 1972. Chapters 8–12. Chapters 10 and 11 include basic discussions of organic compounds and the physics and chemistry of life.

chapter

4

Water: Properties and Significance

The Earth is the only body in our solar system that can truly be called the "watery planet." Water is such a common substance that it is usually taken for granted. However, it plays an essential role in the functioning of both the abiotic and the biotic portions of the environment.

An appreciation of the significance of water is gained by considering our water requirements. An average person cycles about 2.5 quarts (2.4 liters)* of water per day through his body by drinking liquids (45 percent), by eating water containing foods (40 percent) (Table 4.1), and by respiration of food (15 percent). This water is lost through excretion (60 percent), perspiration (20 percent), and expiration through the lungs (20 percent). The human body is approximately 65 percent water, but the water is not evenly distributed. Blood is 90 percent water, muscle tissue is 75 percent, and bones about 20 percent. A mere 12 percent loss of the body's water content is fatal. Water is essential for digestion, transporting nutrients and oxygen, movement of carbon dioxide to the lungs, and regulation of body temperature.

However, it is in maintaining our standard of living that we use the

OUR WATER NEEDS

Table 4.1
Water content of nine selected foods.

Food	Percentage of water
Wheat flakes	3.8
Wheat flour	12.0
White bread	35.0
Apple pie	48.0
Peanuts	2.6
Hamburger	47.0
Lobster	78.0
Eggs, whole	74.0
Carrots, raw	88.0

* See inside back cover for conversion tables to volume.

71

most water. Each of us uses about 150 gallons per day (Table 4.2). Just flushing the toilet uses five gallons of water. Huge quantities of

Table 4.2
Domestic water uses.

Use	Percentage of total consumption
Flushing toilet	41
Washing and bathing	37
Kitchen use	6
Drinking	5
Washing clothes	4
Household cleaning	3
Watering lawns and gardens	3
Washing car	1
Total	100

Source: C. N. Dufor and E. Becker, "Public Water Supplies of the 100 Largest Cities in the U.S.," United States Geological Survey, Water Supply Paper 1812, 5 (1964).

water are used in industry: 43,000 gallons to produce a ton of paper, 88,000 for a ton of steel, 350,000 for a ton of aluminum. The most staggering water usage is in food production: one egg, 130 gallons; a quart of milk, 1,000 gallons; a pound of beef, 3,500 gallons. Adding water requirements for food to other needs raises our individual consumption to 3,500 gallons a day. Most of the water is expended for raising crops and not for livestock or food processing. And about 99 percent of the water taken up by crop plants is not used in photosynthesis but is given off to the atmosphere. An acre of corn may lose 4,000 gallons of water in a single day. In contrast to agricultural usage, water used by industries and municipalities is returned to the source and can be re-used.

Each organism has a characteristic water requirement. Higher animals use water to carry out functions similar to those of man. Although plants are simpler, water is needed for transporting nutrients between roots and leaves. In all organisms water serves as the medium in which all life-sustaining chemical reactions such as photosynthesis and respiration take place. In short, no water, no biosphere.

PROPERTIES OF WATER

A Polar Molecule

Many of the properties of water can be understood only by examining the intricacies of the water molecule. In the previous chapter we saw that the water molecule is held together by electron-sharing covalent bonds. The arrangement of electrons in the water molecule gives it a characteristic shape and unique properties. The bonded atoms in a water molecule do not lie on a straight line but instead form a 104-degree angle described between the hydrogen, oxygen, and hydrogen atoms (Figure 4.1). In addition, the electrons are not distributed uniformly over the entire molecule. Because the oxygen atom has a stronger attraction for the shared electrons than do the hydrogen atoms, the electrons spend more time in the region of the oxygen atom. Hence the ends of the molecule are oppositely charged, the hydrogen end positive and the oxygen end netative. Coupled with the 104-degree bond angle, this uneven charge distribution causes the molecule to be very *polar,* the charges acting as tiny magnets. These charged sites residing on a water molecule allow it to interact with other charged particles. Figure 4.2 shows that the water molecules align themselves so that they are attracted to either positive or negative sources.

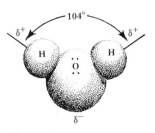

Figure 4.1
Shape and charged regions of the water molecule. The δ indicates a partial charge.

Hydrogen Bonding

Polar water molecules are aligned in such a way that the positively charged region on one molecule orients itself toward the negatively charged region on a neighboring molecule (Figure 4.3). The attraction between neighboring molecules is called *hydrogen bonding.* Because two hydrogen bonds can be formed per molecule, bonding takes place in three directions.

As a result of this bonding, water has many unusual properties. On a weight per unit basis, water has the highest heat of vaporization of all substances (Table 4.3), and except for ammonia it has the highest heat of fusion and specific heat. In addition, on a weight per molecule basis the freezing and boiling points of water are unusually high compared with other substances. For example, molecules of ammonia (NH_3), hydrogen fluoride (HF), and water weigh 17, 20, and 18 atomic mass units per molecule respectively, yet their boiling points are -33, 19, and 100°C (-27.4, 66.2, 212°F). These unique properties, the consequence of hydrogen bonding, give water greater stability. Hence it not only melts and boils at elevated temperatures, but more energy is required in the processes.

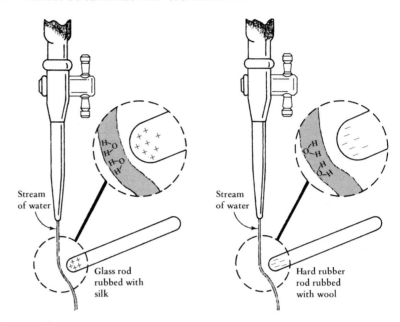

Stream
of water

Glass rod
rubbed with
silk

Stream
of water

Hard rubber
rod rubbed
with wool

Figure 4.2
A stream of polar water molecules is attracted to either positively or negatively charged objects. Nonpolar liquids such as gasoline are not affected.

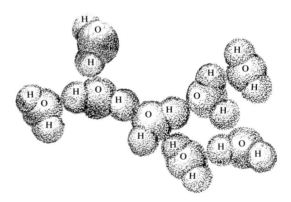

Figure 4.3
Charged sites on the water molecule result in an added attraction between molecules called hydrogen bonding.

Table 4.3
Comparison of properties of water and other substances.

	Melting point (°C)	Heat of fusion (cal/g)	Heat of vaporization (cal/g)	Specific heat (cal/g/°C)
Water	0	79.7	539.6	1.00
Acetone	−95	23.4	125	0.51
Ethyl alcohol	−117	25	204	0.52
Benzene	5.5	30.3	94.3	0.40
Carbon tetrachloride	−23	4.2	46.4	0.20
Mercury	−39	2.8	70.6	0.033
Sulfuric acid	−10.5	24	122	0.27
Ammonia	−77.7	108.1	327.1	1.05

The environmental implications of these unique properties of water are many and far reaching. Water's exceptionally high boiling and freezing points, specific heat, and heats of fusion and vaporization are key factors in moderating (regulating) temperature fluctuations in the environment. An example of the influence of water's high specific heat is seen by contrasting the climates of San Francisco and St. Louis (Figure 4.4). Although at the same latitude, San Francisco next to the

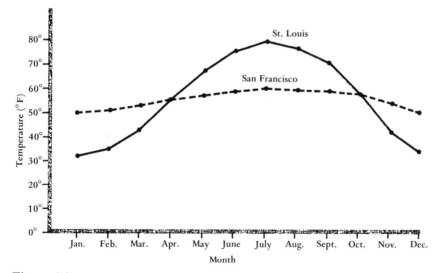

Figure 4.4
Contrast of the average monthly temperture at a continental location, St. Louis, and a maritime location, San Francisco. *(From local climatological data, U.S. Department of Commerce-National Weather Service.)*

ocean experiences much smaller annual temperature variations than St. Louis. Because of the high specific heat of water, large bodies of water tend to maintain a fairly constant temperature throughout the year. In the winter, the ocean surface water is warmer than the air passing over it, so heat energy is supplied to the air by conduction. In the summer, the water is cooler than the air, so heat energy is conducted from air to water. As a result, coastal areas subject to on-shore winds do not experience wide temperature variations.

Solutions

CONCENTRATION OF
SOLUTIONS

Water has the ability to dissolve many substances. A measure of the amount of a substance in a given volume or weight of water is referred to as its *concentration*. Concentrations are expressed in several ways. For example, 1 gram of salt dissolved in 99 grams of water is a solution of 1 percent salt concentration or 1 part per hundred. Lower concentrations are expressed in terms of parts per thousand (ppt), parts per million (ppm), or parts per billion (ppb). A solution with a concentration of 1 part per million is 1,000 times more dilute than a concentration of 1 part per thousand. The values 1 percent, 10 ppt, 10,000 ppm, and 10,000,000 ppb are alternative ways of expressing a concentration of 1 gram of salt dissolved in 99 grams of water. Although concentrations in the part per million range seem insignificant, Table 4.4 gives an indication of the importance of some substances even at low concentrations.

Table 4.4
Selected drinking water standards recommended by the United States Public Health Service, 1962.

Chemical	Suggested concentration limit in ppm
Arsenic	0.01
Chloride	250
Copper	1
Iron	0.3
Nitrate	45
Phenols	0.001
Sulfate	250
Zinc	5

Everyone has put sugar in solutions such as coffee, tea, or Kool-Aid. If more sugar were added in an attempt to see how much would dissolve, it would be seen that there is a definite limit to the amount that will dissolve in a fixed volume of water. At this limit, the solution is said to be *saturated*. One hundred grams of water will dissolve no more than 204 grams of sugar at 20°C (68°F).

It is the polar nature of the molecule that is responsible for water's ability to dissolve many substances. Figure 4.5 demonstrates how it dissolves an ionic substance, table salt (NaCl). The water molecules are aligned so that the negative region of the water molecule interacts with the positive sodium ions, the positive region with the negative chloride ions.

Dissolving a substance involves an interaction between the solvent (water) and ions. If the interaction yields sufficient energy to overcome

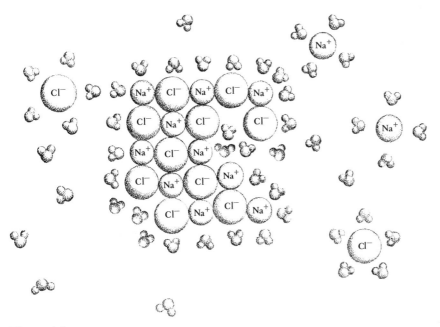

Figure 4.5
Schematic drawing of water dissolving an ionic substance. The water molecules are aligned so that the negative region of the molecule attracts the positive ions, while the positive region attracts the negative ions.

the forces that hold the ions together in the solid state, the substance dissolves. When both solid and water are present, there is continual competition between the reactions that dissolve the ions and the reactions that return ions to the solid crystalline state. In a saturated solution the rates of the two processes are identical, and the system is said to be in moving, or dynamic, equilibrium despite the absence of visible activity.

Water interacts with some nonionic molecules that have polar bonds. Glucose, one of several compounds called sugars, is such a molecule (Figure 4.6). The O-H part of the molecule is polar. Because there are five such sites, water molecules interact and readily dissolve glucose. Other sugar molecules such as sucrose (table sugar) also contain large numbers of O-H groups and are easily dissolved by water. This explains how blood (90 percent water) transports chemical energy.

The wide variety of substances that water dissolves is demonstrated by the composition of seawater. Table 4.5 lists the most abundant ions dissolved in seawater, which contains traces of nearly all of the naturally occurring elements. As a result of human activity during the past three decades, pollutants such as radioactive wastes and pesticides are also present.

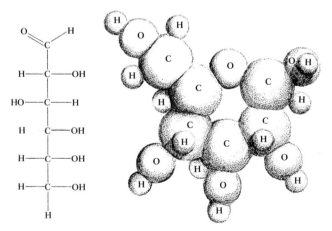

Figure 4.6
The glucose molecule contains five polar —OH sites that interact with polar water molecules. The glucose molecule is thus dissolved.

Table 4.5
Concentration of the major ions dissolved in seawater.

Positive ions	Percentage	Negative ions	Percentage
Sodium, Na^+	1.06	Chloride, Cl^-	1.9
Magnesium, Mg^{2+}	0.13	Sulfate, SO_4^{2-}	0.26
Calcium, Ca^{2+}	0.04	Bicarbonate, HCO_3^-	0.01
Potassium, K^+	0.04	Bromide, Br^-	0.006
Strontium, Sr^{2+}	0.01	Fluoride, F^-	0.0001
		Iodide, I^-	0.000005

Not all substances are soluble in water. Gasoline and oil are made up largely of mixtures of compounds that contain few polar groups, so oil slicks do not dissolve. Some proteins, fats, and carbohydrates (components of all organisms) are also insoluble because they are made up of very large molecules with insufficient polar sites to allow them to be dissolved. If these substances were soluble it would be fatal to shower, or swim, or get caught in the rain. As most rocks and minerals do not readily dissolve, we can expect little alteration of landforms resulting from the dissolution of rocks during a lifetime (Figure 4.7).

Figure 4.7
Limestone caves such as the Guacharo Cave result when limestone is dissolved by groundwater over a long period of time. (De Wys, Inc.)

EFFECT OF
TEMPERATURE

The solubility of solids and liquids usually increases with increasing temperature. The effects of temperature on the solubility of some common chemicals are shown in Table 4.6. An important exception to the rule is calcium carbonate ($CaCO_3$), whose solubility decreases with increasing temperature. Because of this, calcium carbonate in many domestic and industrial water supplies may form deposits in hot water pipes, even completely fill them.

Gases are also soluble in water, but unlike most solids, gases decrease in solubility with increasing temperature (Figure 4.8, Table 4.6). This characteristic is important because during summer months, when river or lake temperatures can rise to near 30°C (86°F), the water's capacity to hold oxygen is decreased, thereby exerting an additional stress on aquatic organisms.

EFFECT OF PRESSURE

The solubility of gases also depends upon pressure. An increase in pressure causes an increase in solubility, so precaution must be taken by any diver who descends below 60 feet (18.6 meters). As a diver

Table 4.6
Effect of temperature on the water solubility of some substances.

Substance	Solubility in grams per 100 grams of water			
	0°C	20°C	50°C	100°C
Solids				
Sodium chloride (table salt)	35.7	36.0	37.0	39.8
Sodium hydroxide (lye)	42	109	145	347
Barium sulfate	0.000115	0.00024	0.00034	0.00041
Calcium sulfate (Gypsum)	0.176	0.201	0.210	0.162
Calcium chloride (road salt)	58	79	134	161
Gases[a]				
Oxygen	0.0070	0.0044	0.0026	0
Carbon dioxide	0.335	0.169	0.076	0
Carbon monoxide	0.0044	0.0028	0.0018	0
Nitrogen	0.0029	0.0019	0.0012	0
Nitric oxide	0.0098	0.0062	0.0038	0
Methane	0.0040	0.0023	0.0014	0
Sulfur dioxide	22.83	11.28		

[a] Solubility at 1 atmosphere pressure.

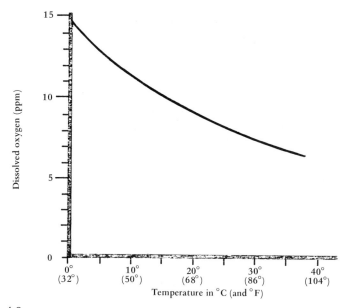

Figure 4.8
Dissolved oxygen in natural waters illustrates the decrease in solubility of gases with increasing temperature.

descends the increasing pressure results in increasing solubility of nitrogen gas. If he rises too rapidly, the decrease in pressure causes bubbles of nitrogen gas to form in his bloodstream. This condition is called the "bends," which can be fatal.

The effect of pressure on gas solubility is also important for other organisms. Increased concentrations of nitrogen gas in the Columbia River result from water surging out of huge dams (Figure 4.9). Tiny

Figure 4.9
The Bonneville Dam between Washington and Oregon on the Columbia River is one of a series of dams on this river that has contributed to young salmon mortality from nitrogen bubble disease. *(Monkmeyer.)*

air bubbles are carried down into deep pools below the dams (Figure 4.10). The increased water pressure causes the air bubbles to dissolve, and the fish living in this environment acquire high concentrations of gases in their bloodstreams. When the fish swim out of deep pools into shallower water, decompression causes nitrogen bubbles to form in their blood (Figure 4.11) and death ensues quickly. This problem has caused multimillion-dollar losses in the salmon runs of the Columbia and Snake Rivers in the Pacific Northwest. To solve the problem, the dams must be restructured to prevent deep turbulent flow of water leaving the dam.

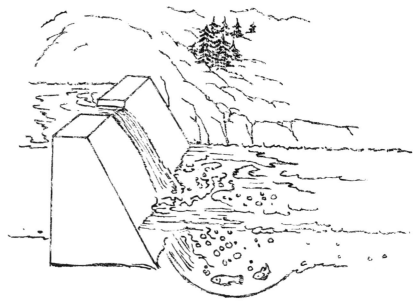

Figure 4.10
Increased pressure on bubbles carried into deep pools behind dams results in increased concentrations of nitrogen gas in water. Fish acquire these higher concentrations in their blood and die from the bends when they rise to the surface.

Figure 4.11
A young salmon killed by nitrogen bubble disease. The bubbles are under the skin to the right of the pen point. *(Washington State Game Department.)*

An environment of the proper acid level is essential to all living organisms. Water containing no dissolved substances has its own characteristic acidity because water molecules react among themselves to form positive hydronium ions and negative hydroxide ions:

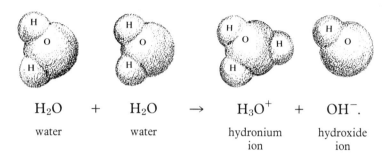

$$H_2O \quad + \quad H_2O \quad \rightarrow \quad H_3O^+ \quad + \quad OH^-.$$

water   water   hydronium   hydroxide
                                        ion   ion

At any given time only one out of every 550 million water molecules is in the form of hydronium and hydroxide ions. Certain types of chemical compounds react with water so as to increase the hydronium ion concentration; these are called *acids,* and the solution they form is termed acidic. Some of the more common acids are hydrochloric, HCl; sulfuric, H_2SO_4; nitric, HNO_3; and carbonic, H_2CO_3. When one of these acids is dissolved, it reacts with water to produce a positive hydronium ion and a negative ion. For example:

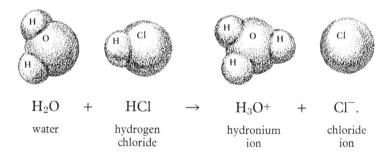

$$H_2O \quad + \quad HCl \quad \rightarrow \quad H_3O+ \quad + \quad Cl^-.$$

water   hydrogen   hydronium   chloride
             chloride   ion   ion

Other types of compounds, termed *bases,* increase the hydroxide concentration when dissolved in water. Such solutions are called basic, or alkaline, solutions. Common bases include ammonia, NH_3; sodium hydroxide, $NaOH$; potassium hydroxide, KOH; and calcium hydroxide, $Ca(OH)_2$. For example:

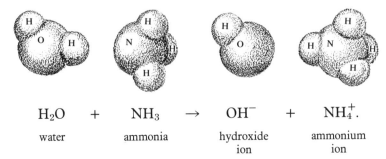

$$H_2O \quad + \quad NH_3 \quad \rightarrow \quad OH^- \quad + \quad NH_4^+.$$

water   ammonia   hydroxide   ammonium
ion   ion

The hydronium ion concentration, or acidity, of a solution is usually stated in terms of *pH*, a scale that ranges from 0 to 14. Water with no substances dissolved in it has a pH of 7 (the neutral point on the acidity scale). From pH 7 to pH 0 the acidity of a solution increases, whereas the alkalinity increases from pH 7 to pH 14. Figure 4.12 gives pH values of some common liquids.

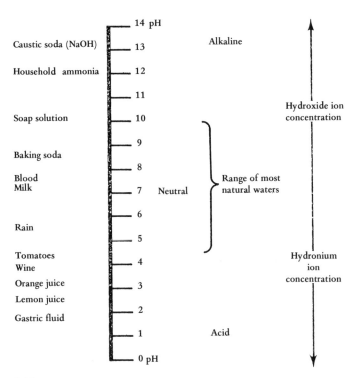

Figure 4.12
The pH scale and the pH values of some common liquids.

The pH scale is not linear. For example, hydronium ion concentrations increase by a factor of 10 when the pH decreases by one unit. And an increase of one pH unit represents a ten-fold increase in hydroxide ion concentration.

The control of the acidity of environments is essential to the well-being of organisms. Certain plants grow best when the soil is slightly acid whereas other types grow much better in alkaline soils. The pH of human blood must remain relatively constant; a change from the normal 7.35 to a value of 6.9 causes death. Acidity also affects the maintenance of structures; for example, the rates of corrosion of metals are much higher under acidic conditions.

Solutions of acids and bases react with one another to produce water, a positive ion, and a negative ion. For example:

$$NaOH \quad + \quad HCl \quad \rightarrow \quad H_2O \quad + \quad Na^+ \quad + \quad Cl^-.$$

| sodium hydroxide | hydrochloric acid | water | sodium ion | chloride ion |

Such a reaction is called a *neutralization reaction*, because if proper amounts of the acid solution and the base solution are mixed, the pH returns to 7, the neutral point. If the resulting solution were evaporated, only the sodium chloride would remain.

Suspensions

When a substance dissolves completely in water, a homogeneous solution results. Such a solution does not disperse light because the dissolved ions or molecules are too small. Natural waters, however, are seldom homogeneous solutions. They are mixtures that also contain suspended solid particles such as clay or microscopic organisms. Light is scattered or absorbed by the suspended material (Figure 4.13), causing the water to appear *turbid*, or cloudy. High levels of turbidity have a marked effect on aquatic plants that require light for photosynthesis. Some fish also require clear water to find food. Turbidity also causes abnormal warming of surface water because of the absorption of solar radiation by the suspended particles.

Suspended particles can be removed by physical methods such as settling or filtering. Large particles, including sand, settle out rapidly, but very small clay particles or bacteria may require a month to settle out (Figure 4.14). Dissolved substances, however, cannot be settled or filtered out of solution. Since the composition of a suspension changes and the composition of a solution remains constant, the methods used

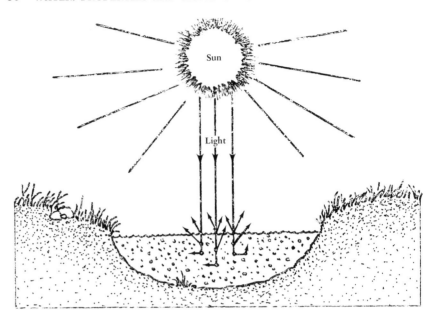

Figure 4.13
In water, light is scattered by suspended particles that make the water appear turbid and cause shorter penetration distance. Some of the light is scattered back out of the water and some is absorbed.

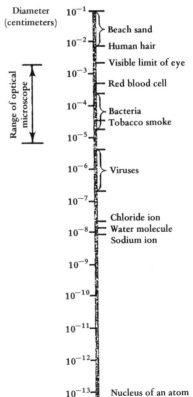

Figure 4.14
Comparative sizes of some small particles.

to remove pollutants depend upon whether the pollutant is in suspension or solution.

We have already discussed the anomalous values of water's high heats of fusion and vaporization and its high freezing and boiling points. Water also exhibits unusual density variations with temperature. Except for water, all liquids expand or increase in volume as they are heated above their melting point. Water contracts as its temperature rises from 0 to 4°C (32 to 39.2°F). Thereafter, it expands upon further heating, as other liquids (Figure 4.15). Hence, water has its greatest density at 4°C.

This unusual density characteristic has a significant effect on lakes in the temperate regions of the world. During the winter the lake is

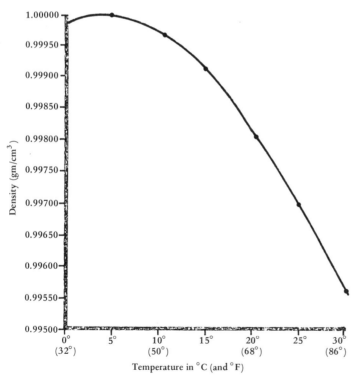

Figure 4.15
The effect of temperature on the density of water.

ice-covered, and the water temperature varies from 0°C just below the ice to 4°C near the bottom. When spring arrives, the ice melts and surface waters warm. However, because water becomes more dense as its temperature rises toward 4°C, the warmer but denser water sinks. Convection currents aided by wind mix the lake until its temperature is uniformly 4°C. The density throughout the entire lake is then the same. This mixing is called the spring turnover. As the surface water continues to warm through the summer, the density differences between surface and bottom increase. The result is a stable stratification of lighter and warmer water overlying denser and colder water on the bottom. Very little mixing takes place between these two layers. The top layer is called the *epilimnion,* the bottom layer the *hypolimnion,* and the transition zone the *thermocline* (Figure 4.16). When cooler weather arrives in the fall the temperature of the surface layer decreases. Eventually, the densities of the epilimnion and the hypolimnion become equal. Under these conditions, the entire lake can again be easily mixed by the wind. This mixing period is called the fall turnover (Figure 4.17).

In lakes the major source of dissolved oxygen for fish is an exchange between the atmosphere and surface waters. During periods of lake

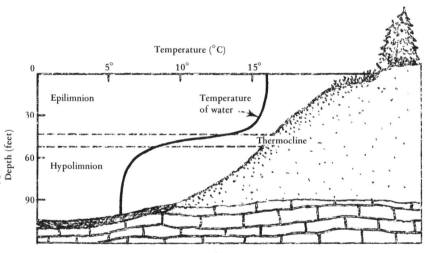

Figure 4.16
A lake in summer stratifies into two layers as a result of temperature differences.

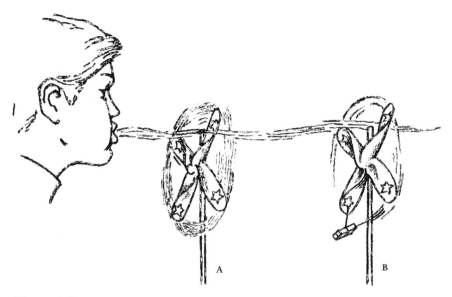

Figure 4.17
The pinwheel with evenly distributed density will be set into motion much more easily than the pinwheel that is heavier at the bottom. Pinwheel A is analogous to a lake with constant temperature. Pinwheel B is analogous to a stratified lake.

stratification the oxygen supply of the epilimnion is replenished, whereas that of the hypolimnion may be depleted. Because certain species of fish require cold temperatures and high oxygen concentration (lake trout, whitefish, and cisco are examples), turnover periods are essential for replenishing oxygen.

For most other substances the solid state is heavier than its liquid state, so the solid sinks to the bottom. However, the density of ice is 10 percent less than that of water, thus ice floats. If the reverse were so, ice formed at the surface would sink to the bottom. During winter months there would then be a continual accumulation of ice until the body of water was completely frozen. Under such conditions little aquatic life would exist.

Because ice is a good insulator, ice depths on lakes seldom exceed three or four feet. The rest of the lake stays at a temperature between 0°C (32°F) and 4°C (39°F) thereby preventing the exposure of aquatic organisms to subfreezing temperatures.

DENSITY OF
SOLID STATE

The expansion of water upon freezing is a major factor in the physical disintegration of rocks and requires that water pipes be buried deep beneath the soil and automobile radiators be filled with antifreeze in regions where winters are severe.

KEY WORDS
AND SUMMARY
STATEMENTS

polar	acid	turbidity
hydrogen bonding	base	epilimnion
concentration	pH	hypolimnion
saturated	neutralization reaction	thermocline

Tremendous volumes of water are required to raise and process our food; thus our water requirements are much greater than the 2.5 quarts per day needed to maintain the water balance in our bodies.

Many of water's unique properties can be understood by realizing that water is a polar molecule, i.e., a molecule without an even distribution of electrons over the entire molecule. Polarity and the 104° bond angle in water account for the hydrogen bonding that in turn accounts for water's high boiling and freezing points.

Water's specific heat and heats of fusion and vaporization are unusually high compared with other substances. These properties moderate temperature fluctuations, making the environment hospitable.

Water is a good but not unlimited solvent. It does not dissolve nonpolar molecules to a significant extent. The amount of a substance that water will dissolve depends on both temperature and pressure, especially for gases.

Added to water, certain substances called acids and bases alter the pH. Proper acidity or alkalinity are necessary for organisms to survive. Acids and bases are capable of neutralizing each other.

Suspensions are not true solutions. Because they scatter light they make their surroundings appear cloudy, or turbid. Suspended material can be separated from water by physical methods such as filtering or settling.

Water becomes more dense when it is warmed from 0 to 4°C. Thereafter, it behaves like other liquids and expands upon further heating. In addition, the solid state of water (ice) is less dense than the liquid state, causing it to float. These two unique properties are important in maintaining aquatic life throughout an annual cycle, especially in lakes.

1. Give an example of water in the lithosphere, atmosphere, and biosphere. How did it get there and how can it escape?

2. What would happen to the surface temperature of a waterless Earth?

3. Compare the cost of dehydrated fruits with that of ordinary fruits. Why don't the dehydrated fruits spoil as the others do?

4. Speculate on the consequences to man if all water were absolutely pure.

5. Why do aquatic organisms use the oxygen dissolved in the water rather than the oxygen in the water molecule?

6. Suggest reasons why the concentration limits for substances in drinking water vary so widely (see Table 4.4).

7. From your knowledge of the physical properties of water, suggest reasons why water is used to put out fires. Why isn't it used on gasoline fires?

Davis, K., and Day, J. *Water: The Mirror of Science.* Garden City, N.Y.: Doubleday and Co., Inc., 1961. Discusses further unique properties of water and the importance of water for life.

Laas, W., and Beicos, S. *Water in Your Life.* New York: Popular Library, 1967. Deals with topics from the physical properties of water to composition of natural waters.

Platt, R. *Water: The Wonder of Life.* Englewood Cliffs, N.J.: Prentice-Hall, Inc., 1971. Includes a variety of topics related to water, e.g., structure, life within water, thermal pollution.

chapter

5

The Lithosphere: Characteristics and Degradation

To this point we have dealt with the concepts of matter and energy and the important underlying principles governing their distribution and roles in the environment. Having seen that it is convenient to view our environment as being composed of four interdependent spheres, we shall now investigate them, first by means of an overall perspective of the composition, structure, and functions of each and then by considering the ramifications of man's impact upon them. Given the scope of this work, however, we shall examine their characteristics and processes only to the extent that they help us to understand environmental problems.

The lithosphere is composed of *rock* distributed into four concentric spheres within the Earth: crust, mantle, and the inner and outer core (Figure 5.1).

SUBDIVISIONS OF THE LITHOSPHERE

The view that the Earth is composed of concentric rock spheres was not always held. At one time the Earth was thought to have a hollow interior. There was no scientific basis for this belief; rather it evolved from speculation and eventually became widely accepted. Even in the 1960s, when Congress was considering financing the drilling of a well through the crust and into the mantle, some congressmen received letters from irate constituents who feared that drilling such a hole

93

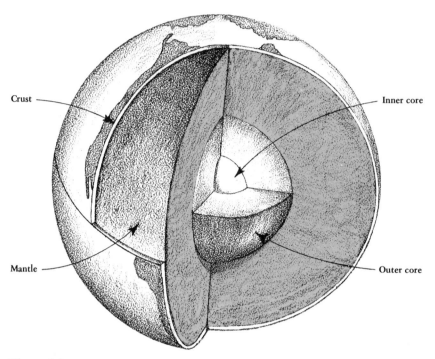

Figure 5.1
The subdivision of the lithosphere into crust, mantle, and core. *(U.S. Department of Interior, Geological Survey.)*

would be like pulling the stopper in a bathtub, allowing all the ocean water to drain into the Earth's interior.

The Earth's Interior

The *crust* is the only lithospheric subdivision that man has studied directly, yet even the deepest oil wells have failed to penetrate it completely. Scientists have had to rely upon indirect means to study most of the Earth's interior. As meteorites, or "shooting stars," probably had the same origin as the Earth, they offer clues to the composition and structure of the interior. Some meteorites are composed of iron and magnesium, others are mixtures of iron and nickel. These materials are likely the dominant constituents of the Earth's interior.

Analyses of seismic (earthquake) waves, however, have provided the most significant insight regarding the Earth's interior. An *earthquake* is a consequence of long-term accumulation of potential energy in crustal blocks of rocks. Eventually, a critical point is reached and the blocks fracture, releasing their stored energy. The energy is propagated in the form of waves along the Earth's surface and through its interior. The latter, called body waves, travel at varying velocities depending upon the properties of the materials through which they travel. Following an earthquake, sensitive instruments located at monitoring stations around the globe record these waves and evaluate the changes they've undergone after they have passed through the Earth. Scientists have noted a sudden change in wave speed at the base of the Earth's crust. They have therefore concluded that the underlying *mantle,* which is about 1,800 miles (2,900 kilometers) thick and accounts for 80 percent of the total volume of the Earth, is of a markedly different type of material from that composing the crust. It is apparently made up of a very dense material rich in iron and magnesium. The behavior of seismic waves also indicates that the Earth's *core* consists of two parts, an outer liquid core and a solid inner core. Studies of meteorites suggest that the core is composed of iron or possibly of an alloy of iron and nickel.

The rock that composes the crust is classified as either igneous, sedimentary, or metamorphic. This is not an arbitrary classification scheme; rather, each name specifies the general environment in which the rock evolved.

Igneous rocks are the ancestors of all rocks (Figure 5.2). It is even said that there was igneous rock in the beginning and that from it all other things have been derived. Igneous rocks evolve as a result of

The Crust: Composition and Structure

IGNEOUS ROCK

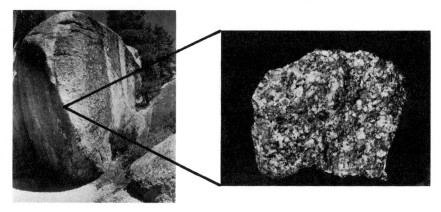

Figure 5.2
A close-up of granite isolated from an outcrop of igneous rock at Lake Tahoe. (Left: *Palmer from Monkmeyer.* Right: *Field Museum of Natural History, Chicago.*)

the cooling and solidification of a hot, molten material called *magma*. Magma may remain within the Earth and slowly solidify, forming coarse-grained rock; or it may spew forth as lava through vents of volcanoes or cracks in the Earth's crust and rapidly solidify, forming fine-grained rock. Thus igneous rocks evolve either upon the Earth or within the crust — an environment characterized by high, confining pressures and high temperatures.

SEDIMENTARY ROCK

Sedimentary rocks are derived rocks (Figure 5.3), many consisting of particles resulting from the *weathering* (chemical decomposition or physical disintegration) of other rocks. One process of forming sedimentary rock involves the breaking of sea waves against a rock-bound coast. Waves gradually grind shoreline rocks into small particles, which are sorted by size, carried away, and deposited elsewhere as beach sand. As the sand accumulates the grains are packed by their own weight and cemented together *(lithification)*. This common sedimentary rock is called sandstone. Energy is expended in initially breaking down the material, transporting it, and eventually lithifying it. Sediments may also consist of the excretions or skeletal remains of members of the biosphere. For example, when accumulations of calcareous (containing calcium carbonate) shell remains of shallow-water organisms are lithified, the result is limestone, a widespread and useful sedimentary rock.

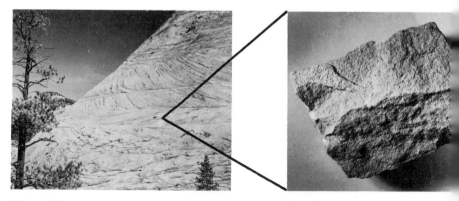

Figure 5.3
A close-up of sandstone isolated from an outcrop of sedimentary rock in Zion National Park, Utah. (Left: *Rathbone from Monkmeyer.* Right: *M. L. Brisson, University of Wisconsin, Green Bay.*)

Metamorphic rocks (Figure 5.4) are also derived. A rock is metamorphosed when it is subjected to the high confining pressures, intense heat, and chemically active fluids that exist deep within the Earth's crust. By definition, the metamorphic environment is never severe enough to melt the rock and return it to the magmatic state; the rock is simply deformed.

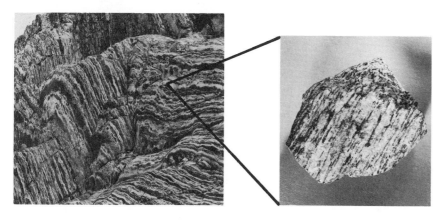

Figure 5.4
A close-up of gneiss isolated from an outcrop of metamorphic rock in Titus Canyon, California. (Left: *Ed Cooper, Photofind, S.F.* Right: *M. L. Brisson, University of Wisconsin, Green Bay.*)

During metamorphic deformation the particles that compose the rock sometimes become aligned, giving the rock a banded appearance. Such alignment may facilitate the cleaving of these rocks into platelike slabs. Slate is one example. When some rocks are subjected to the metamorphic environment, their constituent particles are recrystallized to a different size. For instance, when limestone is metamorphosed the result is the metamorphic rock, marble.

Each of the three major rock categories includes many rock types. Specification (whether it be a sandstone, limestone, or slate) is a function of small variations in available materials and the environmental conditions that prevailed during its formation.

A crustal rock generally contains two or three dominant minerals (Figure 5.5) and several minor ones (Table 5.1). *Minerals* are solids that are characterized by an orderly internal arrangement of atoms

Figure 5.5
Rock is made up of one or more minerals. Here, the dominant minerals are isolated from a sample of granite, in the center. *(M. L. Brisson, University of Wisconsin, Green Bay.)*

Table 5.1
Some common rock types and their major mineral constituents.

Rock classification	Rock type	Important minerals
Igneous	Granite	Quartz (silicon dioxide)
		Muscovite (potassium aluminum silicate)
		Feldspars (potassium, calcium, and sodium aluminum silicates)
	Dunite	Olivine (iron, magnesium silicate)
	Basalt	Feldspars
		Pyroxenes (iron, magnesium silicate)
Sedimentary	Sandstone	Quartz
	Limestone	Calcite (calcium carbonate)
	Dolomite	Dolomite (calcium, magnesium carbonate)
Metamorphic	Quartzite	Quartz
	Marble	Calcite

(Figure 5.6). They usually have a definite composition, or at least a limited range of composition. The most abundant minerals in the Earth's crust contain primarily oxygen and silicon atoms (Table 5.2). Oxygen atoms account for about half the total mass of atoms contained in rock-forming minerals, silicon, the next most abundant atom, for about one-quarter. They are usually combined in the form of silicate ions (SiO_4^{4-}) that are in turn combined with aluminum, iron, and calcium ions to form the common minerals of the Earth's crust.

   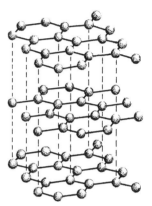

Figure 5.6
The physical properties of a mineral are determined by its internal atomic structure. Carbon (C) in the form of diamond *(left)* has considerably different characteristics from carbon in the form of graphite *(right)*. (Left photograph: *Field Museum of Natural History, Chicago.* Right photograph: *M. L. Brisson, University of Wisconsin, Green Bay.*)

Table 5.2
The ten most abundant elements
in the Earth's crust.

Element	Percentage by weight
Oxygen	46.60
Silicon	27.72
Aluminum	8.13
Iron	5.00
Calcium	3.63
Sodium	2.83
Potassium	2.59
Magnesium	2.09
Titanium	0.44
Hydrogen	0.14
Total	99.17

CONTINENTAL AND
OCEANIC CRUST

The portion of the crust that comprises the continents is composed chiefly of the igneous rock called *granite* (Figure 5.7), which is light in color and coarse-grained. It overlies a thinner layer of *basalt*, a denser, darker, and finer-grained igneous rock. The granitic layer has an average thickness of about 20 miles (32 kilometers), the basalt layer about three miles (five kilometers). In most land regions of the world, the granitic bedrock is not visible but is covered by a relatively thin wedge of sedimentary and metamorphic rocks and soil derived from rock. The crust under the oceans is composed of a thin layer of sediment over a basaltic substratum; granite is absent.

Given this, the less dense granitic portion of the crust may be considered as floating upon the basaltic substratum. The entire crust, in turn, floats upon the upper portion of the mantle. Hence like an iceberg in water, the crust is thickest where it is highest (Figure 5.8), i.e., along the mountainous belts of the world. The overall thickness variation of the continental portions of the crust ranges from 12 to 36 miles.

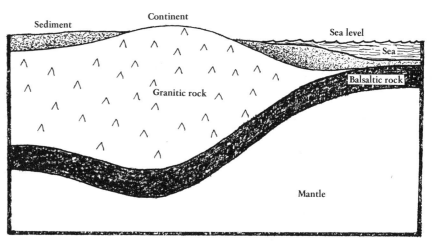

Figure 5.7
A schematic cross-section through the ocean-continent crustal boundary.

Figure 5.8
When wood blocks of different lengths are floated in water, the larger the block, the more water that is displaced, and the deeper the block floats. An analogous situation exists for granitic mountains "floating" on a basaltic substratum.

A fundamental characteristic of the crust is that it is dynamic; i.e., it is continually undergoing change. Through the long period of the Earth's history, the landscape has been repeatedly reshaped by events such as mountain building and earthslides (Figure 5.9), glaciation (Figure 5.10), and faulting. Its appearance (Figure 5.11) is a response to stresses acting both from the Earth's interior and from outside the Earth's crust. The former include volcanic activity and folding and fracturing of rock — processes that derive energy from the vast store of energy in the Earth's interior. The latter include interactions between the crust and the other three spheres (atmosphere, hydrosphere, and biosphere) with the sun as the direct sustaining energy source.

LANDSCAPE EVOLUTION

Figure 5.9
Small-scale earth movements may result in sudden and damaging landscape alterations. *(Authenticated News International.)*

Figure 5.10
A glacier near Mount Cook on South Island of New Zealand. *(American Airlines photograph.)*

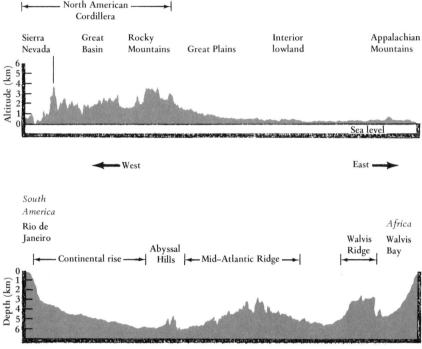

Figure 5.11
Landscape profiles from west to east across continental and oceanic portions of the Earth's crust. *(Redrawn with permission from transparency LFS-19 to accompany Chester R. Longwell, Richard Foster Flint, and John E. Sanders,* Physical Geology *[New York: John Wiley & Sons, 1969], © 1970 John Wiley & Sons.)*

Soil Development

In many areas where bedrock is not exposed, the crust is blanketed by a layer of *soil* only a few feet thick. Soil forms at the interface between the atmosphere and the lithosphere as the end product of physical, chemical, and biological weathering of rock. The properties of soil are determined by five factors: the composition of parent bedrock, climate (prevailing moisture and temperature), topography (quality of drainage), types of organisms (forests versus grasslands), and time.

The vertical cross-sectional profile of most soils consists of a sequence of layers, called *soil horizons,* produced by the gradual upward transition from undisturbed bedrock to surface vegetation (Figure 5.12). Horizons are classified on the basis of physical and chemical characteristics that in turn are determined by the degree of leaching to which each layer is subjected. *Leaching* is the process by which downward seeping water dissolves, transports, and redeposits soluble soil constituents.

Three horizons can be identified in most soil profiles. Surface soil, or topsoil (called the A-horizon), usually contains abundant roots and a dark layer of decaying vegetation termed humus. This is the zone from which soluble soil constituents (e.g., calcium carbonate) are removed (leached). Soil fertility refers to the ability of a soil to support vegetation and is determined by the supply of both organic and inorganic materials (e.g., nitrates, phosphates, and potassium) in the A-horizon. The subsoil (called the B-horizon) is the zone of accumulated leached materials. The C-horizon is composed of the partially decomposed parent substratum.

Because soil is the reservoir of water and nutrients for vegetation, it ultimately maintains the entire biosphere.

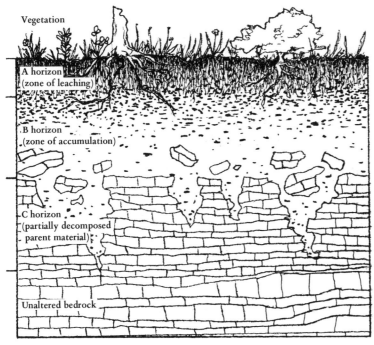

Figure 5.12
A soil profile demonstrating the transition from deep unaltered bedrock to surface vegetation.

Work of Water and Wind

Soil and rock undergo removal *(erosion)* from one area and are transported, and deposited elsewhere (conservation of matter) primarily by running water (and glaciation) and secondarily by wind. For example, soil is eroded from the Nile River Valley, transported downstream, and ends up as part of a delta in Egypt. Each year the Nile River transports more than 75 million tons of crustal material in solution and suspension toward the Mediterranean Sea (Figure 5.13).

Wind is also an effective agent of erosion, transport, and deposition. Sand and dust storms transport large amounts of material. In the 1930s the dust bowl area of the United States suffered a considerable loss of valuable topsoil, which brought about the destruction of many farms and the displacement of large numbers of people. In some parts of the Great Plains more than a foot of topsoil was lost in less than three years (Figure 5.14).

Figure 5.13
An aerial view of the Nile River delta taken during NASA's Gemini 4 spacecraft orbit, June 3–7, 1965. The dark regions are under cultivation. *(NASA.)*

Figure 5.14
Top: The sky is darkened by an approaching dust storm in Prowers County, Colorado (1937). *Bottom:* As a result of wind erosion, sand drifted around these barns in Beadle County, South Dakota (1935). (Top: *USDA–Soil Conservation Service.* Bottom: *Monkmeyer.*)

The Rock Cycle

The three rock categories are interrelated in such a way that one may be transformed into another (Figure 5.15). An igneous rock may be transformed into a sedimentary rock. A sedimentary rock may become a metamorphic rock or may revert back to the magmatic form by melting, and eventually it may solidify to an igneous rock. However, in order for these transformations to occur, two conditions are required. The first condition is environmental change. To change, say, the sedimentary rock, sandstone, to its metamorphic equivalent, quartzite, the sandstone must be immersed in the metamorphic environment. Geologic time — millions or even billions of years — is the second condition. This vast time scale has important environmental implications in that it essentially fixes man's supply of the various rock types and their mineral components. These materials cannot be renewed within his life span.

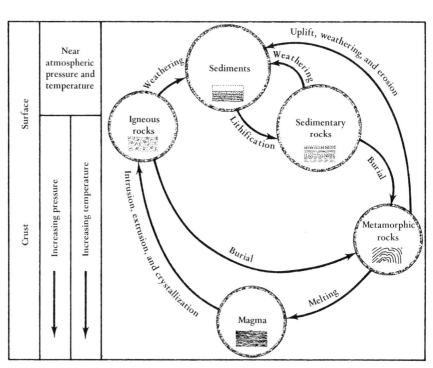

Figure 5.15
The rock cycle: adjustments of rocks to changes in their environments.

Volcanic activity produces great quantities of rock, ash, and lava (Figure 5.16) that after solidifying markedly modify the topography. Over the past 30 million years, the Columbia Plateau of the Pacific Northwest (Figure 5.17) has been covered with accumulations of basalt that in places is 4,500 feet (1,400 meters) thick.

During many periods within the span of geological time, stresses within the crust have alternately increased and waned. Some stresses merely bent (folded) rock strata; others exceeded the strength of the rock and shattered (fractured) it. An important determinant of the critical stress required for fracturing is the type of rock involved. For example, sandstone is usually more brittle than limestone, so stress that will fracture the sandstone may only bend limestone.

Volcanism, Folding, and Fracturing

Figure 5.16
Lava flows from the volcano Cerro Negro in Nicaragua. This eruption occurred in 1968. *(U.S. Department of the Interior, Geological Survey.)*

Figure 5.17
The location of exposures of solidified lava flows (shaded) in the Pacific Northwest. *(After Geologic Map of the United States, U.S. Department of the Interior, Geological Survey.)*

Bending and fracturing of rock strata have taken place over much of the Earth. Folds range from microscopic crinkles to broad warps hundreds of miles across. Fracturing (Figure 5.18) may involve rock displacements *(faulting)* that range from less than an inch to more than 100 miles (e.g., the San Andreas fault in California). The great mountain systems of the globe are the product of large-scale folding and faulting.

Figure 5.18
Structural damage resulting from an earthquake in downtown Anchorage, Alaska, on Good Friday 1964. *(Authenticated News International.)*

In many instances, man modifies his lithospheric landscape in complete disregard of the natural processes of landscape evolution. He fails to take into account the fact that type and distribution of soil and rock are the consequence of a complex interplay of geologic forces.

One important consequence of the action of natural landscape-sculpturing agents is the selective distribution of crustal resources. Our way of life is built upon a base of metallic minerals. However, only three metals — aluminum (8 percent), iron (5 percent), and magnesium (2 percent) — exceed 1 percent of the total weight of crustal rock material. If these small amounts of metal were uniformly distributed in the crust, their removal would not be feasible.

Industrially important lithospheric resources include not only the metallic ores (Table 5.3) but many nonmetallic minerals and rocks as well. Diamonds (C), for example, are displayed as decorative gems and used for cutting and drilling hard materials. Fluorite (CaF_2) is important in steel processing, muscovite ($KAl_3Si_3O_{10}(OH)_2$) as an electrical insulator, and crushed stone, sand, and gravel in building and road

IMPACT
OF MAN'S
LANDSCAPE
MODIFICATION

Exploitation of
Lithospheric
Resources and
Its Consequences

Table 5.3
Mineral sources of some common metals.

Metal	Source minerals or ores	Composition
Aluminum	Bauxite	$Al_2O_3 \cdot n\, H_2O$
Antimony	Stibnite	Sb_2S_3
Beryllium	Beryl	$Be_3Al_2Si_6O_{18}$
Chromium	Chromite	$Fe(Cr,Fe)_2O_4$
Cobalt	Cobaltite	$CoAsS$
Copper	Bornite	Cu_5FeS_4
	Chalcocite	Cu_2S_4
Iron	Hematite	Fe_2O_3
	Magnetite	Fe_3O_4
Lead	Galena	PbS
Mercury	Cinnabar	HgS
Tin	Cassiterite	SnO_2
Titanium	Ilmenite	$FeTiO_3$
	Rutile	TiO_2
Uranium	Pitchblende	U_3O_8
	Uraninite	UO_2
Vanadium	Carnotite	$K_2(UO_2)_2(VO_4)_2 \cdot 3H_2O$
Zinc	Sphalerite	ZnS

construction. In fact, the total value of sand and gravel mined in the United States per year exceeds that of all metallic ores. Coal, oil, and natural gas — found within layers of ancient rock — are our major sources of energy.

Lithospheric resources are essential to maintaining our standard of living, but the environmental impact of the methods of extracting these materials is far-reaching. Air and water are often polluted. Lands are stripped bare of soil and vegetation. The severity of the damage varies with the method of extraction, the physical and chemical properties of the material, and the location of the deposit.

SURFACE MINING

Surface mining has a particularly disastrous effect on the landscape. To reach the resource the overlying material (overburden) must first be removed. Even when alternative mining techniques exist, this extraction method is favored by mine operators because it permits more complete extraction and poses fewer safety hazards. The danger of collapse or explosion is virtually nil compared with that in underground mines. And fear that new federal safety regulations, if vigorously enforced, would close many subsurface mines has accelerated the trend toward surface mining.

There are several techniques of surface mining. Sand, gravel, and crushed stone are removed from the small quarries (Figure 5.19) that dot the countryside. In parts of the West and in the Mesabi Range along Lake Superior, metallic ores are removed from large open-pit mines (Figure 5.20) that often comprise many square miles. In some instances powerful jets of water are used either to remove the overburden or to wash out the mineral itself (hydraulic mining). Where more extensive surface mining methods are not feasible, coal is often extracted with huge drills called augers.

It is *strip mining*, however, that results in the most extensive disruption of the landscape (Figure 5.21). Huge power shovels literally chew up the land in individual gulps of 140 cubic yards (97 cubic meters). This technique is used primarily to recover coal deposits that lie within 100 feet of the surface. The United States Bureau of Mines reports that more than 1.8 million acres of land have so far been disturbed by strip mining, and the figure is expected to rise to nearly 5 million acres by 1980 — an area the size of the state of New Jersey (Figure 5.22).

Figure 5.19
A small limestone quarry disrupts the countryside in Pennsylvania. *(Grant Heilman, Littitz, Pa.)*

Figure 5.21
The GEM of Egypt, an enormous earth mover, is used to strip mine for coal in Ohio. *(Rotkin, Photography for Industry.)*

Figure 5.20
An open pit copper mine in Twin Buttes, Arizona. *(The Anaconda Company.)*

Figure 5.22
The United States Bureau of Mines estimates that the amount of land in the United States disturbed by strip mining will, by 1980, be equivalent to the area of the state of New Jersey.

By 1970, coal mining operations had accounted for about 41 percent of total land disruption by surface mining. Sand and gravel operations were second with 26 percent. However, restored land had risen to only about 33 percent by 1970.

SUBSURFACE MINING

The many metallic and nonmetallic resources mined by subsurface shafts in the United States are estimated to underlie eight million acres of land surface. However, land subsidence (Figure 5.23) has affected about 25 percent of this area primarily because of collapse of subsurface coal mines. Pillars of coal left to support the ceilings of subsurface caverns are weak and subject to failure. Withdrawal of oil, natural gas, and water from their subsurface reservoirs also leads to land subsidence and is particularly costly when it occurs beneath urban areas. For example, the land surface in the Central Valley of California has sunk as much as 20 feet as the result of removal of ground water.

DEGRADATION OF AIR, WATER, AND SOIL

Exploitation and processing of lithospheric resources may set off a chain of deleterious environmental consequences. The National Academy of Sciences reports that excavation and milling of asbestos ores release enough asbestos fibers into the air to contribute to an unusually

Figure 5.23
The land subsidence here is due to withdrawal of brine from subsurface salt mines on Grosse Ile near Detroit. (Earth Science *magazine.*)

high incidence of lung cancer among the mine and mill workers. Annually, more than 20 million tons of waste (tailings) from processing iron ore are dumped into Lake Superior. The resulting turbidity of the lake waters may in turn endanger aquatic life.

Mine waste heaps currently exceed 20 billion tons, covering more than a million acres of our land, and are increasing by a billion tons per year. The lack of nutrients in waste piles inhibits the establishment of potentially stabilizing vegetation, resulting in rapid erosion and dangerous sliding. Several years ago in Aberfan, Wales, a 600-foot slag pile (coal mine wastes) suddenly slid down into the town, smashing houses and taking more than 150 lives.

Rain seeping through mine wastes rich in sulfur compounds produces sulfuric acid. More than 60 percent of acid drainage in the United States is from abandoned coal mine remains. When it drains into

Figure 5.24
Acid drainage from industrial processing plants may be lethal to aquatic life. (Left: *Brody, Editorial Photocolor Archives*. Right: *Environmental Protection Agency*.)

rivers, aquatic life is threatened and water supplies are contaminated. Values of pH in the range of 1.5 to 3.5 are common near sites of contamination, and a pH of 5 is lethal to most aquatic life. It is estimated that in Appalachia more than 10,000 miles of waterways have been seriously impaired by runoff from coal wastes. In the summer of 1969, the Associated Press reported that 500,000 fish were killed in a 90-mile stretch of the Monongahela River of Pennsylvania because of an influx of acid mine waters (Figure 5.24).

In addition, winds lift dust from mine dumps adding to atmospheric pollution, sediments are washed from mines into drainage ways, wildlife and human habitats are fouled and made ugly.

RESOURCE
MANAGEMENT

Unlike resources of the biosphere (e.g., wood), crustal resources are depletable, or nonrenewable. Fossil fuels, for example, are not regenerated even within thousands of lifetimes. Extracted metals are not destroyed but are dispersed over the Earth as diverse items ranging from airplanes to zithers; limited recovery capacity makes management of crustal resources a unique and pressing problem.

There are efforts to make more efficient use of existing lithospheric resources and to reduce their present rates of depletion. Mine operators are encouraged to effect a more complete removal of ore because they often bypass low-grade ore in quest for more valuable grades. A mine is frequently abandoned because it may not be economically worthwhile to remove low-grade ore. If, however, both high- and low-grade material are removed together, the low-grade ore can be stockpiled until technology or industrial demand makes processing feasible.

Another management technique is the substitution of renewable for lithospheric resources: replacing fossil fuels with direct solar energy sources, for example. Alternatively, one depletable resource may be replaced by another that is in greater supply, perhaps the substitution of aluminum for iron. However, caution should be taken that in the process one set of environmental problems is not substituted by a more serious set.

Although metals are widely dispersed in the environment, *recycling* is a feasible means of resource conservation. For example, of the more than seven million motor vehicles junked each year, the metallic portions of more than 80 percent are reclaimed. In fact, recycled metals make up a significant percentage of the total amount of metals used in the United States (Table 5.4).

Table 5.4
Recycled metals in the United States in 1966 in percentage of total used.

Metal	Percentage
Aluminum	20
Copper	42
Iron and steel	45
Zinc	25

Source: Data from American Chemical Society, *Cleaning Our Environment: The Chemical Basis for Action* (Washington, D.C., 1969).

Man is continually modifying the terrain to accommodate a burgeoning population, reshaping it for housing, commercial, and industrial purposes (Figure 5.25). Hillsides are terraced, lowlands filled in, surfaces sealed by asphalt and concrete, and campsites and playgrounds

Landscape Disruption by Nonmining Activity

Figure 5.25
Man's occasional disregard of a region's terrain when he expands urban industrial complexes may have disastrous consequences. In Bound Brook, New Jersey, a chemical plant constructed in a flood plain is engulfed by rising river waters. *(American Cyanamid Company.)*

are whittled out to meet recreational requirements. Meanwhile, we heap the ever-mounting wastes of our society upon the land, in amounts significant enough to undermine the quality of the environment.

HIGHWAYS

U.S. highways now occupy about 24,000 square miles — an area about the size of West Virginia (Figure 5.26). Road construction often diverts streams, resulting in disruption or destruction of animal and plant communities, distorts scenic panoramas, and creates sites of disposal of vast quantities of trash. During winter months, millions of tons of salt (usually 95 percent $NaCl$ and 5 percent $CaCl_2$) are dumped on road surfaces for ice control, a practice harmful to roadside vegetation, wildlife, vehicles, metallic highway structures, and even the roads themselves. Some salt finds its way into neighboring streams and may contaminate drinking water supplies. Roads also act as concentrated line sources of the noxious emissions of the principal air polluter — the motor vehicle.

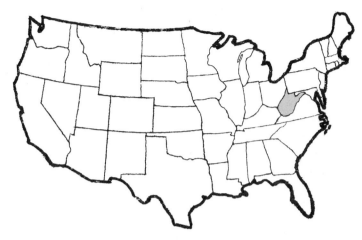

Figure 5.26
In the United States, highways presently cover an area of land equivalent to the area
of the state of West Virginia.

In some areas of the world short-sighted agricultural practices threaten to remove or destroy essential topsoil. When furrows are plowed up and down rolling hills rainfall runoff flows rapidly down-hill, accelerating soil erosion. The silty soil particles turn waterways turbid and may degrade reservoirs. To alleviate this problem farmers are encouraged to plow furrows parallel to land contours and to flatten local slopes into terraces. *Contour plowing* (Figure 5.27) and terracing impede runoff flow and decrease the energy available for erosion of soil.

AGRICULTURAL
PRACTICES

Cultivating land year after year without crop rotation depletes the soil's nutrients more quickly than they can be replenished by physical, chemical, and biological weathering processes. Nutrient depletion requires artificial recharge by fertilization. And regions that cannot afford fertilizers are usually those of increasing populations where food is in great demand.

Tens of thousands of years may be required for the redevelopment of soil exposed to avoidable erosion. Centuries may be needed for natural processes to revive a soil that has been depleted of nutrients. These factors alone make the current rate of soil wastage a matter of high environmental concern.

Figure 5.27
Contour-plowed farmland in Pennsylvania. *(Grant Heilman, Littitz, Pa.)*

Stream channelization involves the straightening and ditching of meandering stream channels (Figure 5.28). Its avowed purpose is to accelerate the transport of water downstream, thereby controlling upstream flooding. Channelization projects are sponsored by such agencies as the Soil Conservation Service of the U.S. Department of Agriculture and the U.S. Army Corps of Engineers.

But stream channelization, though significantly decreasing the danger of upstream flooding, merely displaces the flood problem downstream and sets off a whole chain of environmental problems. Upstream marshes and swamps are drained, destroying the habitats of wetland animals such as waterfowl; removal of vegetation from stream banks leads to destabilization of soil and acceleration of erosion; increased sediment load of streams reduces aquatic life — in some areas to the extent of virtually destroying the recreational fishing potential. (The Sport Fishing Institute, for example, reports that game fish in some North Carolina streams have been reduced by 90 percent since channelization.)

Figure 5.28
The appearance of a stream before *(top)* and after *(bottom)* channelization. *(Tennessee Game and Fish photographs by Charles Jackson.)*

JETTIES

To assure boaters calm waters for docking, rock barriers are sometimes constructed offshore. But these structures seriously disrupt the pattern of beach sedimentation. Because sea waves usually approach the shore at an angle, some water motion occurs parallel to the shore. This *longshore current* carries sand along the beach and maintains a consistent supply of sand along the entire length of the shoreline. *Jetties,* or piers, constructed perpendicular to the shore disrupt longshore sand transport. Sand accumulates on the upcurrent side of them, leading to a widening of the beach. A gradual removal of sand takes place downcurrent from the jetty, thereby cutting back the beach (Figure 5.29). In some instances, beach erosion on the lee side of jetties completely removes beaches and undermines adjacent roads and buildings. On Santa Monica Bay in Redondo, California, many city blocks were lost to an encroaching sea as a consequence of a harbor jetty.

WASTE DISPOSAL

Much of the 1,600 pounds (725 kilograms) of waste disposed of each year by the average person in our nation is a potentially valuable resource. Unfortunately, more than 90 percent of the 190 million tons of refuse collected annually in the United States is abandoned in land disposal sites. Though most of the remainder is incinerated it does provide a residue of reusable metals. The average annual yield of one of the larger municipal incinerators includes more than 3,000,000 tons of iron and 200,000 tons of such metals as aluminum, copper, and zinc. But an effective community recycling program directed at solid waste requires an initial expenditure for the separation of organic and recyclable materials from such nonreusable substances as plastics and other synthetics.

The organic fraction of refuse has a potentially significant value as an inexpensive fertilizer, i.e., as *compost*. In the United States, farmers generally prefer inorganic fertilizer to compost because the latter is relatively poor in nutrient content. The nutrient content of compost may, however, be enhanced by the addition of partially treated sewage.

Although disposal of solid waste in landfill sites excludes recovery of lithospheric resources, proper methods of disposal at least contribute to the quality of our surroundings. When successive layers of compacted refuse are sealed between layers of clean earth, the numerous deleterious effects of open dumps are eliminated. In such *sanitary landfills* (Figure 5.30), there is no open burning to foul the air, no proliferation

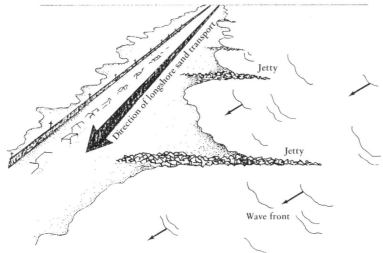

Figure 5.29
The disruption of longshore sand transport. The beach is widened on one side of a jetty and eroded back on the other side. *(Photograph courtesy of the U.S. Army Coastal Engineering Research Center.)*

of disease-bearing insects and rodents, no contamination of water by surface runoff, and no offensive odors.

As long as the potential effects of natural landscape-sculpturing agents are not disregarded, sanitary landfills can restore landscapes

Figure 5.30
Mile-High Stadium in Denver, Colorado, was constructed on a sanitary landfill site.
(Environmental Protection Agency.)

scarred by mining or make an area more productive. One example of
the latter is the construction out of solid waste of Mount Trashmore
in DuPage County, Illinois, which is to be used for recreational purposes. Unfortunately, very few of our land disposal sites are sanitary
landfills. In 1971, only 13 percent of the nation's solid waste was
disposed of in sanitary landfills.

In an effort to reduce contamination of surface lands and waters,
some areas of industry are practicing subsurface disposal as a favorable
alternative. Noxious waste products are pumped into pore spaces, frac-
tures, and man-made cavities in subsurface strata: For example, each
day in the United States more than a million barrels of chemical fluid
waste are injected into 175 deep wells. Obviously, though, the practice
is not without its negative aspects.

By *deep-well injection* of waste, man alters the character of a portion of the upper crust and may as a result upset a prevailing natural balance. As an illustration, in March, 1962, workers at the Rocky Mountain Arsenal near Denver, Colorado, began to pump fluid chemical warfare wastes into a 12,000-foot deep well. One month later a series of earthquakes began to shake the region and continued even after the well was shut down in February, 1966. As many as 20 tremors a day causing minor damage were reported in the Denver area. Apparently, the fluids upset the subsurface stress field by lubricating a rock fracture zone at the base of the well, thus releasing energy in the form of potentially destructive earthquake waves.

			KEY WORDS
rock	metamorphic rocks	strip mining	AND SUMMARY
crust	minerals	recycling	STATEMENTS
earthquake	granite	contour plowing	
mantle	basalt	stream channelization	
core	soil	longshore current	
igneous rocks	soil horizons	jetty	
magma	leaching	compost	
sedimentary rocks	erosion	sanitary landfill	
weathering	faulting	deep-well injection	
lithification			

Rock is distributed in a series of concentric spheres within the lithosphere: crust, mantle, and inner and outer core.

The crust, the lithospheric subdivision that is the chief target of man's exploitation, is composed of three rock classes: igneous, sedimentary, and metamorphic.

Through the vast expanse of geologic time, the landscape has evolved as a consequence of running water, wind, biotic activity, rock cycling, volcanism, and the folding and faulting of rock strata.

Man's extraction of resources that are selectively concentrated by geological processes within the crust often has a deleterious impact upon the quality of air, water, and land and a lethal or disruptive effect upon biotic communities.

Because crustal resources are renewable only within the scale of geologic time, steps must be taken to ensure proper management of lithospheric resources if our standard of life is to be maintained.

In response to the demands of an increasing population, man often indulges himself with short-sighted modifications in terrain and natural geologic processes. In many instances, his actions (e.g., stream channelization, deep-well waste disposal) set off a chain of environmental disturbances.

QUESTIONS AND
PROJECTS

1. Government-sponsored stream channelization projects make more land available for agriculture, yet farmers are subsidized to keep land out of cultivation. Comment on this paradox.

2. Although salt used for highway ice control endangers roadside biota and soil quality, it is considered almost essential for safe winter travel in many places. Are there alternatives to salt application that would maintain safety but lessen environmental impact? Consider the economic aspects of the problem.

3. Given the world's limited supply of fossil fuels and our accelerating energy demand, speculate on the possibility of tapping the energy in wind, running water, earthquakes, and volcanoes. What do you envision as the environmental consequences of such a procedure?

4. Should metals be given priority over glass and paper in community recycling efforts?

5. What lithospheric resources are extracted in your community? What mining techniques are involved? Do local or state laws require the restoration of the landscape after mining is completed? If so, are the laws enforced?

6. What geological processes are primarily responsible for the appearance of the landscapes of your locality? Enumerate both the landscape alterations that activity has brought about and also some of the positive and negative consequences.

7. Classify the things you consider essential to maintain our nation's present standard of living as either renewable or nonrenewable resources.

8. Dollars and energy are used to distribute lithospheric resources across the face of the Earth, and dollars and energy must be expended to recover these materials for recycling. Suggest measures that could be taken to reduce this double spending.

9. What are the fundamental reasons for the marked contrasts between lunar and Earth landscapes?

SELECTED
READINGS

Cailleux, Andre. *Anatomy of the Earth.* New York: McGraw-Hill, 1968. A well-illustrated general introduction to the properties of the Earth and the processes shaping its landscapes.

Dasmann, R. F. *Environmental Conservation.* New York: John Wiley and Sons, Inc., 1968. Includes sections on man's impact on soils and methods of conservation.

Gillette, Robert. "Stream Channelization: Conflict between Ditchers, Conservationists." *Science,* vol. 176, no. 4037 (1972), pp. 890–894. An article that considers the conflicting views on stream channelization.

Longwell, C. R., Flint, R. F., and Sanders, J. E. *Physical Geology.* New York: John Wiley and Sons, Inc., 1969. An in-depth study of the external and internal geologic processes that control the evolution of the Earth's landscapes.

McDivitt, James F. *Minerals and Men.* Baltimore: The Johns Hopkins Press, 1965. A survey of the economic importance of minerals.

Marx, W. *Man and His Environment: Waste.* New York: Harper and Row, 1971. Considers environmental problems from the point of view of waste disposal.

Steinbeck, John. *The Grapes of Wrath.* New York: Viking Press, 1939. A fictional account of people who suffered displacement by the Dust Bowl.

29 SEPTEMBER 1971
TIME OF PHOTO 1700 GMT

GINGER

30 SEPTEMBER 1971
TIME OF PHOTO 1500 GMT

GINGER

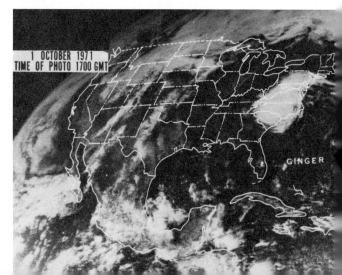

1 OCTOBER 1971
TIME OF PHOTO 1700 GMT

GINGER

chapter

6

The Atmosphere: Characteristics and Motion

The focus of Chapters 6 and 7 will be the atmosphere. Weather in its myriad forms and temperaments is the consequence of the ceaseless and rapid processes taking place within the atmosphere. Local weather is an important regulator of the rate of landscape sculpturing and the types of organisms that may exist and is a limiting factor for countless other environmental interactions. To appreciate the potential effects of air pollution upon weather, we shall consider the fundamental principles that govern atmospheric phenomena.

In the beginning the Earth's atmosphere was composed of a mixture of methane (CH_4) and ammonia (NH_3). Through the vast expanse of geologic time these gases escaped to space and were gradually replaced by accumulating gaseous emissions of ancient lava flows. Oxygen was added by the dissociation of water into its constituent atoms and by photosynthetic organisms.

The present atmosphere is a mixture of many different gaseous molecules and variable quantities of solid and liquid particles. Because of continual, vertical mixing, atmospheric gases exist almost everywhere in about the same relative proportions up to altitudes of about 50 miles (80 kilometers). Normally, we may travel about over the Earth's surface and confidently breathe essentially the same type of air.

COMPOSITION
OF THE
ATMOSPHERE

However, in some regions man's activities are beginning to significantly alter the composition of the atmosphere.

By volume, nitrogen (N_2) normally occupies 78.08 percent of the atmosphere, oxygen (O_2) 20.95 percent. The next most abundant gases are argon (0.93 percent) and carbon dioxide (0.03 percent). There are also trace volumes of the gases neon (Ne), helium (He), krypton (Kr), hydrogen (H_2), xenon (Xe), ozone (O_3), methane, water vapor, and several others (Figure 6.1). The percent volume of some of these gases (e.g., carbon dioxide and water vapor) varies from place to place and with time.

The environmental significance of an atmospheric gas is not necessarily related to its comparative abundance. Collectively, water vapor, carbon dioxide, and ozone exist in minute concentrations yet are vital to maintenance of the biosphere. There is a very small amount of water vapor in the atmosphere — no more than about 4 percent by volume in the lower 7 miles, even in tropical rain forests — but rainfall is

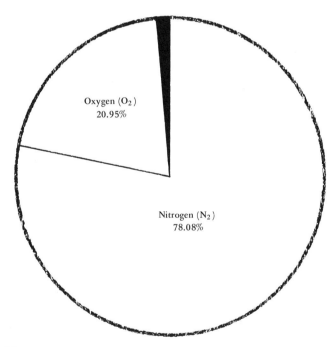

Figure 6.1
Nitrogen and oxygen are the prime components of the atmosphere (in percentage by volume).

essential to replenish the water supplies of terrestrial ecosystems. Concentrations of carbon dioxide seldom exceed 0.1 percent by volume and yet it is required for photosynthesis. In effect, carbon dioxide, water vapor, and ozone together act as a blanket over the Earth's surface that causes the lower atmosphere to be more amenable to life than it would be without these trace components.

The weight of the atmosphere over a unit area of the Earth's surface is called pressure. At a given locale the *atmospheric pressure* varies slightly with time. In mid-latitudes our weather is dominated by a continuous procession of areas of relatively high and low atmospheric pressure. Centers of high pressure, "highs," are characterized by fair weather, whereas "lows" are usually accompanied by stormy conditions.

Gravity causes most of the atmosphere's mass to be concentrated close to the Earth's surface. Air density and pressure drop rapidly with increasing altitude. However, it is impossible to specify an altitude at which the atmosphere definitely ends. On an interplanetary journey, there would be no point en route that could clearly be identified as the beginning of the "atmosphere" of space.

We can speak of the vertical extent of the atmosphere only in terms of the relative distribution of its mass. Half the atmosphere lies between the Earth's surface and a height of about 3.5 miles. At 20 miles about 99 percent of it lies below. Beyond 50 miles, there is a pronounced decrease in the heavier atmospheric gases, and beyond 600 miles the atmosphere merges with the interplanetary gases, hydrogen and helium.

MASS OF THE ATMOSPHERE

The atmosphere is not readily divisible into concentric shells according to compositional variations, as is the lithosphere, but it can be subdivided on the basis of vertical temperature variations (Figure 6.2). The *troposphere,* the lowest layer of the atmosphere, extends from the Earth's surface to an altitude that ranges between 10 miles at the equator and 5 miles at the poles. It is normally characterized by temperatures that decrease with height. Air temperatures atop mountain peaks are usually colder than those in surrounding valleys. Most weather occurs in the troposphere, making it the exclusive atmospheric interface with the abiotic and biotic components of the environment.

The *stratosphere* is the next zone, extending to an altitude of about 30 miles. It is characterized by isothermal (constant temperature) conditions in its lower portion and by a gradual increase in tempera-

SUBDIVISIONS OF THE ATMOSPHERE

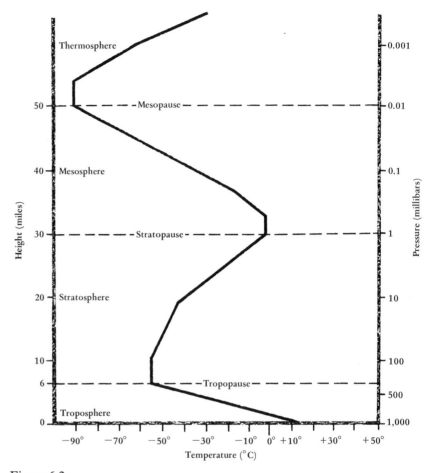

Figure 6.2
The atmosphere is subdivided into a series of concentric spheres based on vertical temperature variations (1 mile = 1.61 kilometers).

ture with height in its upper portion. In recent years there has been considerable concern about possible detrimental effects of aircraft traveling through the stratosphere. Because there is little exchange of air between troposphere and stratosphere, pollutants introduced into the stratosphere tend to stay there. On occasion, dust thrown into the stratosphere during volcanic eruptions has remained there as long as three to five years, resulting in a noticeable cooling of the atmosphere because incoming solar energy was blocked.

The *mesosphere,* beyond the stratosphere and up to an altitude of 50 miles, is characterized by a decrease of temperature with height. Above this is the *thermosphere,* which is marked by temperatures that increase with height.

More than 99 percent of the energy available for all activity on Earth comes from the sun; less than 1 percent is conducted from the Earth's interior. The sun's source of energy is a nuclear fusion process whereby hydrogen nuclei (protons) are combined to produce helium nuclei (alpha particles). During this fusion reaction small amounts of matter are converted into enormous quantities of energy in accordance with Einstein's equation, $E = mc^2$. Some of this energy is used to hold the helium nuclei together; the remainder is continually radiated off to space. About 4×10^{27} calories are radiated each minute, but only about half a billionth of the energy is intercepted by the Earth-atmosphere system. The Earth's movements in space (rotation and revolution) result in an unequal distribution of this energy over the Earth's surface.

As solar energy travels through the atmosphere, it interacts with atmospheric components. Some of it is absorbed by molecular oxygen (O_2), ozone, water vapor, ice crystals, water droplets, and dust particles. Some is reflected — primarily by clouds — back to space. Another portion is scattered, dispersed in all directions. In fact, it is the preferential scattering of the blue portion of visible light that gives the sky its blue color. Solar energy that is not reflected, scattered back to space, or absorbed is transmitted to the Earth's surface, where further interactions occur.

Experienced skiers are well aware that snow has a high reflectivity that can result in sunburn. Fresh-fallen snow has a reflectivity (or *albedo*) of between 75 and 90 percent; i.e., this amount of the solar energy incident on the snow is reflected away. At the other extreme dark surfaces such as road blacktop and green forests may have albedos as low as 5 percent. Depending upon the reflectivity and, hence, the nature of the Earth's surface cover, a certain amount of energy that gets through the atmosphere is reflected back into the atmosphere while the remainder is absorbed.

Recent satellite measurements indicate that about 29 percent of the incoming solar energy is reflected by the Earth-atmosphere system and lost to space. Hence, about 71 percent of the solar energy that is intercepted by the Earth-atmosphere system is finally available for functioning of the environment. Alteration of the Earth's atmospheric

ENERGY IN THE ATMOSPHERE

composition or surface characteristics could reduce the amount of energy available. Because energy is required for the maintenance of the many interrelated processes acting within ecosystems, the implications of such changes may be far-reaching. We will see later that man is indeed effecting such changes.

Of the solar energy intercepted by the Earth-atmosphere system, 20 percent is absorbed directly by the atmosphere and 51 percent by the Earth's surface. The Earth's surface is therefore the prime recipient of solar energy (Table 6.1). The Earth's surface, in turn, continuously reradiates this absorbed energy to the atmosphere and then to space. That the Earth surface functions as the prime energy source for the atmosphere is verified by consideration of the normal temperature behavior in the troposphere. Air is warmest close to the surface and cools with height, i.e., away from the energy source — the surface.

Table 6.1
Budget of incoming solar radiational energy.

	Percentage
Absorbed by the atmosphere	20
Absorbed at the Earth's surface	51
Reflected back to space by Earth-atmosphere system	29
Total	100

Wien's Law

Solar energy is transferred through the atmosphere to the Earth's surface and then back to the atmosphere by means of electromagnetic waves, i.e., radiation. Energy emission by a radiating body takes place over a band of wavelengths. The wavelength within the band at which the greatest intensity of energy is emitted is designated λ_{max} (the Greek letter *lambda* and *max* for maximum).

According to *Wien's Law*, the higher the temperature of a radiating body, the shorter is its λ_{max}. Warm objects emit shorter waves than cold ones. The effective radiating temperature of the sun is about 6,000°C (11,000°F) and thus emits relatively short waves. The band of solar radiation includes the visible portion of the electromagnetic spectrum, the peak energy intensity occurring at a wavelength of about 0.48 microns (1 micron $= 10^{-4}$ centimeters) (Figure 6.3). On the other hand, the much cooler Earth (radiating at a temperature of about 20°C or 68°F) emits longer waves (Figure 6.4). The value of λ_{max} for the

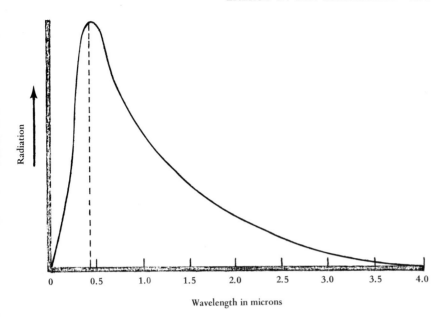

Figure 6.3
The relative intensity of radiational energy emitted by the sun over the band of solar wavelengths. Notice that the wavelength of maximum radiation emission (λ_{max}) is about 0.48 microns (dashed line). *(After H. R. Byers,* General Meteorology, *3rd ed. [New York: McGraw-Hill, 1959], p. 19.)*

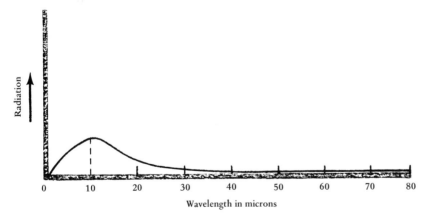

Figure 6.4
The relative intensity of radiational energy emitted by the Earth over the band of terrestrial wavelengths. Notice that the wavelength of maximum radiation emission (λ_{max}) is about 10 microns (dashed line). *(After H. R. Byers,* General Meteorology, *3rd ed. [New York: McGraw-Hill, 1959], p. 19.)*

Earth is approximately 10 microns (in the infrared region), so it responds to the input of solar short wave radiation by emitting long wave radiation.

Greenhouse Effect

Because solar and terrestrial radiation represent different portions of the electromagnetic spectrum, their respective interactions with atmospheric components are also different. We have noted that the atmosphere absorbs only 20 percent of the incident solar radiation passing through the atmosphere from outer space. It absorbs a much larger percentage of the terrestrial radiation that is radiated primarily by the Earth's surface. A portion of the terrestrial radiation is reradiated back toward the Earth's surface, thereby making efficient use of the available energy (Figure 6.5). As a result, the temperature of the lower atmosphere is made more hospitable for members of the biosphere.

The atmospheric components that impede the loss of terrestrial energy are primarily water vapor and carbon dioxide and, to a much lesser extent, ozone (Figure 6.6). Because greenhouses retain terrestrial energy in a similar manner, the process is known as the *greenhouse*

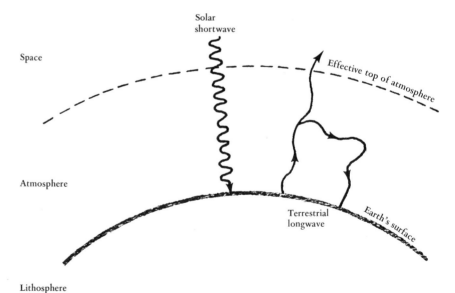

Figure 6.5
The paths of incoming solar shortwave radiation and outgoing terrestrial longwave radiation through the atmosphere. A portion of the terrestrial radiation is absorbed and reradiated back to the Earth's surface as the result of the greenhouse effect.

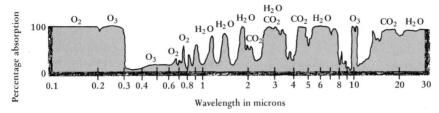

Figure 6.6
Percentage absorption of solar and terrestrial radiation by atmospheric gases as a function of wavelength. *(Redrawn with permission from A. Miller and J. C. Thompson,* Elements of Meteorology [*Columbus, Ohio: Merrill, 1970*], *p. 69.)*

effect; a common example of this is the intense heating of the interior of an auto left in the afternoon sun (Figure 6.7).

To illustrate the greenhouse effect in the atmosphere, let us compare the typical summer weather of the Southwest with that of the Gulf Coast. Both areas are at the same latitude and therefore receive about the same amount of incoming solar energy; and both commonly experience afternoon temperatures above 90°F (30°C). However, at night there is a marked difference. In the Southwest the atmosphere is rela-

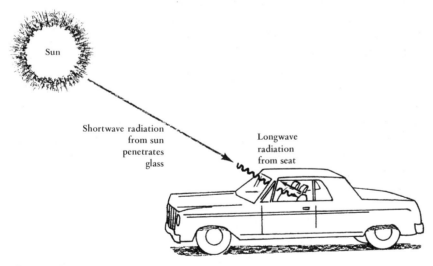

Figure 6.7
An illustration of the greenhouse effect. The windshield glass acts as atmospheric gases to readily transmit solar radiation and trap longwave radiation. *(Redrawn with permission from Albert J. Read,* Physics: A Descriptive Analysis [*Reading, Mass.: Addison-Wesley, 1970*], *p. 99.)*

tively dry, allowing terrestrial waves to readily escape into space; energy is lost and the Earth-atmosphere cools rapidly. The temperature may fall below 55°F (13°C) by dawn. Along the Gulf Coast, however, the air is more humid, resulting in a greater absorption of terrestrial radiation. Because a portion of this energy is reradiated back toward the Earth's surface, the temperature may fall only into the 70's°F(20's°C).

Vertical Energy Transport

If the net radiant (solar short wave and terrestrial long wave) energy distribution is calculated separately for the Earth's surface and the atmosphere, we find that more energy enters the Earth's surface than leaves it and that more energy leaves the atmosphere than enters it. This would imply a continuous accumulation of energy at the Earth's surface and a continuous depletion of energy from the atmosphere. But the atmosphere is not experiencing long-term cooling, nor is the Earth's surface warming. Hence, a transfer must be occurring from the reservoir of excess energy (the Earth's surface) to the reservoir of deficit energy (the atmosphere). The result is a tendency toward a smoothing out of the inequality in energy distribution (a consequence of the Second Law of Thermodynamics).

The movement of energy from Earth to atmosphere is brought about primarily by *latent heat transfer* (about 80 percent) and, to a much lesser extent, by *sensible heat transfer* (about 20 percent). The more readily understood of the two mechanisms is sensible heat transfer, the term "sensible" being used because energy redistribution brought about by this method can be monitored as temperature changes. By this process, heat is transported by conduction from Earth to atmosphere by direct physical contact between air and the Earth's surface. As the lower portion of the atmosphere is heated, it becomes lighter than the surrounding air and begins to rise. The surrounding air then sweeps into its place, is heated, and also rises. The result is a transfer of energy by convection from the Earth's surface to the atmosphere (Figure 6.8).

Latent heat transfer is a more subtle process because it involves the energy differences in the states of water. Energy must be supplied in order to evaporate water from oceans, lakes, and rivers. The change from the liquid to the vapor state (evaporation) requires the addition of heat energy; conversely, when water changes back from the vapor to the liquid state (condenses) within the atmosphere, energy is re-

Figure 6.8
A motorless sailplane remains aloft as the result of vertical convective air currents. *(Schweizer Aircraft Corporation.)*

leased. Both condensation and evaporation take place with little apparent temperature change. The energy required by evaporation is supplied at the Earth's surface, the reservoir of excess energy, and is released by condensation to the atmosphere, the reservoir of energy deficit.

Inequalities in radiant energy distribution occur not only vertically (Earth to atmosphere), but also horizontally (from latitude to latitude). Because the Earth is nearly spherical in shape, parallel beams of incoming solar energy are more directly incident on equatorial regions than at higher latitudes (Figure 6.9). Hence solar energy is spread out over a greater area at high latitudes than at low latitudes. Over the course of an entire year, more solar energy per unit area enters the Earth-atmosphere system from 0 to 38 degrees latitude than leaves by terrestrial long wave radiation. From 38 to 90 degrees latitude, there is a greater per unit area loss of terrestrial radiational energy than is supplied by solar radiation. Hence polar latitudes are sites of net radiant energy loss, and tropical latitudes are sites of net radiant energy gain (Figure 6.10).

However, tropical latitudes are not continually warming, nor are higher latitudes continually cooling. Hence, a transport of energy takes place from south to north across 38 degrees latitude, primarily by the following means: Masses of warm, moist air that form in the lower latitudes move northward to replace the masses of cold, dry air moving

Horizontal Energy Transport

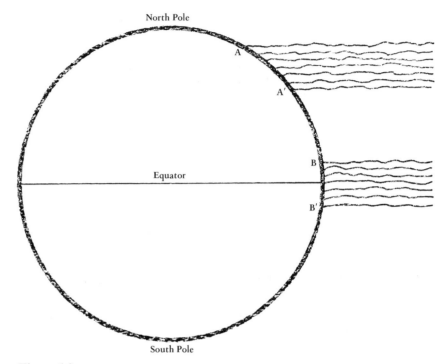

Figure 6.9
A beam of solar energy incident at high latitudes is spread over a wider area (A to A') of the Earth-atmosphere system than is a similar beam incident at equatorial regions (B to B').

in from the higher latitudes (Figure 6.11). Around 50 percent of the resulting poleward energy transport is in the form of sensible heat, whereas latent heat transfer — evaporation of water in lower latitudes and condensation at higher latitudes — accounts for only 30 percent. The remaining 20 percent of poleward energy transport is brought about by the movements of cold and warm ocean currents.

In the case of both vertical and horizontal energy transport in the atmosphere, an even distribution of energy is never actually achieved. If all inequities in energy distribution were smoothed out, the temperature would become uniform throughout the entire Earth-atmosphere system and all transfer processess would cease. However, the factors that result in unequal energy distribution operate continually and thereby trigger ceaselessly the mechanisms of transfer.

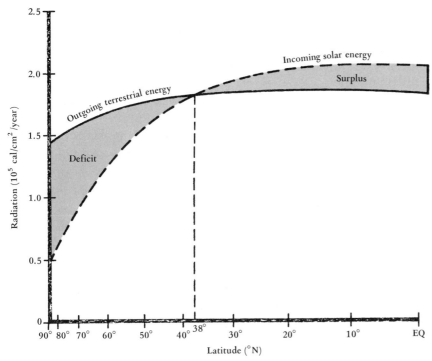

Figure 6.10
A comparison between the amounts of incoming solar radiation and outgoing terrestrial radiation by latitude belt per year. *(After R. E. Newell, "The Circulation of the Upper Atmosphere," Scientific American 210 [March 1964], p. 69; data from Henry G. Houghton.)*

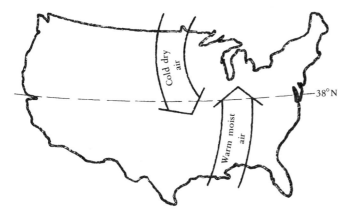

Figure 6.11
Air mass exchange across the 38°N latitude belt in the United States.

ATMOSPHERIC MOTION

Thus, in response to inequalities in both vertical (Earth-to-atmosphere) and horizontal (latitude-to-latitude) energy distribution, processes occur that bring about a continual redistribution of energy in the Earth-atmosphere system. The mechanisms by which this energy redistribution is achieved involve movement of air. There is, then, a cause-effect chain that starts with the sun as the prime energy source and results in atmospheric motion.

Meteorologists usually subdivide observed air motion on the basis of spatial dimensions. From largest to smallest, the scales of motion are designated global, synoptic, meso, and micro. The large-scale wind systems of the world (polar easterlies, the westerlies, and the trade winds) are features of *global-scale circulation* (Figure 6.12). *Synoptic-scale air motion* is continental; migrating storms and air masses are examples (Figure 6.13). *Meso-scale systems* include thunderstorms (Figure 6.14), hailstorms (Figure 6.15), and sea breezes — phenomena that may influence the weather in one section of a city while leaving the remainder unaffected. The flow of air within a cranberry bog (Figure 6.16) and the emission of smoke from a chimney are examples of the smallest subdivision of atmospheric motion — the *micro-scale*.

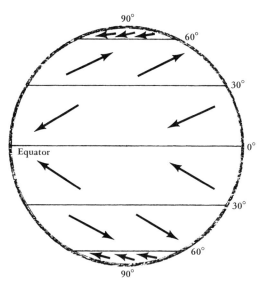

Figure 6.12
The global-scale surface wind systems.

Figure 6.13
Synoptic-scale low pressure systems may spread persistent rain or drizzle over wide areas. *(Merrim from Monkmeyer.)*

Figure 6.14
A thunderstorm is a meso-scale circulation phenomenon that will affect a local area for a very brief time, usually less than an hour. *Left:* A thunderhead cloud. *Middle:* Lightning, usually present during a thunderstorm. *Right:* An approaching thunderstorm. (Left and middle: *NOAA.* Right: *NCAR photograph.*)

Figure 6.15
Some thunderstorms are intense enough to produce destructive hailstones. *Left:* A cornfield in northeast Colorado was stripped by a brief but potent hailstorm. *Right:* Hailstones may be enormous. This hailstone, weighing 1.67 pounds, is one of the largest recorded in the United States. *(NCAR photographs.)*

Figure 6.16
The micro-scale climate that characterizes low-lying cranberry bogs may result in frost formation even during summer months. Bogs must be flooded intermittently throughout the growing season to prevent freezing of the plants. *(Ocean Spray Cranberries, Inc.)*

Each smaller-scale circulation unit is part of and dependent upon larger-scale units. For example, a thunderstorm (a meso-scale circulation system) is only possible during a certain synoptic condition (distribution of warm and cold fronts), which is in turn a unit of global circulation. Extreme radiational cooling (rapid night-time loss of terrestrial radiation) that results in local frost formation (micro-scale) requires a synoptic circulation pattern that favors clear skies and light winds.

Our analysis of the links between solar energy input and atmospheric motion allows us to appreciate the potential of man's environmental tampering. Man-made changes in atmospheric composition and in the nature of the Earth's surface could significantly alter the Earth-atmosphere radiation balance. Because of the interdependence of the various scales of atmospheric motion, change of the radiation balance may ultimately influence all scales of atmospheric motion — with adverse results.

			KEY WORDS
atmospheric pressure	albedo	global-scale circulation	AND SUMMARY
troposphere	Wien's Law	synoptic-scale air motion	STATEMENTS
stratosphere	greenhouse effect	meso-scale systems	
mesosphere	latent heat transfer	micro-scale	
thermosphere	sensible heat transfer		

The atmosphere is a mixture of gases that exist in nearly constant relative proportions from place to place and up to an altitude of 50 miles.

The environmental significance of an atmospheric gas is not necessarily related to its relative concentration in the atmosphere (e.g., water vapor).

Atmospheric pressure and density decrease rapidly with height, but the atmosphere has no clearly defined upper limit.

Division of the atmosphere into a series of concentric spheres is on the basis of vertical variations in temperature.

The portion of solar short wave radiation that is not absorbed by air or returned to space by reflection or scattering is absorbed at the Earth's surface and reradiated into the atmosphere as long waves.

The Earth's surface is the prime, direct energy source for the atmosphere.

Atmospheric water vapor, carbon dioxide, and ozone absorb and reradiate terrestrial long waves back to the Earth's surface, thereby moderating the lower portion of the atmosphere.

Energy transport takes place from the Earth's surface to the atmosphere (vertical) and from tropical latitudes to polar latitudes (horizontal) primarily by means of sensible and latent heat transfer.

Energy transport in the Earth-atmosphere system results in a series of interdependent scales of air motion.

QUESTIONS AND PROJECTS

1. Prepare a list of the varied ways in which our daily lives are influenced by the weather.

2. Suppose our eyes were not sensitive to solar radiation but were sensitive to terrestrial radiation. Would we not all be sources of light for one another?

3. Over the course of a year, how does the amount of incoming solar energy in your locality compare with the amount of outgoing terrestrial energy?

4. On a given winter's day, is the air temperature more likely to be higher if the ground is snow covered or if it is bare? Explain your answer.

5. In your own words, explain the following statement: The sun drives the atmosphere.

6. What is the purpose of the large fans used in some orange groves during calm, clear winter nights?

7. The maximum transport of energy toward the poles takes place at what latitude? Would you expect this latitude belt to be particularly stormy? Explain your answers.

8. Why do Russians spread coal dust over the snow cover in late spring?

9. Why is it incorrect to use the term "air molecules"?

SELECTED READINGS

Flohn, H. *Climate and Weather*. New York: McGraw-Hill, 1969. A concise consideration of the fundamental factors governing meteorological phenomena.

Gates, D. M. *Man and His Environment: Climate*. New York: Harper and Row, 1972. An elementary treatment of climate and weather with an emphasis upon interactions with the biosphere.

Hare, F. K. *The Restless Atmosphere, An Introduction to Climatology*. New York: Harper and Row, 1963. A general introduction to the characteristics and factors involved in determining the climate of a region.

Lehr, P. E., Burnett, R. W., and Zim, H. S. *Weather*. New York: Golden Press, 1965. A well illustrated and clear consideration of weather phenomena and forecasting.

Longley, R. W. *Elements of Meteorology*. New York: John Wiley and Sons, Inc., 1970. An in-depth presentation of radiation, atmospheric stability, and air motion.

chapter

7

The Contaminated Atmosphere

Through his diverse activities man is carrying out his inadvertent modification of the atmosphere's composition with such fervor that virtually no portion of the atmosphere is not affected to some degree. In view of the fact that the biosphere evolved in an atmosphere of specific composition, any significant alteration in this composition threatens the stability of ecosystems by approaching the tolerance limits of their biotic members.

Man is both accelerating transfer rates among the normal components of the atmospheric reservoir and introducing new substances into it. After varying lengths of time in the atmosphere, pollutants are eventually cycled into one or more of the other spheres. Liquid or solid particles may remain in the troposphere for a month or in the stratosphere for a matter of years before they settle to the ground or are carried to it by wind or rain. The mobility of gaseous pollutants permits them to remain in the atmosphere as long as four months before entering the other three spheres.

Air pollution is the consequence of natural processes as well as human activity. Natural sources of pollutants include forest fires, pollen dispersal, wind erosion, organic decay, and volcanic eruptions (Table 7.1). The single most important source of atmospheric pollutants

SOURCES OF POLLUTANTS

Table 7.1
Volcanic gas emissions from Mauna Loa
and Kilauea, Hawaii, in weight percentage.

Gas	Percentage
Water vapor, H_2O	57.8
Carbon dioxide, CO_2	23.5
Sulfur, S	12.6
Nitrogen, N_2	5.7
Argon, A	0.3
Chlorine, Cl_2	0.1
Hydrogen, H_2	0.04

Source: Reprinted with permission from
A. N. Strahler, *The Earth Sciences* (New York:
Harper and Row, Publishers, 1971), p. 485.

fostered by human activity is the motor vehicle (Table 7.2). In 1969,
the Environmental Protection Agency reported that transportation vehicles exhausted more than 144 million tons of air pollutants. There
are also many industrial sources (Figure 7.1), including pulp and paper
mills, iron and steel mills, oil refineries, smelters, and chemical plants.
Additional contributions come from fuel combustion by industrial and
domestic furnaces, refuse burning, and various agricultural activities
(e.g., crop dusting, fall plowing). Annually, more than 280 million tons
of contaminants are emitted into the atmosphere as the result of human
activity in the United States, about one and one-half tons per person.

Table 7.2
Sources of air pollutants emitted in the United States in 1969, in millions of tons.

Sources	Carbon monoxide	Sulfur oxides	Hydro-carbons	Oxides of nitrogen	Partic-ulates	Totals
Transportation	111.5	1.1	19.8	11.2	0.8	144.4
Fuel combustion in stationary sources	1.8	24.4	0.9	10.0	7.2	44.3
Industrial processes	12.0	7.5	5.5	0.2	14.4	39.6
Solid waste disposal	7.9	0.2	2.0	0.4	1.4	11.9
Miscellaneous	18.2	0.2	9.2	2.0	11.4	41.0
Totals	151.4	33.4	37.4	23.8	35.2	281.2

Source: 1969 data from *Environmental Quality: The Second Annual Report of the Council on
Environmental Quality* (August 1971).

Figure 7.1
The Fruitland Power Plant in the Four Corners area of New Mexico as seen close up and from a distance of fifteen miles. *(Richard Weymouth Brooks, Photofind, S.F.)*

Substances listed in Table 7.2 are termed *primary pollutants.* Some of these undergo reactions leading to the production of *secondary pollutants,* which include acid mists and photochemical smog. In some instances the environmental impact of individual primary pollutants is less severe than when they occur in combinations as secondary pollutants.

Two notable products of burning organic fuels include carbon dioxide (CO_2) and carbon monoxide (CO). Carbon dioxide results from complete combustion, carbon monoxide from incomplete combustion. From 1958 to 1969 the atmospheric content of carbon dioxide increased at a rate of 0.7 ppm per year. We noted previously the role of CO_2 in the greenhouse effect. In a later section we shall examine the possible impact of increased CO_2 on world climate.

AIR POLLUTANTS

Oxides of Carbon

Carbon monoxide (CO) is a colorless, odorless, toxic gas that competes with oxygen for bonding sites on the hemoglobin molecule in the blood. Because CO forms the more stable bond, increasing amounts of inhaled CO decrease the quantity of oxygen that the blood can carry from the lungs. Most people experience no ill effects at concentrations of less than 10 ppm. However, at 100 ppm some show symptoms of dizziness, headache, and impaired perception. In concentrations of 300 to 400 ppm, vision impairment, nausea, and abdominal pain may result; 1,000 ppm is fatal. While typical urban air contains 20 to 30 ppm, concentrations of CO may reach 100 ppm in highway tunnels and immediately behind auto exhausts (Figure 7.2).

Figure 7.2
A rush-hour traffic jam on the San Francisco Bay Bridge. *(Jim Stewart, Photofind, S.F.)*

Hydrocarbons include many of the compounds of carbon and hydrogen. They are introduced into the atmosphere primarily as the result of incomplete combustion of gasoline. In low concentrations hydrocarbons do not present important environmental problems, but in high concentrations or in combination with other pollutants, they can have serious effects. Some, in fact, are believed to be carcinogenic (cancer-inducing).

Hydrocarbons

Nitric oxide (NO) is the product of the combination of atmospheric oxygen and nitrogen at high temperatures. Here again the major source is the internal combustion engine. Reaction of NO with oxygen yields the more toxic nitrogen dioxide (NO_2). Like carbon monoxide, nitric oxide reduces the blood's oxygen-carrying capacity. Because NO_2 is brown in color, it reduces visibility. When combined with water vapor, it forms nitric acid (HNO_3), a highly corrosive substance.

Oxides of Nitrogen

The smelting of iron ore and the processing of ceramics and phosphate rock put fluorides into the atmosphere. Hydrogen fluoride (HF) at a concentration of only 0.1 ppb damages some species of vegetation. Other plants, including alfalfa and orchard grass, combine the fluorides with organic compounds to detoxify the fluoride. Fluorides can reach concentrations of 40 ppm in these forage plants, and to the livestock that consume the plants, the organic fluorides are lethal. Substantial losses in cattle (Figure 7.3) and citrus groves in Florida are attributed to fluoride emissions from processing phosphate deposits for fertilizers.

Fluorides

Figure 7.3
A cow afflicted with fluorosis, a bone-weakening disease resulting from fluoride accumulation in the body. *(Robertson Studio.)*

Compounds of Sulfur

Sulfur compounds are cycled naturally in the environment (Figure 7.4). They are emitted into the atmosphere as volcanic gas, by sea spray, and as hydrogen sulfide (H_2S) from the decay of organic matter. Sulfur is removed from the atmosphere by rainfall and absorbed by soil, vegetation, and ocean waters. Combustion of sulfur-containing fuels (coal and oil) and the smelting of certain metals introduce sulfur oxides into the atmospheric reservoir. When inhaled, sulfur dioxide (SO_2) and sulfur trioxide (SO_3) in concentrations of only a few ppm irritate respiratory passages and can contribute to asthma, emphysema, and bronchitis. When sulfur dioxide combines with water in plant leaves, it destroys leaf cells; alfalfa, cotton, barley, and tulips are particularly susceptible (Figure 7.5). Average annual concentrations as low as 0.03 ppm may have long-term effects upon some vegetation (Figure 7.6).

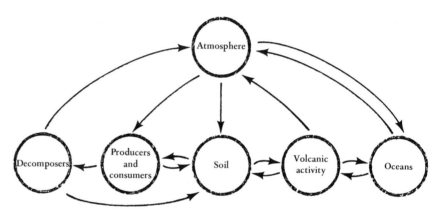

Figure 7.4
The sulfur cycle.

Figure 7.5
These tulip leaves have been damaged by sulfur dioxide gas. *(Authenticated News International.)*

Figure 7.6
Sulfur dioxide fumes from a smelter have destroyed this hardwood forest near Copper Hill, Tennessee. *(U.S. Forest Service.)*

Sulfur dioxide and sulfur trioxide combine with atmospheric water vapor to produce a mist of sulfuric acid droplets. This is both a corrosive and a visibility-restricting mixture. Industrial activities such as paper and pulp processing emit hydrogen sulfide and a family of organic sulfur-containing gases called mercaptans. Even in extremely small concentrations, these compounds cause foul odors. In addition, hydrogen sulfide damages copper facing, silverware, lead-based paints, and statuary (Figure 7.7).

Figure 7.7
This statue of Alexander Hamilton is soiled as the result of air pollution in Washington, D.C. *(Environmental Protection Agency.)*

Particulate Matter

To the particulate matter introduced into the atmosphere as the result of natural events (e.g., pollen rains, volcanic eruptions), man adds millions of tons. The most common of these pollutants are dust and soot. *Dust* is primarily the product of wind erosion of soil accelerated by agricultural activity, whereas *soot* (tiny, solid particles of carbon) is emitted during combustion of fossil fuels and refuse. There is also a wide variety of other particles whose composition is governed by activities carried on in a given area, i.e., the local types of mining, milling, and manufacturing. These particulates may include asbestos, arsenic, selenium, beryllium, cadmium, and the many pesticides and fertilizers. Further, man's unceasing quest for the ultimate weapon of destruction has resulted in the emission of such fission products as strontium-90, cesium-137, and iodine-131.

The burning of gasoline to which lead has been artificially added to control engine knock is the prime contributor to an enormous increase in the atmosphere's particulate lead content. In the northern hemisphere, lead concentration is now about 1,000 times its natural, or background, level. A recent study shows that concentrations of lead in air extend well beyond the bounds of well-traveled highways (Figure 7.8) and present a significant hazard to roadside livestock. The environmental danger of lead lies in the fact that it is a poison that may accumulate in the body more rapidly than it is excreted. However, little is known of its toxic threshold for man. Only 5–10 percent of ingested lead is retained by the body, but 50 percent of inhaled lead is retained. The nationwide average daily intake of lead is about 400 millionths of one gram (0.000014 oz.) per person, and except in a few urban areas, it is still primarily due to food and water intake and not to breathing.

Smog

Smog is a noxious mixture of gaseous, solid, and liquid pollutants. In urban regions where sulfur-containing fuels (e.g., coal and fuel oil) are burned, soot and sulfur dioxide are the prime constituents of smog. In cities where there is a high concentration of automobiles, hydrocarbons react with nitric oxides in the presence of sunlight to produce photochemical smog, ozone (O_3) being a major component. While the background level of ozone is about 0.02 ppm at the Earth's surface, it may reach 0.5 ppm during very smoggy periods. At these high concentrations ozone impairs vision, respiration, and mental function. It degrades rubber and cloth and damages such vegetation as tobacco plants, spinach, and grapes. Wind-borne ozone from Los Angeles is

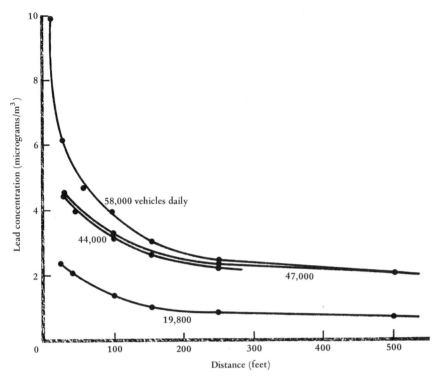

Figure 7.8
Concentration of lead in the air varies with traffic volume and the distance from roadway. Concentration, expressed in terms of micrograms (10^{-6} grams) of lead per cubic meter of air, was measured on sections of U.S. Highway 1. *(Redrawn with permission from Robert H. Daines, Harry Motto, and Daniel M. Chilko, "Atmospheric Lead: Its Relationship to Traffic Volume and Proximity to Highways,"* Environmental Science and Technology, *4 [March 1970], pp. 318-322. Copyright 1970 by the American Chemical Society.)*

destroying hundreds of thousands of ponderosa pines in the San Bernardino and San Jacinto Mountains 60 miles (96 kilometers) from the city.

Ironically, ozone formation in the stratosphere is a life-preserving mechanism. Ozone forms as a result of absorption of solar ultraviolet radiation (UV) by oxygen molecules. This filtering process prevents organisms at the Earth's surface from being exposed to lethal intensities of UV. Hence, although the production of ozone in the stratosphere is essential for existence of the biosphere, its presence at the Earth's surface has a deleterious effect upon organisms.

DISTRIBUTION OF POLLUTED AIR

Concentration levels of contaminants in the air are determined by the degree to which pollutants are mixed with cleaner air. The more effectively they mix, the more dilute the concentrations. In view of our concern with air quality, it is important that we consider the factors that directly influence the amount of mixing that takes place. One critical factor is stability of the atmosphere.

Atmospheric Stability

In our discussion it is convenient to distinguish initially between polluted air and the relatively clean air into which the polluted air is introduced. The polluted air is considered to be composed of discrete volume units termed parcels, whereas the clean air is referred to as surrounding air. This differentiation fades as mixing proceeds.

If a parcel of polluted air is warmer than its surrounding denser air, it will rise. Such a parcel is said to be *buoyant* with respect to its air environment. The atmospheric pressure on a rising air parcel steadily decreases, so the parcel expands (just as a helium-filled balloon expands as it ascends). As long as there is no heat flow through the imaginary walls of a parcel, its heat content remains unchanged. But because a parcel expands while rising, its heat energy spreads out and occupies the continually increasing volume, which steadily lowers its temperature. A parcel cools at a constant rate of about 5.4°F per 1,000 feet (9.8°C per 1,000 meters) of vertical displacement.

If the temperature profile of a layer of air is such that the temperature at every elevation is lower than the temperature of an air parcel rising through the layer (Figure 7.9), the surrounding layer is called an *unstable air layer*. The parcel will continue to rise. If, on the other hand, the parcel enters a layer of air whose temperature at every elevation is warmer than the temperature of the air parcel, it is no longer buoyant and begins to sink. Such a layer is said to be a *stable air layer*. A parcel experiences more mixing when emitted into unstable air than when emitted into stable air. Stable air layers inhibit vertical transport of air pollutants and thus may act as canopies over the lower atmosphere. Continual emission of contaminants into stable air layers results in continual accumulation and concentration of pollutants.

A physical analogy may help to illustrate parcel behavior within stable and unstable air layers. Consider a golf ball placed at the bottom of a mixing bowl (Figure 7.10). Movement of an air parcel within a stable air layer is like the displacement of the golf ball. After any movement the ball returns to the base of the bowl. Now invert the

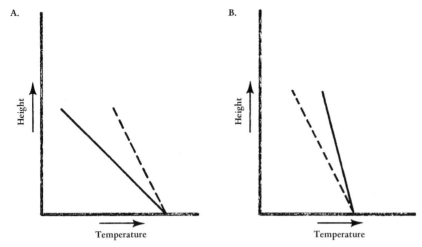

Figure 7.9
The solid line represents typical temperature variation with height of an unstable air layer *(figure A)* or a stable air layer *(figure B)*. Dashed line indicates the temperature behavior of an air parcel that is lifted within the air layer, i.e., cools at a rate of 5.4°F per 1,000 feet (10°C/1000 meters).

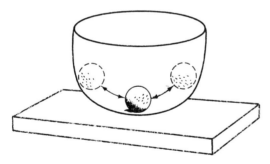

Figure 7.10
The movement of a golf ball placed in the bottom of a mixing bowl is analogous to the movement of an air parcel introduced into a stable air layer. Both the golf ball and the air parcel return to their original positions.

mixing bowl and place the golf ball on top (Figure 7.11). If the golf ball is moved now, it accelerates away from its original location just like an air parcel introduced into an unstable air layer.

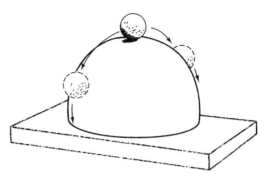

Figure 7.11
The movement of a golf ball placed on the top of an inverted mixing bowl is analogous to the movement of an air parcel introduced into an unstable air layer. Both the golf ball and the air parcel accelerate away from their original positions.

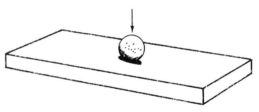

Figure 7.12
The movement of a golf ball placed on a horizontal plane is analogous to the movement of an air parcel introduced into a neutral air layer. Both the golf ball and the air parcel remain in their original positions.

There may be occasions when the rate of cooling of a rising air parcel matches the temperature profile within an air layer. Such an *air layer* is said to be *neutral*. Vertical parcel displacement within a neutral air layer is like the movement of the golf ball along a horizontal plane (Figure 7.12). The ball and the air parcel remain at the position at which they are placed.

We can gain a qualitative estimate of the stability of air layers by observing the behavior of a plume of smoke belching from a stack (Figure 7.13). If the air layer is unstable, looping occurs, which allows polluted air parcels to mix readily with surrounding air and thus facilitate dispersal. If, though, smoke plumes flatten and spread out, stable conditions are indicated and pollutant concentrations increase.

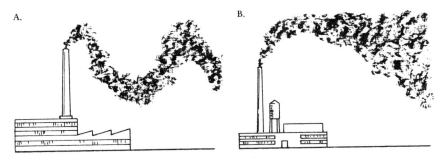

Figure 7.13
The appearance of a smoke plume in an unstable air layer *(figure A)* and in a very stable air layer *(figure B)*.

The troposphere is normally stable and thus retards pollutant dispersal. On some occasions layers of the troposphere are extremely stable. This occurs when the temperature within the air layer increases with height (Figure 7.14), a condition known as a *thermal inversion*. There are two important types: subsidence inversion and radiation inversion.

The *subsidence inversion* forms a canopy over an area usually as large as several states. It develops during a period of fair weather when the global circulation pattern favors the stagnation of a center of relatively high atmospheric pressure (synoptic pattern). This type of weather system is characterized by descending (hence warming) air currents

The Thermal
Inversion

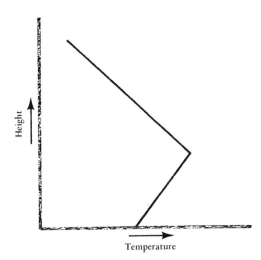

Figure 7.14
Temperature profile in an air layer characterized by a thermal inversion in the lower portion and a decrease of temperature with height in the upper portion.

that spread out near, but not at, the Earth's surface. It is prevented from reaching the surface by a shallow air layer at ground level known as the *shielding layer*. The frictionally maintained shielding layer is not displaced upward, so its vertical temperature profile remains unchanged. However, the air just above the shielding layer experiences warming because of its descent and may be significantly warmer than the air immediately beneath the upper boundary of the shielding layer. A transitional thermal inversion forms, joining the air of the shielding layer with the modified air above (Figure 7.15).

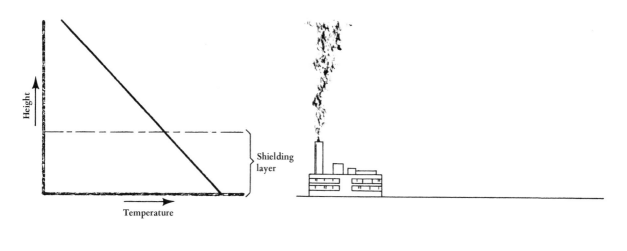

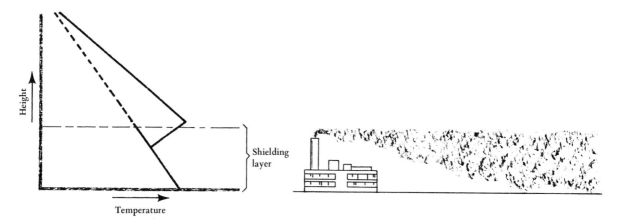

Figure 7.15
Development of a subsidence inversion and the resulting behavior of a smoke plume.

The *radiation inversion* is more common and more localized. At night, the loss of the Earth's warmth by long wave radiation cools the ground surface. Surface air layers are then chilled by contact (conduction) with the cooler ground. Because the coldest air is at the surface, a thermal inversion results, usually in the early morning hours. Often the inversion gradually disappears as the day's solar energy is absorbed by the ground and reradiated to the lower troposphere, and normal thermal behavior is restored.

The frequency of stable atmospheric conditions varies from place to place and, in some areas, with the season of the year (Figure 7.16). In the United States, regions of particularly high atmospheric pollution potential include the coast of Southern California, portions of the Rocky Mountain states, and the western sections of the mid-Atlantic states. On the West Coast, conditions are potentially most severe during the summer months, when an inversion forms on at least 90 percent

Frequency of Stable Conditions

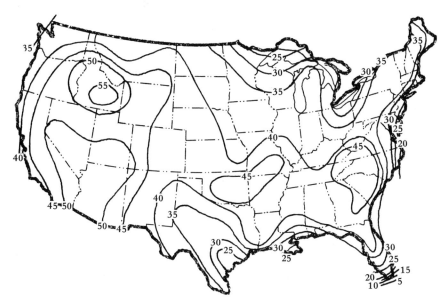

Figure 7.16
Frequency of temperature inversions in near surface air layers in percentage of inversion hours per day in the autumn. *(Redrawn with permission from D. H. Pack, "Meteorology of Air Pollution," Science, 146 [November 1964], p. 1125. Copyright 1964 by the American Association for the Advancement of Science.)*

of the days, whereas little seasonal frequency change is noted in the western Carolinas.

Effect of Terrain

Hills and mountain ranges may act as horizontal barriers to the dispersal of polluted air. In addition, thermal inversions in such regions as river valleys are often strengthened by the accumulation of cold, dense air that drains downward from surrounding highlands. The result is a stable (and therefore persistent) stratification of cold dense air overlayed by warmer, lighter air. A region's topographic relief and its frequency of atmospheric stability should therefore be essential considerations in the construction or expansion of industrial complexes.

Los Angeles

The sprawling metropolis of Los Angeles is especially susceptible to the accumulation of air pollutants. The exceptionally high incidence of stable atmospheric conditions along the California coast is aggravated in Los Angeles by topographic barriers. The city lies in a bowl that has on one side the Pacific and on the other mountains that effectively encase the city in its own fumes during thermal inversions. The weather of Los Angeles, like that of most of the West Coast, is under the influence of the eastern edge of a semipermanent center of high atmospheric pressure centered over the tropical Pacific. The resulting descending air currents induce subsidence inversions over Los Angeles for perhaps two-thirds of the days of the year (Figure 7.17). The consequence is frequent formation of photochemical smog with its attendant plant damage and human irritation.

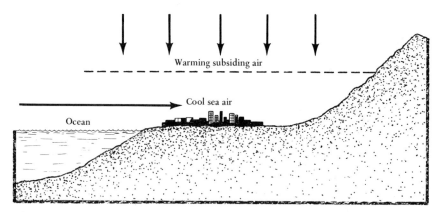

Warming subsiding air

Cool sea air

Ocean

Figure 7.17
Schematic representation of the Los Angeles air pollution situation.

AIR POLLUTION AND CLIMATE

Urban Air Circulation

Travelers approaching an urban area are often introduced to it by the blanket of dust, smoke, and haze that often overhangs a city. This dome of dust and dirt is the consequence of a convective atmospheric circulation pattern that characterizes many urban-industrial areas. This air motion is in turn a product of thermal contrasts between the city and surrounding rural areas.

The average annual temperature of a city is typically about 0.7°C (1.3°F) higher than that of the surrounding countryside. On certain days, however, the thermal contrast may be as much as 15°C (27°F). Among the several factors contributing to this *urban heat island* are the city's great concentration of heat sources (e.g., people, cars, space heaters) and the fact that it is constructed of materials (e.g., concrete, asphalt, and brick) that more readily conduct heat than does the vegetative cover of rural areas. Thus the heat a city loses at night by radiation is partially compensated by a release of heat from buildings and streets. The contrast is further accentuated by the city's lack of standing bodies of water. Urban drainage systems quickly and efficiently remove rainfall runoff, so a city uses less of the available solar energy for evaporation. This results in more solar energy available for the direct heating of the ground and air.

The relative warmth of many cities compared with their surroundings promotes development of a convective air circulation (Figure 7.18). Warm air at the city's center rises and is replaced by cooler, denser air from the countryside. With light winds, rising columns of air concentrate particulates in a *dust dome* over the city. Over the industrial sector, the dust concentration may be 1,000 times that in the air of the open countryside. As the synoptic-scale winds increase to more than about 8 miles per hour (3.6 meters per second), the dust dome is elongated downwind in the form of a *dust plume,* spreading the city's pollutants over the distant countryside. The Chicago dust plume is sometimes visible as far away as 150 miles.

The dust dome decreases the amount of solar radiation that penetrates the urban atmosphere. This reduction is particularly marked (typically about 30 percent) in the ultraviolet portion of the solar spectrum. Such a depletion in ultraviolet radiation probably contributed to the high incidence of rickets in industrialized European cities prior to the supplementing of diets with Vitamin D. In addition, urban dust concentration reduces visibility and enhances urban rainfall.

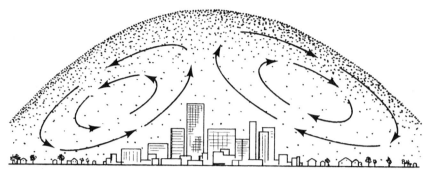

Figure 7.18
Development of a city air circulation pattern that concentrates dust in a dome over the urban center. *(Redrawn with permission from W. P. Lowry, "The Climate of Cities," Scientific American, 217 [August 1967], p. 20 Copyright © 1967 by Scientific American, Inc. All rights reserved.)*

Change in Global Air Temperature

Concern is expressed over the possible impact of atmospheric pollution upon the Earth-atmosphere radiation balance. This concern is primarily directed at the effects of the increased atmospheric content of dust particles and carbon dioxide. The impact of increased concentrations of carbon dioxide is an increase in the greenhouse effect. The result is a greater absorption and reradiation of terrestrial energy, which warms the atmosphere.

The impact of *atmospheric turbidity* (dustiness) upon global air temperature is a controversial subject. According to Reid A. Bryson of the University of Wisconsin, the effect of increased atmospheric turbidity is opposite that of carbon dioxide: An increase in turbidity leads to an increase in the reflectivity of the Earth-atmosphere system. The reduction of solar energy that reaches the Earth's surface results in a cooling of the atmosphere. According to Bryson, it appears that in the past few decades, an increase in atmospheric turbidity caused by human activity has slightly prevailed over the effect of an increase in atmospheric CO_2. As a result, the average world temperature has begun to drop. The cooling is very gradual (about 0.2°C from 1940 to 1967) and its effects will probably be almost unnoticeable in mid-latitudes for many years to come, except, of course, in regions already only marginally habitable. A slow but persistent cooling of world temperature would gradually increase the extent and duration of pack ice on the North Atlantic, and fishing-oriented countries like Iceland would find their short fishing season growing even shorter.

An opposing point of view is held by Helmut Landsberg of the University of Maryland. He argues that man's contribution to atmospheric turbidity has the same effect on climate as the increase in atmospheric CO_2, i.e., global warming. Landsberg agrees that introduction of volcanic dust into the stratosphere leads to atmospheric cooling, but he notes that most particulates resulting from man's activities do not reach the stratosphere; rather they are confined to the lower troposphere by stable atmospheric conditions. In the troposphere, the dust scatters solar radiation primarily back to the Earth's surface and absorbs both solar and terrestrial radiation. The net effect of the dust, then, is a warming of the lower atmosphere. This point of view has led alarmists to forecast eventual melting of the Greenland and Antarctic ice sheets, which would flood many of the populous coastal areas of the world.

Resolution of the controversy surrounding the effect of turbidity upon global air temperature awaits further research, but it is clear that air pollution is influencing climate on at least a local scale (urban dust dome) and probably on a global scale.

THE COST OF AIR POLLUTION

Human Health

It is difficult to determine the exact relationship between the incidence of human illness and the levels of specific air pollutants. This is partly because an individual's resistance is a function of numerous factors (e.g., age, general health, personal hygiene, and habits such as smoking) and partly because pollutants occur in a wide range of concentrations and combinations. There are well-documented cases of air pollution disasters (e.g., London in 1952; Donora, Pa., in 1948; New York City in 1953) when fatalities dramatically increased. However, in these episodes the unusual numbers of deaths occurred mainly among the very young, the very old, and those already suffering from respiratory and heart diseases. Still to be fully evaluated are the health effects on the general populace of long-term exposure to moderate and low levels of air pollution.

There is evidence that an urban dweller is much more likely to contract respiratory and other diseases than is his rural counterpart. For example, the death rate from coronary heart disease can be from 37 to 46 percent higher in a city than in a rural area. The number of deaths resulting from chronic respiratory illness or lung cancer can be twice as high, and the incidence is increasing as our skies become more contaminated. Although there is a definite connection between air pollution and illness, we must be cautious in accepting correlations between a specific air pollutant and a specific illness until a physical relationship is clearly established. Still the lack of such evidence should not be used as an excuse for inaction.

Dollar Loss

The exact monetary cost of polluted air is difficult to evaluate because its direct and indirect effects vary so widely. There are the costs of medical care and lost man-hours, of cleaning and replacement of soiled and corroded metals, building stone, and fabric, and the incalculable losses in the beauty of our air environment. Annual agricultural losses in the United States are at least $500 million. Conservative estimates place the total overall cost in excess of $16 billion per year — more than $95 for each man, woman, and child in our nation. If we are to continue as a progressive industrial society, positive measures must be taken to reduce the accelerating toll of air pollution. This requires further expenditures for development, installation, and maintenance of devices and techniques for emission control. In time, the initial costs of control will be far outweighed by the reduction of air pollution damage and the aura of clean skies. A 1972 study shows that a $3.9 billion annual expenditure for cleanup would reduce the cost of air pollution by 66 percent in only four years.

AIR QUALITY CONTROL

The only reasonable, or indeed feasible, method of air pollution control must be directed at sources. This may involve one or more of several control techniques. Potential pollutants could be largely removed from fuels or raw materials prior to their use, either at the refinery or at the ore-processing plant. Or less polluting substances could be substituted for more polluting materials. An example is the use of low sulfur fuels; between 1964 and 1971, New York City required the sulfur content of fuel oils to be reduced from 3 percent to 1 percent.

Industrial processing methods may either be altered or replaced to reduce air pollution. An example of the former is the reduction of automobile hydrocarbon emissions by the PCV (positive crankcase ventilation) system that has been mandatory on all new cars since 1963. An example of the latter is possible phasing out of the present internal combustion engine in favor of steam, battery, or turbine engines.

Air quality control is often aimed at reducing the particulates and the liquid and gaseous contaminants of industrial stack effluents. Particulates may be removed by electrostatic precipitation, filtering, or gravitational settling. In *electrostatic precipitators* particles are electrically charged and then collected on plates of opposite charge, a process that removes an estimated 99 percent of fly-ash emissions from power plant stacks. A particle-containing air stream can be passed through a series of filters of varied compositions (e.g., spun glass, cotton, cellulose-asbestos) that are sufficiently porous to permit air to escape while trapping particulates. Solid air pollutants are also separated from air by a *cyclone collector,* a device that induces gravitational settling of heavier solid particles (Figure 7.19). As the result of application of these techniques, particulate emissions from some paper-pulp mills have been reduced by as much as 90 percent.

Noxious gases that are water soluble (e.g., ammonia) can be removed by water sprays directed at the effluent stream. This process is called

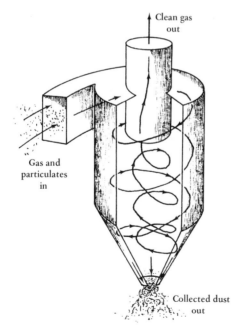

Figure 7.19
Schematic diagram of a cyclone collector used to separate particulates and gases from an effluent air stream. *(Redrawn with permission from Walker,* Operating Principles of Air Pollution Control Equipment *[Bound Brook, N.J.: Research-Cottrell, Inc., 1968].)*

scrubbing (Figure 7.20). Filters composed of substances to which certain gases are adsorbed (e.g., activated carbon filters) are also effective removers of gaseous pollutants. In other processes chemical reactions convert gaseous or liquid contaminants to products either less hazardous or more readily removable from the effluent. A case of the former would be the neutralization of acidic and basic pollutants. An example of the latter is a method of sulfur dioxide removal: Sulfur dioxide (SO_2) combines with oxygen to form sulfur trioxide (SO_3), which in turn is combined with water vapor to produce sulfuric acid mist that is subsequently trapped.

The specific method of control that is chosen is a function of economic and technical feasibility and also resource availability, all of which are dependent upon the type of processing and pollutants involved. There is, however, need for further research to enable more effective abatement. The elimination of some important air pollutants (e.g., oxides of nitrogen formed in internal combustion engines) has not yet been made practical.

Oddly, universal implementation of adequate air quality control programs could, if successful, give impetus to another environmental

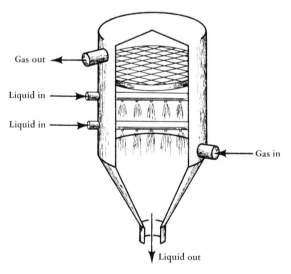

Figure 7.20
Schematic diagram of a spray collector or scrubber. *(Redrawn with permission from A. C. Stern,* Air Pollution, *2nd ed. [New York: Academic Press, 1968].)*

problem. Air contaminants that are removed from effluents do not disappear but must be put to use or disposed of (conservation of matter). In many cases these products have economic value and are recycled. Too often, however, the extracted air pollutants are simply added to the mounting heaps of industrial waste and end up in a river or landfill. Although the air pollution problem is abated, the solid waste and water pollution problems are enhanced. A truly effective program must not only require adequate control devices but also include provisions for proper disposal of extracted air pollutants.

air pollution	unstable air layer	urban heat island	**KEY WORDS AND SUMMARY STATEMENTS**
primary pollutants	stable air layer	dust dome	
secondary pollutants	neutral air layer	dust plume	
dust	thermal inversion	atmospheric turbidity	
soot	subsidence inversion	electrostatic precipitators	
smog	shielding layer	cyclone collector	
buoyant	radiation inversion	scrubbing	

Man's activities accelerate the transfer rates of some natural components into the atmosphere and introduce new materials.

Stability of air layers is a critical factor in determining the degree of air pollutant dispersal.

Thermal inversions consist of the extremely stable stratification of warm, light air over cool, denser air. Radiation inversions are generally more common but less persistent than subsidence inversions.

Many urban-industrial areas are sufficiently warmer than surrounding rural regions to produce a convective air circulation pattern that concentrates air pollutants in a dome over the city center.

Man-made increases in atmospheric dustiness and carbon dioxide may be gradually modifying the climate.

There is a general relationship between high levels of air pollution and the incidence of respiratory and heart diseases, though correlations between specific air pollutants and specific illnesses are as yet unproved.

Implementation of adequate air quality control techniques and devices promises to reduce the present costs of polluted air.

QUESTIONS AND
PROJECTS

1. What steps could be taken to reduce the thermal contrast between city and countryside in order to decrease the frequency of dust dome formation?

2. Set up a program of air quality control legislation, keeping in mind the interstate transport of air pollutants.

3. Is there an advantage in locating industry at the periphery of an urban area rather than close to the city center? Discuss the social and economic ramifications of suburban rather than urban location of industry.

4. Usually, large corporations are more able to absorb the cost of emission control than small ones are. In fact, some small factories have been forced to close because of the costs required to meet air quality standards. Do you see any solution to this problem?

5. The types of pollutants that foul the air over a particular locality are determined by the prevailing industrial and domestic activities. Prepare a list of the sources of air pollutants in your community. Is information available concerning the composition and amount of air pollutants from local industry?

6. Prepare a summary of the "hidden" costs of air pollution. How do these costs compare to the more obvious expenses of polluted air?

7. What procedures could an individual take to reduce his contribution to air pollution?

8. In order to develop meaningful air quality control legislation, standards must first be established. Suggest guidelines that should be followed in determining such standards.

9. Evaluate the air pollution potential of your community in terms of the area's topography, frequency of stable atmospheric conditions, and location of industry.

SELECTED
READINGS

American Chemical Society. *Cleaning Our Environment: The Chemical Basis for Action.* Washington, D.C.: American Chemical Society, 1969. Includes a section on the air environment that emphasizes our technical capability for air quality control.

American Public Health Association. *Guide to the Appraisal and Control of Air Pollution.* New York: American Public Health Association, 1969. Briefly defines the air pollution problem and outlines control procedures.

Battan, L. J. *The Unclean Sky, A Meteorologist Looks at Air Pollution.* New York: Doubleday and Company, Inc., 1966. A popular account of how the atmosphere is being utilized for waste disposal and the consequences.

Bryson, R. A. " 'All other factors being constant . . .', A Reconciliation of Several Theories of Climatic Change." *Weatherwise,* vol. 21, no. 2 (1968), pp. 56–62. A semi-technical account of the roles of carbon dioxide and atmospheric turbidity in climatic change.

Landsberg, H. E. "Man-Made Climatic Changes." *Science,* vol. 170, no. 3964 (1970), pp. 1265–1274. A concise yet clear summary of the numerous ways in which man's activities modify the climate.

chapter

8

The Hydrosphere: Man's Impact on the Hydrologic Cycle

The total volume of water on Earth has remained virtually constant throughout recent geologic time. A very small annual loss of water vapor in the upper atmosphere is compensated for by volcanic emissions.

Water is distributed in oceanic, atmospheric, and terrestrial reservoirs (Table 8.1). Oceans are the largest reservoir, containing over 97 percent of the volume; most of the remainder is tied up as ice in

Table 8.1
The Earth's reservoirs of water.

Reservoir	Volume of water (gal)[a]	Percentage of total
Oceans	$348,700.0 \times 10^{15}$	97.20
Glaciers	$7,700.0 \times 10^{15}$	2.15
Ground water	$2,217.0 \times 10^{15}$	0.63
Lakes and inland seas	60.5×10^{15}	0.02
Atmosphere	34.1×10^{15}	0.01
Biosphere	3.4×10^{15}	0.001
Streams	0.3×10^{15}	0.0001

Source: B. J. Skinner, *Earth Resources* (Englewood Cliffs, N.J.: Prentice-Hall, 1969).
[a] 1 gallon = 3.79 liters.

continental and alpine glaciers. Comparatively speaking, the water contained in lakes, rivers, the atmosphere, the biosphere, and as ground water represents a very small amount.

The *hydrologic cycle* is the ceaseless transfer of water among these reservoirs (Figure 8.1). The water is taken up from the sea to form clouds; rain and snow fall from the clouds to the Earth to supply rivers; and the rivers flow back to the sea.

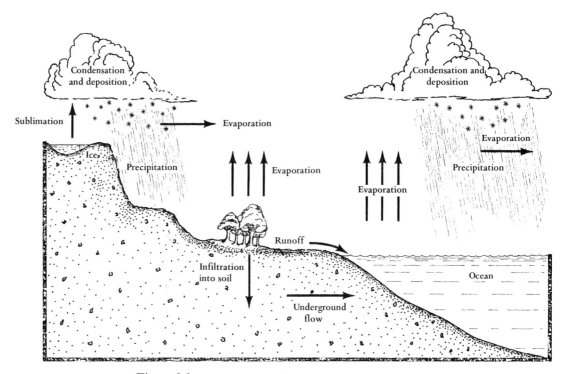

Figure 8.1
The hydrologic cycle.

TRANSFER
PROCESSES

An essential link in the hydrologic cycle is that which joins the atmospheric reservoir with the other reservoirs. It is here that the energy input that sustains the functioning of the hydrologic cycle takes place. The sun supplies energy either to evaporate water from the sea and land reservoirs or to sublime snow and ice. By *evaporation* a substance is changed from a liquid to a vapor at a temperature below its boiling point. *Sublimation* is the direct transition of a substance from solid to vapor without an intervening liquid state. In both instances the substance passes from a lower to a higher energy level, thereby requiring the addition of energy.

Water is returned from the atmospheric reservoir of water vapor to land and sea via the processes of condensation and deposition. *Condensation* is the change from vapor to liquid (droplets); *deposition* is the direct transition from vapor to solid (ice crystals). Precipitation (rain, snow, ice pellets, hail) returns a portion of these products to the Earth's surface.

Let us examine the path of lake water as it moves through the hydrologic cycle. There is a continuous exchange of water molecules at the interface between the lake and atmosphere. If more water enters the atmosphere than returns to the lake, evaporation takes place, transferring water from the lake to the air (Figure 8.2).

Consider a small parcel of air that has received some water vapor from the lake. Its water-vapor content is described in terms of the weight of water vapor divided by the weight of the dry air that contains the water vapor. This parameter is termed the *mixing ratio* (W) and is expressed as grams of moisture per kilogram of dry air (parts per thousand):

AIR-WATER INTERACTION

$$W = \frac{\text{weight of water vapor}}{\text{weight of dry air}} .$$

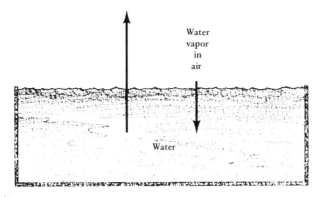

Figure 8.2
During evaporation of water, more water molecules transfer from the liquid to vapor state than return from the vapor to liquid state.

At the lake's surface, the parcel of air has not only an *actual mixing ratio,* Wa, but also a *potential mixing ratio,* Wp. The Wp is the maximum amount of water vapor that can be contained in the parcel of air at the temperature of the parcel. The higher the temperature of the parcel, the higher its Wp; i.e., the warmer the air, the more moisture it can hold.

If wind transports the parcel upward, its temperature cools. As the temperature drops, Wp also decreases but Wa remains constant. As the parcel continues to rise, Wp approaches the value of Wa. When Wp equals Wa, the parcel contains its maximum amount of water vapor and is said to have achieved *saturation.*

Relative humidity (RH) is defined as the ratio of actual to potential mixing ratio multiplied by 100 percent. Relative humidity, therefore, increases as the parcel rises and cools.

$$\text{RH} = \frac{\text{Wa}}{\text{Wp}} \times 100\%.$$

At saturation RH equals 100 percent.

As the parcel approaches saturation, there is a tendency for condensation and deposition to occur on nuclei — tiny, solid particles that are always present in large numbers in the atmosphere. These *condensation nuclei* are products of both natural and human activity. Forest fires, volcanic eruptions, wind erosion of soil, sea-salt spray, and effluents of domestic and industrial chimneys provide a continuous supply of nuclei.

The most effective of these nuclei are *hygroscopic;* i.e., they have a special affinity (attraction) for water molecules. This property results in condensation or deposition on these nuclei at relative humidities of less than 100 percent. In fact, some hygroscopic sea-salts produce condensation at relative humidities as low as 70 percent! From the foregoing it is apparent that cloud formation and attendant precipitation occur more efficiently where there is an ample supply of hygroscopic nuclei.

Clouds in their myriad forms are the visible manifestations of condensation and deposition in the atmosphere. They are composed of water droplets and ice crystals that are so small and light that they tend to remain in suspension. Hence in order for the hydrologic cycle to continue, these cloud particles must somehow become larger and fall toward the Earth's surface as precipitation.

Water droplets and ice crystals can both be present (coexist) in clouds at temperatures well below the freezing point. The liquid is then said to be *supercooled water*. Hence condensation of water vapor may take place at temperatures below and above 32°F (0°C). Supercooled water is an important factor in the *Bergeron-Findeisen theory* of precipitation formation, which applies to those clouds that contain a mixture of ice crystals and supercooled water droplets. In such a cloud, the ice crystals grow at the expense of the water droplets; they become heavier and begin to descend at an accelerating velocity. Because they fall faster than the water droplets, they intercept and capture droplets in their paths and grow still larger. Eventually, the ice crystals are big enough to escape the cloud. If the atmosphere is below the freezing point all the way to the ground, the crystals will reach the Earth's surface in the form of snow; if the air near the ground is above freezing, they reach it as rain.

The Bergeron-Findeisen process applies only to clouds whose temperatures are below the freezing point. However, in the summer in mid-latitudes, and during the entire year in the tropics, clouds form that have temperatures above the freezing point. Hence neither ice crystals nor supercooled water droplets are present. To explain precipitation from this type of cloud, a second theory postulates the presence of relatively large hygroscopic sea-salt nuclei. The larger nuclei result in larger droplets that fall faster. As they fall they intercept and capture smaller water droplets in their paths, thereby growing by what is called the *coalescence process*.

Cloud conditions that favor precipitation formation also favor its preservation, but once precipitation leaves the cloud it enters a hostile environment, and either evaporation or sublimation takes place. In general, the longer its journey to the ground and the drier the air in its path, the greater is the amount of precipitation that will be returned to the vapor state. Often, hilly regions receive a greater amount of rainfall than surrounding lowlands partly because of this effect.

In falling to the ground precipitation performs the important function of cleansing the atmosphere, i.e., it washes pollutants from the air. However, in the process rain and snow may become significantly acidic. Rainfall is normally slightly acidic (pH of about 5.7) as the result of passing through the atmospheric reservoir of carbon dioxide.

Bergeron-Findeisen Process

Coalescence Process

Acid Rains

Wherever the air is polluted with oxides of sulfur and nitrogen, however, rainfall also produces sulfuric and nitric acids. The pH of precipitation that passes through such contaminated air may become as low as 3. Acid rains corrode structures, increase the rate of leaching of many chemicals such as plant nutrients from soils, and threaten aquatic organisms by lowering the pH of lakes and ponds.

ENHANCEMENT AND SUPPRESSION OF PRECIPITATION

Rainfall is enhanced in some localities and suppressed in others by both natural and man-influenced causes.

Orographic Rainfall

A mountain range lying perpendicular to the prevailing wind flow forms a natural barrier that results in heavier rainfall on one side than on the other. As air sweeps up the windward side of the mountain range, its temperature decreases and the value of Wp approaches that of Wa. The relative humidity increases and, eventually, precipitation falls. On the leeward side of the range air descends and warms, and the relative humidity decreases. Thus the mountain range establishes two contrasting climatic zones: moist on the windward side and dry on the leeward side (Figure 8.3).

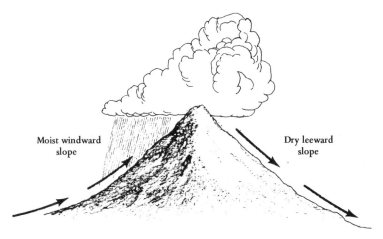

Moist windward slope

Dry leeward slope

Figure 8.3
The effect of air flow over a mountain range on rainfall distribution.

In Washington state this precipitation disparity is especially apparent from west to east. North-south mountain ranges make for exceptionally rainy conditions in the western part of the state and dry conditions in the eastern part (Figure 8.4). On Mount Waialeale, Hawaii, the contrast is spectacular. Annual rainfall varies from 460 inches on one side of the mountain to only 18 inches on the other side. In every case, this *orographic rainfall* results in plant and animal communities markedly different from one side of the mountain range to the other. It also directly affects man's water supply, the type of crops he can grow, and the type of shelter he must build.

Figure 8.4
The orographic effect causes marked differences in rainfall and hence in vegetation from west to east across the state of Washington. The rain forest of the Olympic Peninsula in northwestern Washington *(left)* contrasts dramatically with the dry lands of central Washington, which must be irrigated for cultivation *(right)*. (Left: *Authenticated News International.* Right: *USDA-Soil Conservation Service.)*

Man's Inadvertent Enhancement of Precipitation

Man's inadvertent enhancement of precipitation is due primarily to his contribution, by domestic and industrial processes, of hygroscopic nuclei to the atmosphere. These nuclei include dust particles and droplets of sulfuric and nitrous acid. The tendency toward increased cloudiness and precipitation in urban industrial areas is aided by the convective air circulation pattern that characterizes many cities. As discussed in the previous chapter, this circulation pattern involves rising air currents over the city that help to bring moist air parcels to saturated conditions.

The effect of industry on condensation and precipitation is dramatically illustrated by the climatic contrasts between urban and rural regions. In general, *fog* (ground-level clouds) is two to five times more frequent in cities than in the surrounding countryside. In the downtown sector of Paris, for example, fog days comprise as much as 47 percent of the year. The figure is only 28 percent in the suburbs and 9 percent in the countryside. Cities generally receive 5 to 10 percent more rain than surrounding rural areas. That this precipitation is of industrial origin is suggested by the fact that the excess usually occurs on weekdays, when industrial activity is at its peak.

An unusually pronounced artificial enhancement of precipitation is noted in LaPorte, Indiana, about 30 miles downwind from the East Chicago-Gary industrial complex. From 1951 to 1965 LaPorte received 31 percent more annual precipitation and had 38 percent more thunderstorms and 246 percent more days of hail than surrounding areas (Figure 8.5). There is some controversy surrounding the cause of the LaPorte condition, but it appears that both addition of condensa-

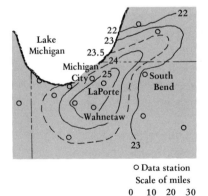

Figure 8.5
The average warm season rainfall in inches in the vicinity of LaPorte, Indiana. *(Redrawn with permission from Stanley A. Changnon, Jr., "The LaPorte Weather Anomaly — Fact or Fiction?"* Bulletin of the American Meteorological Society, *49 [January 1968], p. 6.)*

tion nuclei and stimulation of cloud development by vast quantities of heat liberated by the urban-industrial complex are contributing factors.

Exceptional precipitation and cloudiness in urban areas have serious effects on transportation: Restrictions in visibility slow traffic, impede air travel, and contribute to auto accidents. In recent years, however, there have been reports of locally improved visibilities, apparently the result of stricter enforcement of air quality standards and the trend from coal to petroleum and natural gas for sources of energy. These are reasons why in the past ten years, winter sunshine in London has increased by about 70 percent.

Since the end of World War II there have been numerous attempts to increase precipitation artificially (Figure 8.6). Scientists try to stimulate natural precipitation (Bergeron-Findeisen and coalescence processes) by cloud seeding, that is, by introducing nucleating agents into clouds. Dry ice and silver iodide (a substance with crystal properties similar to ice) are injected into clouds of supercooled water droplets while relatively large water droplets and sea-salt crystals are injected into warm clouds. At first glance, fulfillment of these endeavors would appear to be of great economic value. Cloud seeding offers a promise of restoring farmlands parched by drought and of maintaining water reservoirs in expanding cities. However, much controversy surrounds the amount of precipitation enhancement brought about by cloud seeding and the advisability of large-scale seeding efforts.

On the first count, although claims of precipitation increase range from 0 to 20 percent and more, there is the question of whether the rain that falls following a cloud seeding project would have fallen anyway. On the second count, it must be kept in mind that cloud seeding merely facilitates the transfer of water from clouds to the Earth's surface; it will not produce rain without clouds. On a large scale, successful rainmaking may merely redistribute a fixed supply of rain, so the increase in precipitation in one area may be offset by a decrease in another.

If cloud seeding is successful in a region, moreover, it may not benefit everyone. Some areas in the Southwest rely upon water draining from the snowfields of the western slopes of the Rocky Mountains in order to meet a sizable portion of their water needs. As populations climb and demands for water soar, thought is given to seeding the

Cloud Seeding: Man's Advertent Enhancement of Precipitation

Figure 8.6
This cloud layer was seeded with dry ice pellets dropped from an aircraft. Ice crystals formed and fell out of the cloud, leaving a hole behind, within an hour of the time this photograph was taken. *(Vincent J. Schaefer.)*

clouds over the mountains, increasing the snowpack and hence the water runoff into lower regions. If successful, this project would be of great benefit to the water-users of urban California. However, except for those who rely upon the ski industry for a living, the prospects are less bright for the mountain environment. Lengthening and thickening the winter snow cover would shorten the growing season, reduce the amount of land available for grazing, and increase the danger of avalanches.

Rajputana Desert: Man's Suppression of Rainfall

Man has not only enhanced local precipitation; he has also suppressed it. The development of the dusty Rajputana Desert of northwest India and Pakistan is a good case in point (Figure 8.7). Though this desert region is one that should receive at least moderate rainfall, it is so arid that agricultural production is submarginal. Archeological evidence shows, however, that prior to 1000 B.C., the agriculture-based Indus civilization thrived there in a land rich in vegetation. After 1000 A.D., deterioration set in when forests were cut down and burned. Overgrazing further depleted the vegetative cover, and the loss of this protection induced wind erosion of the soil. Dust was carried into the atmosphere, where its gradual accumulation caused air subsidence. Sinking air warms and dries, i.e., its relative humidity decreases, and the result in this case was the creation of a desert. Moreover, the aridity contributed more dust to the atmosphere, so the desert became self-perpetuating. Only when vegetation is reestablished (perhaps by irrigation) and maintained (by regulation of grazing animals) will this condi-

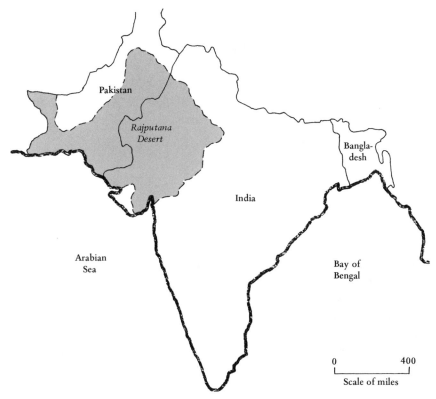

Figure 8.7
The Rajputana Desert.

tion be reversed. In view of India's need for productive lands, these measures would appear to be essential.

HYDROLOGIC BUDGET

The flow of water between land-atmosphere and atmosphere-sea is in two directions. Evaporation of water from the oceanic reservoir is 95.2×10^{15} gallons (360×10^{15} liters) per year, and the amount of evaporation from land reservoirs is 16.4×10^{15} gallons per year. Annual precipitation on the sea is 85.5×10^{15} gallons, on land about 26.1×10^{15} gallons. The reason for the large differences between values for sea and land is primarily the fact that the oceans cover nearly 75 percent of the Earth's surface area. There is an annual gain of water on land and a loss of water from oceans. The excess on land (9.7×10^{15} gallons per year) is about equal to the oceanic deficit (Table 8.2).

Table 8.2
The hydrologic budget in gallons per year.

Precipitation on sea	85.5×10^{15}
Evaporation from sea	95.2×10^{15}
Net loss from sea	-9.7×10^{15}
Precipitation on land	26.1×10^{15}
Evaporation from land	16.4×10^{15}
Net gain on land	$+9.7 \times 10^{15}$

However, the land is not getting any soggier nor are the world's oceans drying up, for the excess water that falls on the land as precipitation eventually recharges the sea's deficit. This excess drips, seeps, and flows from the land back to the sea (Figure 8.8). This is an important consideration in understanding the possible extent of environmental pollution: If water in land reservoirs is contaminated by industrial and domestic wastes, some of these pollutants ultimately find their way to the world's oceans.

On its journey to the sea part of the excess water that falls on the land seeps into the soil and rock, and the remainder flows as rivers and streams. These two components are termed *infiltration* and *runoff* respectively.

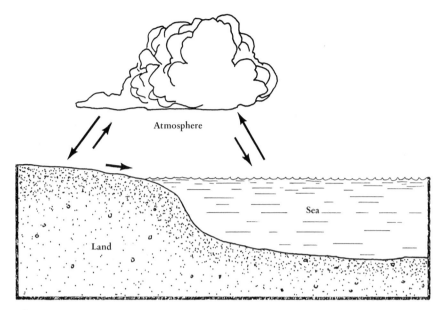

Figure 8.8
Directions of water flow among atmospheric, oceanic, and terrestrial reservoirs.

Water may seep (infiltrate) into the ground directly, as rain, or indirectly, from lakes, streams, or rivers. By both methods the water supplied maintains the ground-water reservoir. Downward-seeping water is distributed in two zones within the surface strata of the crust. In the upper layer, called the *zone of aeration,* pore spaces contain water droplets (held by soil and rock particles) and air. The water requirements of most land plants are supplied by the zone of aeration. The lower zone, the *zone of saturation,* constitutes the ground-water reservoir. Pore spaces in the lithospheric materials of the zone of saturation are completely filled with water.

More than 97 percent of our nation's reserves of fresh water is contained in the subsurface reservoir. Within 3,000 feet of the surface, the volume of water is more than nine times that of the Great Lakes. At present, 20 percent of our population's water needs are met by *ground water.* In 12 states, however, ground water supplies more than half the water supply. In view of the deterioration of surface waters, the value of maintaining the quality of our ground water is obvious.

THE INFILTRATION COMPONENT: GROUND WATER

In many areas, however, our activities threaten the quality of ground water. In order to appreciate the dimensions of the problem, it is necessary that we consider the physical characteristics of ground-water distribution and flow.

Ground-Water Flow

The surface that forms the upper boundary of the ground-water reservoir is called the *water table,* which is not horizontal but rather parallels the overlying topography, i.e., it tends to be higher under hills and lower under valleys. The depth to the ground-water reservoir varies, however, with the amount and frequency of rain. In most areas it is less than 100 feet below the surface, but in arid parts of the world wells must be drilled several hundred feet before they reach the water table. When water is pumped from subsurface reservoirs, the water table drops. Places in the American West and Southwest have rates of withdrawal that exceed the rates of recharge by natural processes. Where artificial recharge is not possible, local agriculture is abandoned.

The property of lithospheric material to transmit water in the zones of aeration and saturation is called *permeability.* The degree of permeability is determined by the volume of pore spaces (porosity) and how effectively the pores are interconnected. Materials of high permeability are called *aquifers.* In general, layers of sand and gravel are good aquifers, whereas clay, shale, and most igneous and metamorphic rocks are poor ones.

In some regions, an aquifer is sandwiched between two folded layers of impermeable rock (Figure 8.9). If a drill taps the aquifer at the trough of the fold, water flows freely from the well under the influence of gravity. Free-flowing wells — called *artesian wells* — are of more value than other wells in that they do not require an expenditure of energy for pumping.

The movement of water through a permeable layer is extremely slow; a velocity of 50 feet (15.2 meters) per year is typical. Hence ground water flows in smooth, continuous lines toward points of discharge, such as rivers and seas. Typical flow lines in a uniformly permeable material are presented in Figure 8.10. Part of the water that seeps in from the surface flows straight downward, and some of it off toward either side, in this case supplying water to a stream and a marsh. Marshes and some streams and lakes are created where the water table intercepts or is above the land surface. In some cases the

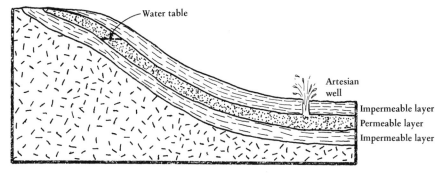

Figure 8.9
Cross-section of the rock stratigraphic situation that results in an artesian flow of water.

water table is below a stream bed and the stream supplies water directly to the ground-water reservoir (Figure 8.11). Because ground water flows in smooth, straight paths, depression of the water table takes the form of a cone (Figure 8.12). Where wells are closely spaced, excessive use of one well causes adjacent wells to quickly run dry.

Another consequence of the slow movement of ground water is the potential residence-time of pollutants. If pollutants are introduced into the ground-water reservoir, they remain there for extended periods before being flushed out. The United States Geological Survey reports that contaminants may remain in subsurface aquifers for periods rang-

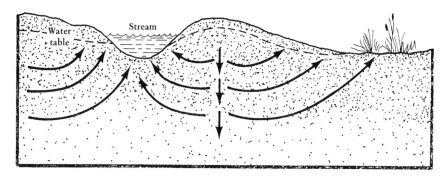

Figure 8.10
Cross-section of the flow of groundwater through a uniformly permeable lithospheric material.

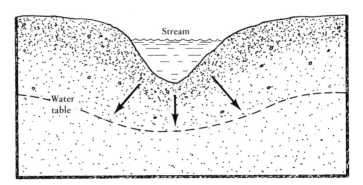

Figure 8.11
Cross-section of a stream supplying water to the ground-water reservoir.

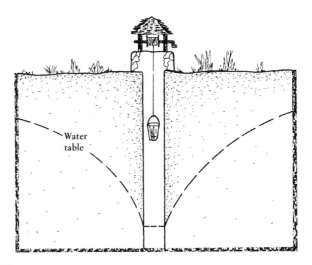

Figure 8.12
Cross-section of the depression of the water table into a cone by pumping from a well.

ing from 200 to 10,000 years — effectively destroying the water supply for generations to come.

Composition of Ground Water

The quality of ground water depends upon its source and its interactions with lithospheric materials in its path. Because surface runoff supplies water to the subsurface reservoir, the same activities that contaminate surface waters can also pollute ground water. Drainage from mine waste-heaps, seepage from septic tanks, and runoff from solid and liquid industrial wastes may seep into ground water. However, infiltration is a natural filtering process that removes suspended solids, bacteria, and viruses; it is so effective a purifying mechanism that fluid wastes are sometimes sprayed on the ground surface for the purpose of removing impurities and recharging the ground-water reservoir.

Filtering is not always sufficient to remove all pollutants, however. In some cases the path of the water through soil and rock particles is not long enough to permit complete purification. In others the pollutant does not interact with lithospheric materials but rather passes directly into the ground-water reservoir. One example is the nitrate ions (NO_3^-) that are released from feed lots, septic tanks, and fertilized fields. This substance is potentially very dangerous in well-water supplies. Nitrates in drinking water are known to induce abortion in cattle and are linked to methemoglobinemia — an often fatal condition in newborn infants that results from oxygen depletion in the blood.

The composition of ground water is also affected by nonhuman activities. For example, beneath swamps and peat bogs, ground water is acidic because of the organic acids released by decaying vegetation. A more familiar example is "hard" water, which is the result of water's passing through limestone and dolomite. Some of the calcium and magnesium ions present in these rocks are dissolved in water. High concentrations of these ions require the use of large quantities of soap. Because of this, detergents containing phosphates that act as water softeners have received wide use in hardwater areas.

Salt-Water Intrusion

An understanding of ground-water movement is especially critical in coastal regions, where there is danger of contamination of fresh ground-water reservoirs by salt water *(salt-water intrusion)* (Figure 8.13). A typical, vertical cross-section of the discharge of ground water into the ocean reveals that there is usually a near-shore interface between salt-water and fresh-water portions of the reservoir. The exact location of this interface is determined by the pressure exerted by the fresh water. If the water table is sufficiently high above sea level, the resulting water pressure will keep salt water offshore; if it is near sea level, water pressure is less and the interface is displaced inland.

The problem is compounded by the fact that salt water is 2.5 percent denser than fresh water because of the greater amount of dissolved substances in salt water. Hence a 2.5 percent greater volume of fresh water is required to exert the same pressure as a given volume of sea water (Figure 8.14). Salt-water intrusion, then, is especially acute in low-lying, flat coastal areas such as southern Florida, where the fresh-water ground reservoir is shallow and subjected to the demands of an expanding population. In such localities, aquifers must continually be recharged artificially to prevent encroachment of sea water and to maintain the supply of fresh water.

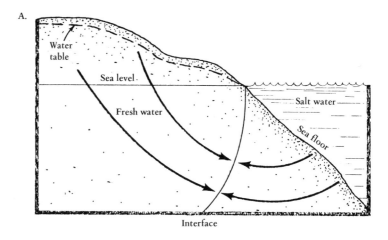

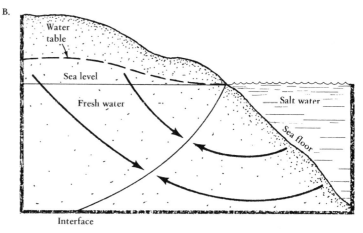

Figure 8.13
Cross-section diagrams of the interface between fresh and salty ground water along a coastal region *(figure A)* and of the landward displacement of the interface following a lowering of the water table *(figure B)*.

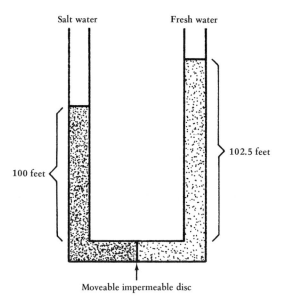

Figure 8.14
A U-tube illustrating the density difference between salty and fresh water. About 2.5 percent more fresh water is required to balance the column of salty water.

Precipitation that does not seep into the ground or evaporate flows into tiny rills that unite to form streams, which join to form rivers that eventually empty into the sea.

Along the downhill course of surface water, a portion of the running water's kinetic energy is expended in erosion and in the transport of rock and soil. Lithospheric materials are carried in solution and suspension and are rolled and slid along the channel bed. It has been estimated that the rivers of the world annually deliver to the oceans 400 million tons of material in solution and another billion tons in suspension. By these processes, running water ranks as the primary sculpturing agent of the landscape.

In each stream there is a balance among four parameters: channel width (W), channel depth (H), stream velocity (V), and water discharge (D), i.e., the volume of water that passes a given point in an interval of time. This balance is expressed as:

$$D = W \times H \times V.$$

Alteration of any of these parameters causes a change in each of the

RUNOFF COMPONENT

other three. For example, if the discharge of a stream is decreased by diversion of water for irrigation, the stream's velocity decreases, resulting in less kinetic energy for transport of the river's sediment load. A portion of this sediment is deposited, decreasing the width and depth of the stream channel, in some instances enough to curtail navigation. Damming also reduces the discharge of rivers, leading to a host of environmental problems.

Each pathway or tributary of surface water drains an area called a *drainage basin*. The activities prevailing within the basin (domestic, industrial, agricultural) determine the quality of its surface waters. Runoff being an essential supplier of water for man and machine, its maintenance is of paramount importance.

KEY WORDS AND SUMMARY STATEMENTS

hydrologic cycle	condensation nuclei	zone of aeration
evaporation	hygroscopic	zone of saturation
sublimation	supercooled water	ground water
condensation	Bergeron-Findeisen theory	water table
deposition	coalescence process	permeability
mixing ratio	orographic rainfall	aquifers
actual mixing ratio	fog	artesian wells
potential mixing ratio	infiltration component	salt-water intrusion
saturation	runoff	drainage basin
relative humidity		

The hydrologic cycle is the circulation of water among terrestrial, atmospheric, and oceanic reservoirs.

As parcels of moist air rise through the atmosphere, they cool and approach saturated conditions.

Hygroscopic nuclei cause condensation or deposition and subsequent precipitation to take place at relative humidities below 100 percent.

The Bergeron-Findeisen theory postulates the way precipitation may form from clouds whose temperatures are below the freezing point, whereas the coalescence process explains how precipitation forms from clouds whose temperatures are above the freezing point.

Precipitation is enhanced and suppressed both naturally (e.g., orographic rainfall) and by man (e.g., cloud seeding, Rajputana Desert).

When total evaporation and precipitation over the oceans and the terrestrial reservoirs are compared in the hydrologic budget, a flow of water from land to sea is indicated.

Water flows from land to sea via infiltration (ground-water flow) and runoff (rivers and streams).

Pollutants that are not filtered out of infiltrating water may contaminate the ground-water supply for generations to come.

Interruption of surface-water flow (e.g., by diversion for irrigation) upsets the balance that exists among the parameters: water discharge, water velocity, channel width, and channel depth.

QUESTIONS AND PROJECTS

1. How will an increase in atmospheric turbidity influence the functioning of the hydrologic cycle?

2. Frequent fogs at airports pose serious hazards to aircraft flight that often result in flight cancellations or diversions that are costly to airlines and their passengers. Suggest a method of fog dispersal that does not require seeding.

3. Present one common example of each of the following water transfer processes: sublimation, deposition, evaporation, and condensation.

4. The residence time of a hydrologic reservoir is the time it takes for a given volume of water to be cycled through the reservoir. Which hydrologic reservoir has the longest residence time? How is this time an important consideration in the problem of environmental pollution?

5. How does man harness the energy of the hydrologic cycle?

6. In your locality, is ground water or surface water the prime source of the public water supply?

7. Usually, there is very little difference between the quantity of water vapor in the air over the Southwest and over the Northeast. There is, though, a large difference in the precipitation amounts received at the two localities. What is the fundamental reason for the contrast in precipitation?

8. By our definition, is cloud seeding a form of pollution? Is legislation needed to regulate cloud seeding? If so, delineate the scope required of such legislation.

9. Enumerate the ways in which water is cleansed of pollutants as the result of its passing through the hydrologic cycle.

SELECTED READINGS

Battan, L. J. *Harvesting the Clouds, Advances in Weather Modification.* Garden City, N.Y.: Doubleday and Company, Inc., 1969. A clear discussion of man's attempts at weather modification.

Battan, L. J. *Cloud Physics and Cloud Seeding.* Garden City, N.Y.: Doubleday and Company, Inc., 1962. A clear consideration of cloud and precipitation formation.

Bryson, R.A., and Baerreis, D. A. "Possibilities of Major Climatic Modification and Their Implications: Northwest India, A Case for Study." *Bulletin of the American Meteorological Society,* vol. 48, no. 3 (1967), pp. 136–142. A semitechnical account of man's climatic modification in the Rajputana Desert.

Changnon, S. A., Jr. "The LaPorte Weather Anomaly — Fact or Fiction?" *Bulletin of the American Meteorological Society,* vol. 49, no. 1 (1968), pp. 4–11. A detailed investigation into the characteristics and contributing factors of the anomalous climate of LaPorte, Indiana.

Likens, G. E., Bormann, F. H., and Johnson, N. M. "Acid Rain." *Environment,* vol. 14, no. 2 (1972), pp. 33–40. A review article that considers the causes and potential environmental hazards of acid rains.

The following books contain more detailed discussions of the characteristics of ground water and ground-water flow:

Foster, R. J. *General Geology.* Columbus, Ohio: C. E. Merrill, 1969, Chapter 12.

Spencer, E. W. *The Dynamics of the Earth, An Introduction to Physical Geology.* New York: T. Y. Crowell Co., 1972, Chapter 16.

Zumberge, J. H., and Nelson, C. A. *Elements of Geology,* 3rd ed. New York: John Wiley and Sons, Inc., 1972, Chapter 10.

chapter

9

The Pollution of Surface Waters

The composition of natural waters is continually changing as the result of gases, rocks, and minerals entering and leaving the water. Normally, water teems with living organisms that in turn affect its composition. Man, in his use of surface waters, has introduced new substances and accelerated the transfer rate of materials. The environmental impact of these activities is the subject of this chapter.

Runoff from the hydrologic cycle furnishes 80 percent of our water needs. People are located in nearly every river and lake drainage basin of the United States, and through their activities pollutants of a complex composition are introduced into the surface waters. Perhaps the most dramatic example of how deteriorated we have allowed some of our waters to become is the Cuyahoga River. This oil-laden river that flows into Lake Erie at Cleveland, Ohio, caught fire in the summer of 1969 and damaged two railroad bridges (Figure 9.1). The Hudson River and the Houston ship canal are two other examples of surface waters that are extremely contaminated.

Figure 9.2 shows a schematic drawing of a typical river drainage basin. The types of activities within the drainage basin largely determine the types of pollutants that enter a river. We will divide these activities into four categories: natural and relatively undisturbed, agricultural, urban, and industrial.

DRAINAGE
BASIN
ACTIVITIES

197

Figure 9.1
Fire on the oil-laden Cuyahoga River in Cleveland, Ohio. (The Cleveland Plain Dealer.)

Figure 9.2
Some examples of how the composition of surface water is altered within a drainage basin. *In natural areas:* (1) Flowing water dissolves and erodes rock; (2) Marshes incorporate nutrients in vegetation; (3) Dissolved gases are added by the turbulence of water below waterfalls. *In urban areas:* (4) The municipal sewage treatment plant does not remove all wastes added to water; (5) Storm sewer water contains wastes washed from the urban area. *In agricultural areas:* (6) Crop dusting adds pesticides and herbicides to rain and runoff; (7) Fertilizers improperly applied are dissolved in runoff; (8) Barnyard wastes may be washed into the river. *In industrial areas:* (9) Industrial waste water effluents vary considerably in composition; (10) Acid water flows from mines; (11) Heated water flows from the power plant; (12) Industrial gases are washed out of the atmosphere by rain; (13) Oil spills result from transportation accidents and the unloading of oil. *(Redrawn with permission from C. Renn,* Our Environment Battles Water Pollution *[Chestertown, Md.: LaMotte Chemical Products Company, 1969].)*

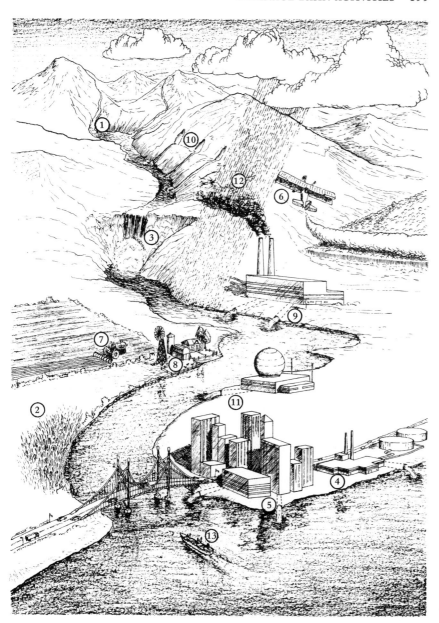

Natural Areas

Forests, marshes, and grasslands generally contribute little to the pollution or alteration of rivers. Water passing through these ecosystems acquires a characteristic "normal" concentration of many substances that foster aquatic organisms. Naturally added materials occasionally cause upsets, but these are usually either rapidly cleaned up by decomposers or of such a small amount that they are readily diluted.

Agricultural Areas

Agricultural areas contribute to the degradation of water quality in several ways. Soil erosion may cause a river to transport a heavy sediment load. Pesticides, fertilizers, and animal wastes may run off into the water from fields, orchards, and the huge feed lots where animals are fattened for market. In rural regions human wastes are usually disposed of by means of septic tanks (Figure 9.3), some of which do not function properly and overflow directly into nearby

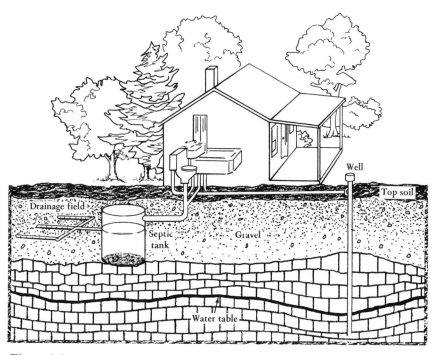

Figure 9.3
Schematic drawing of the waste disposal system used in rural areas. Notice that the waste water from the home will eventually enter the water table.

surface water. High water tables, soils with low permeability, and near-surface bedrock are natural conditions that impair filtration of waste effluents.

A city's sewer system (Figure 9.4) is an important factor in determining the extent of its pollution. Concrete, asphalt, and buildings make for a large part of the urban surface and are impermeable to rain water and snow melt, increasing runoff. To prevent flooding, large *storm-sewer* pipes that are capable of transporting huge volumes of water underlie city streets. Storm sewers usually lead directly to the nearest river, lake, or ocean. During periods of rainfall the air and ground surface are scrubbed, and many of the pollutants (e.g., grime, aerosols, and lawn fertilizers) are carried into the rivers along with the runoff.

A second, smaller sewer pipe called the *sanitary sewer* carries waste water from homes and commercial areas to treatment plants where the water is treated and discharged into the nearest surface water. This two-pipe system is called a *separated sewer system.* The quality of the effluent from treatment plants is directly related to the degree of treatment, which in many cases is totally inadequate. Merely passing sewage through a treatment plant does not magically restore the quality of the water.

Many sewer systems use single pipes to transport water from both runoff and domestic use to the treatment plant. This is called a *combined sewer.* During dry weather this system receives only domestic wastes. However, when it rains the volume of water flowing through the sewer often greatly exceeds what can be properly treated. As a consequence, only a portion of the water is treated, and the remainder — containing raw sewage — is discharged directly into the river. In 1960 an estimated 65 million persons in the United States were served by combined sewers and an equivalent number by separated sewer systems. Even today there are many cities still being served by combined sewer systems.

Raw materials and chemicals used in industrial processing that cannot be economically converted to products are released as air or water pollutants or used as landfill. (Everything must go somewhere: conservation of matter.) Water used by most industries is degraded to the point that when it is released to the environment, undesirable effects

Urban Areas

Industrial Areas

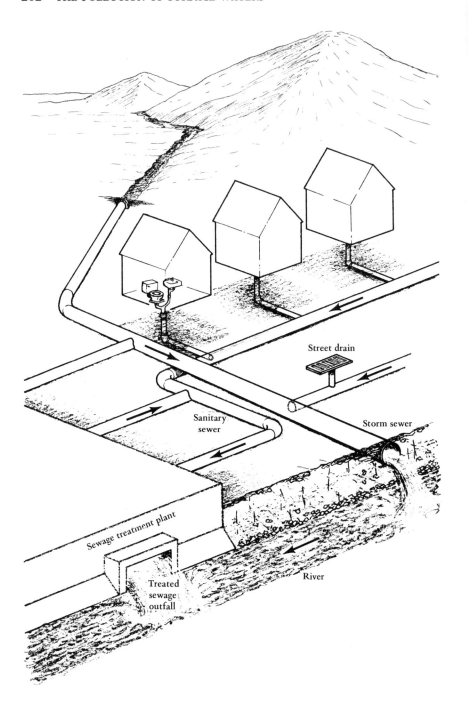

Figure 9.4
Schematic drawing of a separated sewer system used in urban areas. *(After U.S. Department of the Interior, "A Primer on Waste Water Treatment.")*

Figure 9.5
One of the many industrial outfalls that flow into our lakes and rivers. *(Rogers from Monkmeyer.)*

result (Figure 9.5). The waste-water problem of each industry is unique, often requiring special treatment systems to remove particular contaminants.

In the past polluted water meant water that was contaminated with some disease-producing organism, but today many other substances are recognized as water pollutants. These are classified as oxygen-demanding wastes, plant nutrients, inorganic and organic chemicals, sediments, radioactive wastes, and heat discharges.

Organisms that present health hazards are called *pathogenic organisms.* Water-borne pathogens can cause such diseases as dysentery, typhoid fever, cholera, and infectious hepatitis. Analysis of water for specific infectious organisms is a time-consuming and difficult task, so rather then trying to identify specific pathogenic organisms, microbiologists simply analyze for *coliform bacteria* (Figure 9.6). These orga-

WATER POLLUTANTS AND ENVIRON-MENTAL IMPACT
Infectious Agents

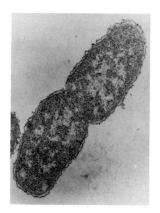

Figure 9.6
Coliform bacteria magnified approximately 60,000 times. *(National Institutes of Health, National Institute of Allergy and Infectious Diseases.)*

nisms are normally present in the intestinal tract of man, so their presence in large numbers in water usually indicates that it has recently been contaminated by raw sewage. Pathogens are also present in the intestinal tract of an infected individual. If coliform organisms are found to be present in significant numbers in the water, there is a possibility that pathogenic organisms are also present. Local health officials set an upper limit on the number of coliform bacteria allowed in recreational waters. If this limit is exceeded, recreational activities such as swimming are prohibited.

Today the probability of disease transmission by water is less than in the past because of chlorination of water supplies (Figure 9.7). Nevertheless, surface waters may be contaminated for several reasons: unchlorinated sewage, combined sewer systems, malfunctioning treatment plants, strikes by sanitary workers, pleasure-boat waste discharge, and the introduction into waters of pathogenic organisms by factories such as meat packing plants (Figure 9.8). Man may not only be infected directly by drinking or swimming in contaminated water, he

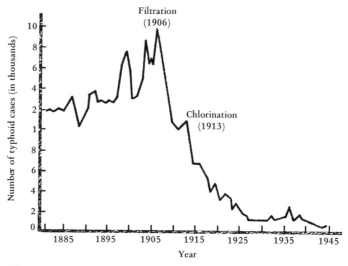

Figure 9.7
Chlorination of water supplies in Philadelphia has drastically decreased the number of water-transmitted cases of typhoid fever. *(Redrawn with permission of The Macmillan Company from W. G. Smillie and E. D. Kilbourne, Preventive Medicine and Public Health, p. 134. Copyright © by The Macmillan Company, 1963.)*

may also be infected via food chains. For example, filter-feeding organisms such as clams and oysters growing in contaminated bays can transmit salmonella microorganisms that cause food poisoning.

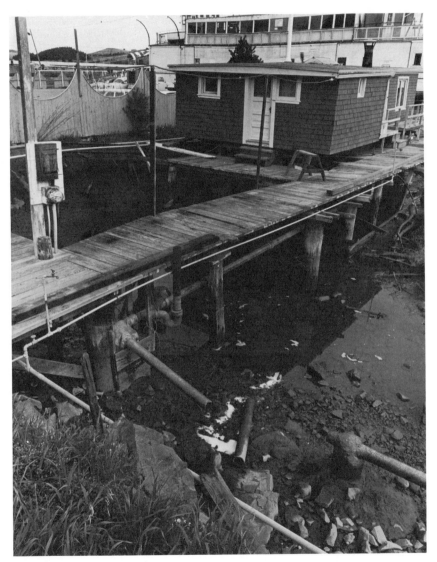

Figure 9.8
Untreated sewage enters surface waters from shoreline buildings such as these in Richardson Bay, California. *(Richard F. Conrat, Photofind, S.F.)*

Oxygen-Demanding Wastes

BIOLOGICAL OXYGEN
DEMAND

Aquatic decomposers, mostly bacteria and fungi, combine dissolved oxygen with organic material, thereby obtaining energy to supply their metabolic needs. In the process organic matter is converted back to carbon dioxide and water (respiration). In a normal aquatic system the quantity of organic material is small, so the oxygen required by decomposers is also small; therefore, the concentration of dissolved oxygen undergoes only small changes. However, some industrial and municipal wastes contain high concentrations of organic substances that require large quantities of dissolved oxygen to be decomposed. The amount of dissolved oxygen needed by the decomposers to decompose the organic material in a given volume of water is called the *biological oxygen demand* (BOD) and is expressed as ppm of BOD.

Human wastes are a major source of BOD, each person adding about 250 ppm of BOD to each of the 150 gallons (567 liters) of water he uses daily. Other major sources of BOD are industries that process organic resources; waste waters from bakeries, dairies, canneries, and packing plants usually have BOD levels of 5,000 to 15,000 ppm or higher. Paper mill and tannery waste waters also have high levels of BOD.

OXYGEN SAG CURVE

When effluents containing BOD are released into a river, dissolved oxygen levels show a characteristic decrease in concentration downstream (Figure 9.9). At the point of discharge, bacteria begin to consume the organic material. The greater availability of food allows the bacteria to rapidly increase in number and consume oxygen faster than it is replenished. As the material moves downstream its decomposition results in a decrease of the BOD. The dissolved oxygen removed by the decomposers is slowly replaced by transfer from the atmosphere into the water. Eventually, the replacement rate exceeds the removal rate and the stream's oxygen level returns to near the original level. This characteristic pattern is called an *oxygen sag curve*.

The shape of the oxygen sag curve is highly dependent upon the processes that transfer oxygen to the river. Oxygen enters an aquatic system through the air-water interface and by the photosynthetic processes of aquatic plants. Turbulence in falls, rapids, or dam spillways causes an increase in transfer of oxygen to the water and a smaller oxygen sag. A wide river has a larger surface area for oxygen transfer than a narrow river. The larger the number of aquatic plants, the more oxygen that is produced.

Water temperature also affects the shape of the oxygen sag curve. The optimal temperature for the decomposition of organic wastes by microorganisms ranges from 25 to 30°C (77 to 86°F). In addition, oxygen is less soluble at higher temperatures, so oxygen levels in rivers

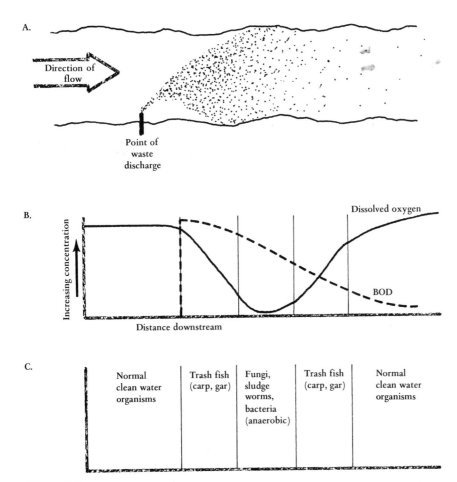

Figure 9.9
The changes that occur in a river receiving oxygen-demanding wastes. Figure A shows the appearance of the river. Figure B shows the oxygen sag curve that results from depletion of oxygen by bacteria decomposing organic wastes. Figure C shows the type of organisms that inhabit the various regions of the river.

receiving organic wastes generally have the lowest oxygen concentrations during the months of July and August.

AEROBIC DECOMPOSITION

When oxygen is present the organic matter undergoes *aerobic* (with oxygen present) *decomposition* (respiration) by microorganisms. The chemical forms of the elements resulting from aerobic conversions are:

$$
\begin{array}{ll}
\text{Organic matter composed} & \left. \begin{array}{c} \text{C} \\ \text{H} \\ \text{O} \\ \text{N} \\ \text{P} \\ \text{S} \end{array} \right\} + O_2 \xrightarrow[\text{organisms}]{\text{Aerobic}} \quad
\begin{array}{l}
CO_2 \\
H_2O \\
H_2O \\
NO_3^- \text{ (nitrate)} \\
PO_4^{3-} \text{ (phosphate)} \\
SO_4^{2-} \text{ (sulfate)}
\end{array}
\end{array}
$$

ANAEROBIC DECOMPOSITION

If the BOD exceeds the amount of available oxygen in the river, *anaerobic* (with no oxygen present) *decomposition* results. In such instances the aerobic organisms are replaced by anaerobic organisms (bacteria). The products of decomposition by anaerobic organisms are:

$$
\begin{array}{ll}
\text{Organic matter composed} & \left. \begin{array}{c} \text{C} \\ \text{H} \\ \text{O} \\ \text{N} \\ \text{P} \\ \text{S} \end{array} \right\} \xrightarrow[\text{organisms}]{\text{Anaerobic}} \quad
\begin{array}{l}
CH_4 \text{ (methane)} \\
CH_4, H_2O, NH_3, H_2S \\
H_2O \\
NH_3 \text{ (ammonia)} \\
PO_4^{3-} \text{ (phosphate)} \\
H_2S \text{ (hydrogen sulfide)}
\end{array}
\end{array}
$$

Under anaerobic conditions the river becomes putrid, unsightly, and a decaying mess.

EFFECT ON AQUATIC LIFE

The response of the aquatic organisms in rivers receiving organic wastes is well known. The portion of a river upstream from a discharge site usually supports a wide variety of fish, algae, and other organisms. In the section of the river where oxygen levels approach zero, only sludge worms (Tubifex) (Figure 9.10) and blood red larvae (Chironomids) survive. As the oxygen level recovers downstream, certain species of trash fish (carp and gar) that can tolerate low oxygen levels appear.

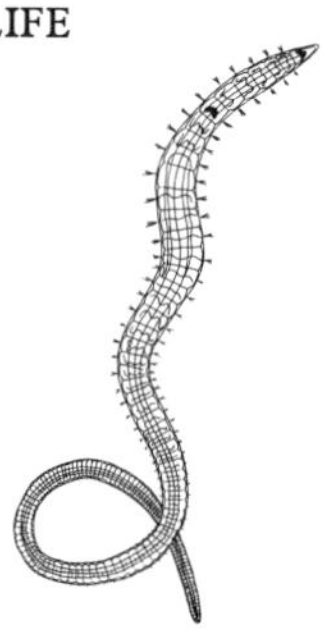

Figure 9.10
The sludgeworm is an organism that thrives on the bottom of organically polluted water. *(Illustration from Science Software Systems, Inc.)*

Eventually a normal community is restored, but a single overloading discharge of BOD can eliminate for a long period the natural aquatic community in an entire river.

Like all ecosystems, aquatic ecosystems require carbon, nitrogen, phosphorus, potassium, and other elements in order to function. The two most common nutrients that act as limiting factors within an aquatic ecosystem are phosphorus, in the form of phosphate (PO_4^{3-}) and nitrogen, in the form of either nitrate (NO_3^-) or ammonia (NH_3). Either of these elements may limit the quantity of aquatic organisms present, though in most cases it is phosphate.

Plant Nutrients

Lakes are classified according to their productivity, the mass of living organisms they support. *Oligotrophic lakes* are characterized by slow rates of nutrient cycling and low productivity (Figure 9.11).

NUTRIENT CYCLING
AND EUTROPHICATION

Figure 9.11
Tipsoo Lake below Mt. Rainier, Washington, is an excellent example of an oligotrophic lake. *(Union Pacific Railroad photograph.)*

Eutrophic lakes have high rates of nutrient cycling, greater productivity, and large numbers but relatively few species of aquatic organisms. Oligotrophic and eutrophic lakes, whose characteristics are summarized in Table 9.1, represent the extremes of a continuous range of productivity.

Table 9.1
General characteristics of oligotrophic and eutrophic lakes.

Characteristic	Oligotrophic	Eutrophic
Rate of nutrient cycling	Low	High
Production by aquatic producers	Low	High
Production of animals	Low	High
Percentage of trash fish	Low	Higher (may dominate)
Oxygen in hypolimnion	Present	Often absent
Depth	Usually deeper	Tend to be shallower
Water quality for drinking and industry	Good	Poor
Number of species of aquatic organisms	Many	Fewer

The quantity of living organisms a lake can support depends upon the rate of cycling of the limiting nutrients (Figure 9.12). The sources of nutrients involved in cycling are the drainage basin, sediments, and organisms within the lake. A few lakes have from their formation been eutrophic because of the influx of high concentrations of nutrients from their drainage basins. Most, however, were originally oligotrophic, becoming more eutrophic over many thousands of years. This natural aging process is called *eutrophication* (Figure 9.13). But man's activities have caused an acceleration in the rates of nutrient cycling called *"cultural" eutrophication.*

Larger and denser growths of aquatic plants develop as limiting nutrients increase. Both rooted and free-floating aquatic plants (Figure 9.14) become so numerous in eutrophic lakes that the water sometimes looks like pea soup or green paint (Figure 9.15). With the onset of warm weather, an explosion in the algae population, an *algae bloom,* may occur. These blooms are usually composed of only a few species of algae, most of them blue-green. Blue-green algae are not eaten by herbivores because the algae are too large for the filter-feeding organisms. The food chain is terminated after the first step.

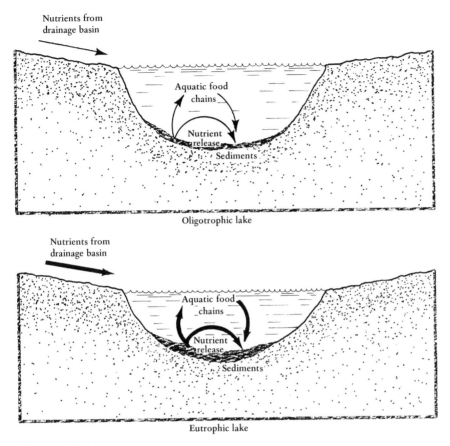

Figure 9.12
Contrast of the rates of nutrient cycling in eutrophic and oligotrophic lakes.

Photosynthesis by algae helps maintain the oxygen content of an aquatic system. After an algae bloom, however, the algae die. Some settle to the bottom, building up an organic sediment that requires oxygen for decomposition. As a result, the hypolimnion of many eutrophic lakes is depleted of oxygen during the summer (Figure 9.16). When this happens, cold-water fish such as lake trout, whitefish, and cisco die. Dead algae also create problems in the epilimnion. Because the wind tends to cause these dead algae to concentrate along the shoreline and in embayments, such regions may also be depleted of oxygen and suffer fish losses. Some species of blue-green algae release

Natural

Time

Man-accelerated

Urban
runoff

Industrial
effluent

Sediment

Fertilizers and
pesticides

Figure 9.13
Eutrophication of lakes, both natural and man accelerated. *(Redrawn from Steven Born and Douglas Yanggen,* Understanding Lakes and Lake Problems, *Upper Great Lakes Regional Commission publication [May 1972].)*

Figure 9.14
Floating aquatic plants become more numerous when fertilizers, such as those from animal wastes, enter the water. *(Authenticated News International.)*

Figure 9.15
Some blue-green algae that produce nuisance blooms. *(Redrawn with permission from Standard Methods for the Examination of Water and Waste Water, 13th ed., American Public Health Association, American Water Works Association, Water Pollution Control Federation [New York, 1971], p. 790 and plates A, B, C, and D.)*

Gleotrichia

Anabaena

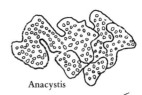

Anacystis

Spirogyra

Chlorella

Aphanizomenon

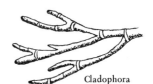

Cladophora

toxic substances that can cause further fish kills. At the very least a dense algae bloom causes a foul smell because of the anaerobic decomposition of algae and fish (Figure 9.17).

Eutrophication of surface water is one of the most significant water quality problems facing man today. Recreation, agriculture, industry, and municipalities are all affected. Dense growths of aquatic plants prevent swimming and boating and seriously impair the aesthetic quality of a lake (Figure 9.18). Eutrophic lakes tend to be taken over by trash fish, which affects both sport and commercial fishing. Municipal water supplies drawn from eutrophic lakes often acquire tastes and odor problems during algae blooms. Removal of compounds causing

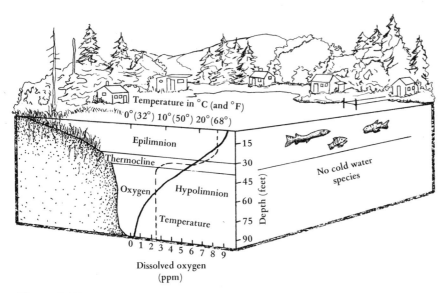

Figure 9.16
Schematic drawing showing the depletion of oxygen in the hypolimnion of a eutrophic lake in midsummer. *(Adapted from Robert L. Smith, Ecology and Field Biology, pp. 164–165, with permission of Harper & Row Publishers, Inc. Copyright © 1966 by Robert Leo Smith.)*

Figure 9.17
Dead fish (alewives) decomposing along the shore of Lake Michigan at Chicago. *(Nancy Hays from Monkmeyer.)*

Figure 9.18
Excessive weed growth because of eutrophication in Lake Mendota, Wisconsin, impairs swimming and boating activities. *(Photograph by Donald Chandler, courtesy of Professor Arthur D. Hasler, Zoology Department, University of Wisconsin.)*

foul tastes and odors, as well as the algae, significantly increase the cost of supplying water to a municipality. Cleanup costs for industrial use can also be considerable.

By limiting nutrient concentration, the quantity of aquatic plants can be controlled. Best estimates by scientists are that excessive growth of algae results if 0.3 ppm nitrogen (as nitrate or ammonia) and 0.03 ppm phosphate are present. With those limits in mind, let us consider the sources of nitrogen and phosphorus compounds within a drainage basin (Table 9.2). Because it is impossible to control the cycles within the lake (Figure 9.12), we must control plant nutrients within the drainage basin. Domestic sewage is an important source of plant nutrients, and the effluent from even a modern treatment plant (one using secondary treatment) usually contains 10 to 30 ppm nitrogen and 5 to 20 ppm phosphorus. These treatment plants remove only about 50 percent of the nitrogen compounds and 30 percent of the phosphorus compounds. A major source (approximately 50 percent) of the phosphate content of sewage is household detergents, so we see the value of the low-phosphate detergents.

Urban runoff is also a significant source of plant nutrients. Studies in Cincinnati indicate that stormwater runoff contains several ppm of both nitrogen and phosphorus. These evidently result from lawn fertilizer misuse, dog-curbing, dust, and combustion products.

Industrial inputs of nutrients vary widely. Paper mills, contributors of high amounts of BOD, release small amounts of plant nutrients. Industries with large surface areas to clean, such as creameries or car washes, contribute large amounts of phosphorus, as do phosphate-mining industries.

Studies indicate that nutrient runoff from some farmland is no greater than that of natural areas. However, where large amounts of

NUTRIENT SOURCES

Table 9.2
Estimated nutrient sources for Lake Mendota, Wisconsin.

| Source | Estimated percentage contribution | |
	Nitrogen	Phosphorus
Municipal and industrial waste water	10	36
Urban runoff	6	17
Rural runoff	11	42
Precipitation on lake surface	20	2
Ground water	52	2
Other	1	1

Source: G. F. Lee, *Eutrophication*. Eutrophication Informational Program, The University of Wisconsin Water Resources Center (1970).

fertilizers are applied and drainage conditions promote runoff, the amount is significant. Water returned from irrigation in the West in some instances has nitrate concentrations approaching 50 ppm. In northern states, the winter practice of spreading manure over frozen ground adds to nutrient levels in spring runoff. Other minor sources of nutrients are ground water and the atmosphere.

The importance of each of the above sources varies with the drainage basin. For example, the 13 million people who live within Lake Erie's drainage basin account for 137,000 pounds (62,200 kilograms) of phosphate per day, with results that are well known. Even for Lake Mendota, Wisconsin, a lake with a large percentage of its drainage basin under cultivation, the major portion of its phosphorus originates in the area's cities (Table 9.2).

In several cases, cultural eutrophication has been reversed. Lake Washington, near Seattle, used to receive nearly 20 million gallons of treated domestic wastes per day. The effluent from the sewage treatment plants contained at least 50 percent of the original nutrient load. As a result, aquatic weeds and algae thrived. Between 1963 and 1968 engineers constructed pipelines that now funnel wastes to a large treatment plant on Puget Sound. From there the treated effluent is discharged into offshore tidal flow that carries the nutrients out to sea. The water quality in Lake Washington has subsequently vastly improved: algae populations decreased and water transparency doubled. Unfortunately, most lakes that receive treated sewage effluent cannot be bypassed.

Inorganic Chemicals

Excluding products of biological origin, elements and compounds found in the lithosphere are classified as inorganic. Man uses the concentrated deposits of these substances to manufacture metals, new compounds, and finished products. However, through mining, smelting, production of goods, and the use and disposal of products, inorganic substances may find their way into surface waters and cycle through ecosystems.

Trace amounts of many metals are required for sustaining life; some are cobalt, zinc, copper, manganese, chromium, and molybdenum. But these can accumulate in food chains to levels potentially harmful to living organisms.

Mercury illustrates the hazards posed by some inorganic wastes in surface waters. The ore is mined as the mineral cinnabar (mercury sulfide) and is converted to the liquid metal by processing. Mercury and its compounds have a wide variety of uses (Table 9.3), so there are many possible routes whereby this element can enter aquatic ecosystems. In 1969 nearly six million pounds of mercury were used in the United States, much of it by the chlor-alkali industry, which produces chlorine, a disinfectant. The initial discovery of high mercury levels in fish was traced back to discharges and losses from these chlorine producing plants. Some marine paints have mercury compounds blended into them that prevent barnacles from growing on boats. Coal and petroleum contain only traces of mercury (typically about 0.15 and 0.07 ppm respectively), but given the vast consumption of these fuels, such sources can be significant.

Mercury is often discharged into the environment as either mercury ions (Hg^{2+}) or mercury metal. Certain microorganisms can convert both to another compound called methyl mercury, which is more toxic than other forms. It appears that only methyl mercury can be accumulated in food chains. Instances of mercury moving through food chains were first noted in Minnamata, Japan. Between 1953 and 1960, 111 persons suffered mercury poisoning, and 43 of them died. The victims' diets consisted largely of fish and shellfish.

Mercury affects mainly the brain and central nervous system, producing numbness, tingling sensations in the hands, feet, or lips, cons-

Table 9.3
United States consumption of mercury, 1969.

Source	Thousands of pounds
Chlor-alkali production	1,575
Electrical apparatus	1,417
Paints	739
Industrial and control instruments	531
Dental preparations	232
Catalysts	225
Agriculture	204
General laboratory use	155
Pharmaceuticals	55
Pulp and paper making	42
Other uses	736
Total	5,911

Source: United States Bureau of Mines.

tricted vision, headaches, and emotional disturbance. Not surprisingly, fetuses and young children are the most susceptible. Mercury in a number of foods has been found at levels sufficient to produce adverse health effects. Tuna and swordfish caught far offshore have been found to contain levels higher than the Food and Drug Administration's recommended maximum of 0.5 ppm mercury for fish. Thus, it appears that the margin between levels of mercury we consume and those that produce harmful effects may not be very far apart. A varied diet is one way to avoid ingesting excess mercury.

Metals such as aluminum, titanium, barium, strontium, and iron occur naturally in soils and do not usually produce toxic effects in ecosystems. However, industrial accidents involving poisoning by metals such as mercury, arsenic, and beryllium point out the need for a better understanding of the movement and effects of metals in ecosystems. For example, because mercury compounds were used to prevent growth of microorganisms, it was assumed that mercury did not cycle through the environment. Yet, under proper conditions, certain bacteria produce methyl mercury that allows subsequent concentration in food chains.

Other substances besides metals are classified as inorganic pollutants. Indeed any inorganic chemical, when present in high concentration, may be toxic to some members of the biosphere: Salt is necessary to our diet, but drinking only seawater is fatal. Industries employ many concentrated salt solutions, e.g., potassium cyanide, which is used in electroplating the silver and gold components of electronic equipment. Accidental discharges of these concentrated waste solutions have, on occasion, eliminated whole communities of aquatic life.

Acidic and alkaline wastes can alter the pH of natural waters beyond the pH level tolerated by aquatic organisms. We have previously discussed the problems of acid mine wastes that are further aggravated by the fact that the solubility of metals increases in acid waters. Concentrations of metals such as zinc, copper, and lead under these conditions can also be increased to toxic levels.

Organic Chemicals

In the laboratory man has synthesized literally millions of new organic compounds that are based on a carbon skeleton, i.e., compounds formed because of the ability of carbon atoms to bond themselves in chains. These compounds are used in the manufacture of products ranging from paints to pesticides to pharmaceuticals to plastics. When present in water, some of these compounds present problems. For example, a class of compounds called phenols, in concentrations of less than 1 ppm, cause taste and odor problems in water. Plastics are not biodegradable, so they are destined to become eyesores on our landscape and in our waters. The problems of pesticides are discussed in Chapter 11.

Oil and its derivatives are made up of a wide variety of organic compounds composed essentially of carbon and hydrogen. Water pollution by oil results from both accidental and thoughtless discharges of oil. The Federal Water Quality Administration reported over 1,000 known oil spills in 1969 of 100 barrels (3,150 gallons) or more. Ocean vessels were responsible for over half the spills, and another one-third involved shoreline facilities such as pipelines, oil terminals, and storage tanks. Spectacular examples of the former include the breakups of the *Torrey Canyon* (1967) in the English Channel and the *Ocean Eagle* (1968) off Puerto Rico. In 1969 an offshore well near Santa Barbara, California, developed a leak releasing an oil slick that at one time covered an estimated 800 square miles (2,070 square kilometers). Destruction of oil rigs by storms and blowouts of offshore wells are additional causes of oil spills.

Some effects of oil spills are well known. Birds that become coated with oil have little chance of surviving (Figure 9.19). Fish that depend

Figure 9.19
These are some of the 10,000 ducks that died from an accidental oil spill on Spring Lake, Minnesota, off the Mississippi River. *(Environmental Protection Agency.)*

upon a sense of smell to find prey or escape predators are confused by compounds present in oil spills, and fish and shellfish in the region of an oil spill often develop a tainted flavor. Beaches are covered and the oil is tracked into motels and homes.

In the past several years there has been a flurry of activity to find ways to contain and clean up oil spills, but most techniques are primitive and expensive. With increases in the amount of oil transported, the size of oil tankers, and the extent of underwater oil exploitation, it is not unreasonable to expect that the problems of oil pollution will also increase.

Radioactive Wastes

During the past three decades, very small amounts of radioactive materials have been released into the environment emitting rays known to be hazardous to the biosphere. Because nuclear reactors are the largest potential source of radioactivity, we will examine the problems of radioactive wastes in discussing energy demands (Chapter 13).

Sediments

Sediments are composed primarily of lithospheric materials that are temporarily suspended in lakes, rivers, and streams (Figure 9.20). Although their presence makes the water turbid, they are not directly toxic to organisms. Some rivers are located in drainage basins with soils made up largely of fine clays that, once eroded, can remain suspended for more than a month even in quiet waters.

Transporting sediments is a normal function of a river, but sediment loads have increased because of soils left unprotected by crop cultivation, timber cutting, strip mining, overgrazed pastures, road building, and construction sites. The Federal Water Quality Administration estimated in a 1969 report that construction sites contribute 2,000 times more sediment than forested land, 200 times more than grassland, and 10 times more than cultivated land. The amount of sediment entering our waterways from erosion exceeds the amount of suspended material discharged from sewage treatment plants by at least 700 times.

Deposition of sediments accelerates the filling of lakes, reservoirs, and harbors, and the resulting increase in nutrient input speeds up natural eutrophication of lakes. However, in areas of heavy deposition, botton-dwelling organisms may be covered and fish spawning areas may be destroyed. For example, a beautiful coral reef that once was a tourist attraction in Kaneohe Bay, Hawaii, is now dead because of the turbidity and sedimentation arising from housing construction

Figure 9.20
Lower Cedar Creek, Minnesota, is choked with sediment from nearby farms in its watershed. *(USDA–Soil Conservation Service.)*

within the drainage basin of the bay. Restoration of filled lakes or basins by dredging is usually economically prohibitive.

Because of its high heat capacity, industries use water to cool machinery. By far the largest user of cooling water is the electric power industry (Table 9.4). Increased demand has necessitated building larger power plants that discharge heat in amounts that can markedly alter the normal thermal conditions of a body of water (Figure 9.21).

Probably the most significant effect of heat discharges is on cold-blooded aquatic organisms whose blood temperatures approximate that of their environment. Because physiological functions are largely regulated by temperature, the well-being of cold-blooded organisms is

Thermal Pollution

Table 9.4
Use of cooling water by United States industry.

Industry	Percentage of total
Electric power	81.3
Primary metals	6.8
Chemical and allied products	6.2
Petroleum and coal products	2.4
Paper and allied products	1.2
Food and kindred products	0.8
Machinery	0.3
Rubber and plastics	0.3
Transportation equipment	0.2
All others	0.5
Total	100

Source: Federal Water Pollution Control Administration, *Industrial Waste Guide on Thermal Pollution* (Washington, D.C., September 1968).

Figure 9.21
Infrared photography is a useful technique for following the movement of heated water. In this infrared photograph, a stream of heated water, which shows white, is being discharged from a nuclear power plant into a cooler river. *(Environmental Sciences Branch, HRB-Singer, Inc.)*

closely governed by water temperature. Gradual seasonal temperature changes affect their reproduction and migration habits (Table 9.5). Increased temperature such as would result from thermal discharges accelerates enzymatic activity and thus the life processes of aquatic organisms. At these high rates more dissolved oxygen is required for

Table 9.5
Provisional recommended maximum temperatures for well-being of various fish species.

Temperature	Fish species
93°F (33.9°C)	Growth of catfish, gar, white or yellow bass, buffalo fish, carpsucker, threadfin shad, and gizzard shad
90°F (32.2°C)	Growth of largemouth bass, drum, bluegill, and crappie
84°F (28.9°C)	Growth of pike, perch, walleye, smallmouth bass, and sauger
80°F (26.7°C)	Spawning and egg development of largemouth bass, white and yellow bass, and spotted bass
68°F (20.0°C)	Growth or migration routes of salmon and for egg development of perch and smallmouth bass
55°F (12.8°C)	Spawning and egg development of salmon and trout (other than lake trout)
48°F (8.9°C)	Spawning and egg development of lake trout, walleye, northern pike, and sauger

Source: Federal Water Pollution Control Administration, *Report of the Committee on Water Quality Criteria* (Washington, D.C., 1968).

respiration, but higher temperatures also cause a decrease in oxygen solubility. The combination of these effects produces stress in some species. Additional stress occurs in polluted water because the toxicity of pollutants generally increases at elevated temperatures.

Temperature controls distribution of aquatic life, each species having its own optimum temperature. For some highly prized species of fish such as lake trout, the optimum temperature is 50°F (10°C). Temperatures much higher than this are lethal to the fish. Generally, freshwater fish will tolerate greater temperature fluctuation than marine fish. Heating marine estuaries only a few degrees may be lethal to some species.

In the summer of 1967 the New York State Electric and Gas Corporation announced plans to install an 830-megawatt (11,600,000 kilocalories per minute) nuclear-powered electric generating plant on Lake Cayuga in upstate New York. The lake is 38 miles long (61 kilometers), averages 1.7 miles in width, and has a maximum depth of 435 feet (133 meters). It is stratified from May through November. The range of the epilimnion temperature is 40–43°F (4.4–6.1°C). The depth of the epilimnion varies between 35 and 50 feet during the summer months.

The company planned to withdraw water from the hypolimnion at the 100-foot depth and return heated water (60–75°F; 15.6–23.9°C) to the epilimnion (Figure 9.22). Our first impression is that returning water at its normal summer temperature would not be detrimental. However, the cooling of an 830-megawatt plant would require the circulation of 500,000 gallons of water per minute through the condensers. Each gallon of water would be heated 25 Fahrenheit degrees (13.9 Celsius degrees). About 10 percent of the lake's total volume would pass through the condenser in a year. As a result, the volume of the lake's epilimnion in autumn would increase by 20 percent. In addition, stratification would begin earlier in the spring and last longer into the fall, thus extending the aquatic growing season.

The power plant would cycle nutrient-rich waters from the hypolimnion to the epilimnion, thus causing the lake to be more eutrophic. Although the plant was originally scheduled for completion in mid-1973, it has been delayed pending the evaluation of the above problems. The proposed reactor is within the size range (500–1,000 megawatts) of those nuclear plants under construction or proposed. The Lake

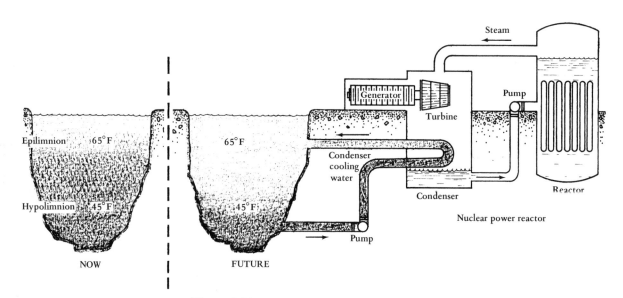

Figure 9.22
Schematic drawing showing how the depth of the epilimnion in Lake Cayuga would increase if the proposed power plant commenced operation. Nutrient cycling would also increase.

Cayuga example illustrates that the aquatic life of even relatively large lakes could be adversely affected by thermal discharge.

Excess heat can be disposed of in two ways, into water or into air. If discharges into water pose potential danger to aquatic ecosystems, power companies should be required to dispose of heat into the air by means of *cooling towers* (Figure 9.23). The towers themselves would add little to the cost of electric power (only about 5 dollars per customer per year), but they would require an additional expenditure of energy to operate them. In addition, intermittent fogging will result when the moist air being emitted from the cooling tower mixes with cold air. Also, the disposal of chemicals used to control slimes that develop in cooling towers may present additional problems. So before cooling towers are advocated to reduce thermal pollution, their negative aspects must also be considered. Each proposed plant site should be evaluated individually with regard to both the positive and negative aspects of thermal discharges.

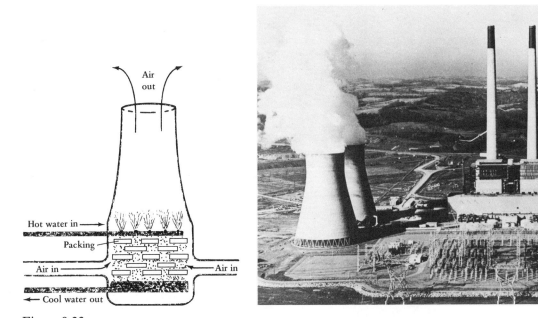

Figure 9.23
Left: Thermal energy in a wet cooling tower is dissipated through evaporation. *Right:* Cooling towers at an electric generating plant near Shelocta, Pa. *(Photograph from National Coal Association.)*

WATER POLLUTION ABATEMENT

We have indicated that human activities exert a significant impact upon the water that reaches rivers and lakes. Water quality in a region is partially dependent upon the effectiveness of sewage treatment (Figure 9.24). Because more citizens are demanding higher water quality, it is important for them to understand the basic sewage-treatment process and its limitations.

Sewage treatment is divided into three steps: primary treatment, secondary treatment, and tertiary treatment. *Primary treatment* is a physical process that removes only the substances in sewage that can be screened out or settled out. Large objects such as sticks, stones, and cans are first separated by a large screen (Figure 9.25). Gravel and sand settle out in a grit chamber. In the next tank, suspended organic material (BOD) is allowed to settle. Processing sewage with primary treatment alone is grossly inadequate (Table 9.6), yet some cities today still do just this. Although the effluent may appear much cleaner with the suspended materials removed, most of the BOD is still present.

Secondary sewage treatment is biological and involves the culturing and harvesting of microorganisms that use the organic material in

Figure 9.24
An aerial view of an activated sludge sewage treatment plant at Knoxville, Tennessee. *(Rotkin, Photography for Industry.)*

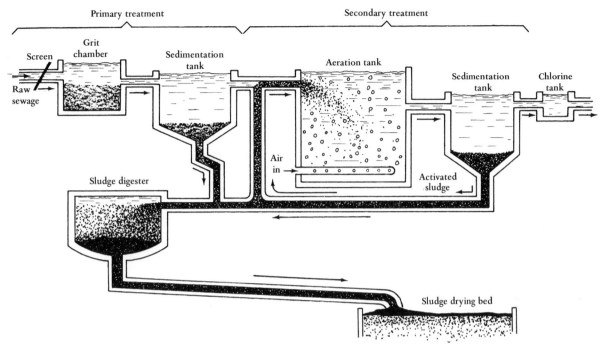

Figure 9.25
Schematic diagram of a sewage treatment plant that uses the activated sludge process. Some of the active organisms in the sludge are recycled, thus the name "activated sludge."

Table 9.6
Performance of the first two stages of sewage treatment.

| Component removed | Removal efficiency of treatment (in percentages) | |
	Primary	Secondary
Biological oxygen demand (BOD)	30	90
Suspended solids	60	90
Nitrogen compounds (total)	20	50
Phosphorus compounds (total)	10	30

Source: American Chemical Society, *Cleaning Our Environment: The Chemical Basis for Action* (Washington, D.C., 1969), p. 108.

sewage as a food source. Secondary treatment removes dissolved BOD such as sugar and starches. The organisms multiply, settle, and accumulate at the bottom of a tank as sludge. The system diagrammed in Figure 9.25 is called an activated sludge plant because a portion of the sludge is cycled back to the point where waste water begins secondary treatment. Organisms in this sludge have been acclimated to the treatment conditions and are therefore able to grow more efficiently. Air is bubbled through the water to furnish the organisms with oxygen, thus maintaining aerobic conditions. If toxic wastes are in sufficient quantities to kill the organisms, the system is actually functioning merely as a primary treatment plant until a new culture of organisms is reestablished. This may require several days to several weeks. Trickling filter plants (water is trickled over rocks coated with organisms to remove dissolved organics) are also used in secondary treatment, but the present trend is toward plants using activated sludge. A final step in sewage treatment involves disinfection by the addition of chlorine.

The disposal of accumulated sludge (dead bacteria) is a major problem for a treatment plant (Figure 9.26). Sludge is sometimes broken

Figure 9.26
Disposal of accumulated sludge represents a major problem for sewage treatment plants. These sludge drying beds are on the outskirts of Chicago. *(Metropolitan Sanitary District of Greater Chicago.)*

down by anaerobic bacteria, and the methane gas produced by the process is used as fuel to operate the plant. In other plants the sludge is filtered out and disposed of in landfills A few cities such as Milwaukee process their sludge to produce an organic fertilizer that is sold commercially.

Treatment plants using primary and secondary processes are most efficient at removing BOD and suspended solids and killing infectious agents. Substances such as nitrates and phosphates require *tertiary treatment* for removal. There are several tertiary methods: Nutrients can be removed by adding chemicals that cause their precipitation; and filtering waste water through activated charcoal removes organic chemicals that resist biological degradation during secondary treatment. Processes are available to remove most contaminants from water, though they are often costly and more complex.

The technology is available to clean up all municipal and industrial waste water. Combinations of the techniques mentioned can accomplish the task. The question is whether we are willing to pay the bill for it.

storm-sewer	biological oxygen demand	eutrophication
sanitary sewer	oxygen sag curve	cultural eutrophication
separated sewer system	aerobic decomposition	algae bloom
combined sewer	anaerobic decomposition	cooling towers
pathogenic organisms	oligotrophic lake	primary treatment
coliform bacteria	eutrophic lake	secondary treatment

KEY WORDS AND SUMMARY STATEMENTS

Pollution of surface waters results from activities within a drainage basin; therefore, surface-water pollution problems should be attacked at that level.

Runoff from agricultural and urban areas and discharges into surface waters from industry substantially render the composition of the water different from that of water that flows through natural areas.

Water pollutants can be classified as follows:

Infectious agents. Included are pathogenic organisms such as bacteria and viruses.

Oxygen-demanding wastes. Wastes decomposed by aerobic bacteria that remove dissolved oxygen from surface waters. The amount of oxygen required to decompose the material in a given volume of water is called its biological oxygen demand (BOD). Depletion of dissolved oxygen results in fish kills and replacement of aerobic by anaerobic decomposers. Anaerobic conditions cause foul odors and unsightly conditions.

Plant nutrients. Usually limit the production of surface waters. Addition of nutrients such as phosphate, nitrate, or ammonia usually lead toward more eutrophic conditions. Eutrophication is the most serious problem facing our lakes. Major nutrient sources include agricultural and urban runoff and municipal and industrial inputs.

Inorganic chemicals. Included are acids, bases, salts, and metals. Certain metals can be converted by bacteria to more toxic compounds. The metal mercury is converted to the more toxic mercury compound, methyl mercury.

Organic chemicals. Examples include pesticides, industrial chemicals for the manufacture of plastics, and oil. Oil spills are devastating for aquatic life.

Radioactive wastes. Includes radioactive isotopes discharged primarily from nuclear power plants and weapons testing.

Sediments. Includes eroded soil and sediment transported by rivers from unprotected crop land, cut forests, construction sites, and strip mining.

Thermal pollution. Results from unusable energy introduced into cooling water from industries, especially electric power plants. The greatest threat is that normal biological cycles of aquatic organisms will be upset, thus eliminating some species.

Sewage treatment plants using primary and secondary treatment are capable of removing suspended materials and BOD wastes in addition to disinfecting the waste water. Not all substances are readily removed in the sewage treatment process, especially nitrogen and phosphorus compounds. A third (tertiary) step beyond normal secondary treatment is required for more complete removal of these substances.

QUESTIONS AND PROJECTS

1. When a body of water becomes polluted, the species present change or die. Comment on the significance of these changes to man.

2. Using a local topographical map, determine the boundaries of the drainage basin you live in. What are the major sources of water pollutants in your drainage basin? What efforts are underway to control these discharges?

3. What is meant by the statement, "A solution to pollution is dilution"? Is the statement still true?

4. Although soil can be a water pollutant, discuss how it can aid in the prevention of water pollution.

5. Would you drink the water out of the well in Figure 9.3? If yes, under what conditions would you not drink it?

6. How can anaerobic decomposition of organic wastes be beneficial to man?

7. What differences are there between dissolved and suspended pollutants? How do the approaches for their removal differ?

8. How does thermal pollution differ from all the other types of pollutants discussed in this chapter?

SELECTED READINGS

Boughey, Arthur S. *Man and the Environment*. New York: Macmillan, 1971. Chapter 11 discusses several other water pollution problems.

Detwyler, T. *Man's Impact on Environment*. New York: McGraw-Hill, 1971. Collection of articles, some dealing with various aspects of water pollution.

Harte, John, and Socolow, Robert H. *Patient Earth*. New York: Holt, Rinehart and Winston, 1971. Article 8 gives a detailed case history of the controversy of siting a large nuclear power plant on Lake Cayuga.

Overman, M. *Water*. Garden City, N.Y.: Doubleday & Co., Inc., 1969. Presents problems of supply and demand for water and various water purification processes.

River of Life. U.S. Dept. of the Interior Environmental Report. Conservation Yearbook Series. Vol. 6. Booklet illustrated in color describing uses of water, pollution and environmental problems of water, and wildlife requirements for water.

chapter
10

The Functioning of the Biosphere

Up to this point we have concentrated primarily on the abiotic spheres of the environment. In the next four chapters we will examine the functioning of the biosphere, focusing on the role of man. Two points need to be emphasized here. First, man himself is a part of the biosphere, so we are actually studying the importance to man of his cohabitants in the biosphere. Second, the biosphere can operate without man. He exerts a significant impact upon the other components of the biosphere, but his presence is not essential to its functioning.

The biosphere is the source of all of man's food energy. We have previously seen that plants are the only organisms capable of photosynthesis, the process of transforming light energy to chemical energy. Man eats the plants, or he eats animals — herbivores and carnivores. In all instances, man is completely dependent upon the producers and other consumers as sources of food energy.

All organisms have certain nutritional requirements. We drink milk to provide calcium for strong bones and teeth, and iron is needed for blood to carry oxygen. The major reservoir for these nutrients is the soil. Plant roots are capable of absorbing nutrients from the soil. Once within the plants, nutrients become part of the molecular architecture of the plant. Thus plants not only fix energy, they also are nutrient

SIGNIFICANCE
OF BIOSPHERE
TO MAN

233

"pumpers"; they pump nutrients out of the soil and make them available to all consumers, including man.

The biosphere also plays a significant role in removing air pollutants. During photosynthesis carbon dioxide moves into the leaves of the plants. If present, gaseous pollutants such as sulfur dioxide, nitrogen oxides, and ozone also move into the leaves. By mechanisms as yet unknown, some of the molecules of these gases remain in the leaves; plants act, therefore, as natural air filters. But they have a limited tolerance, and overloading by pollution will impair their growth and even kill them (Figure 10.1).

The biosphere is also important in cleansing water. We have previously discussed the function of decomposers in removing BOD. Without decomposers (microconsumers) all bodies of water would become completely polluted with organic wastes, just as dead organic material would accumulate on and in the soil in the absence of terrestrial decomposers.

Other cohabitants of the biosphere are important in terms of human health, both from a positive and a negative viewpoint. On the positive side certain members of the biosphere produce *antibiotics,* chemical compounds produced by living microorganisms that are capable of killing other microorganisms. Perhaps the most famous is penicillin, a powerful antibiotic derived from a green fungus (mold) called *Penicillium.* Another group of antibiotics — streptomycin, aureomycin, terramycin, and others — are also natural chemicals obtained from fungus-like organisms.

Some members of the biosphere are the cause of several of man's most serious diseases, including malaria (caused by a single-celled animal), typhoid fever (bacteria), schistosomiasis (blood fluke), plague (bacteria), and two diseases that have recently reached epidemic proportions in the United States — gonorrhea and syphilis (each caused by a different type of bacteria). Bacteria are probably the most important group of organisms pathogenic to humans, but fungi and some of the single-cell and other simple animals are also significant.

Another important role of the biosphere is the prevention of soil erosion. We have seen that plant roots tend to hold the soil in place. If vegetative cover is removed, the soil is exposed and made susceptible to movement by wind and water. Although soil erosion is often neglected in today's concern with pollution, it is nevertheless a major problem. Soil is the main reservoir for nutrients, most of them concen-

Figure 10.1
Pine trees in the San Bernardino, California, National Forest have been killed by air pollutants from the Los Angeles area. *(Authenticated News International.)*

trated in the upper soil layers. When nutrients are lost by erosion of topsoil, plant production decreases, resulting in less food energy available for consumers such as man. Fertile soils are probably our most valuable resource.

ENERGY TRANSFER

Food Chain Efficiency

We have seen that the movement of energy through food chains is a basic function of the biosphere. Via photosynthesis, light energy from the sun is transformed by plants into chemical energy. The plants are eaten by certain types of animals (herbivores) that are eaten by other animals (carnivores). In this manner the energy present in the molecules that make up the bodies of these organisms is passed through the food chain. But transfer of energy between the members of the food chain is not 100 percent efficient (Second Law of Thermodynamics). In fact, producers generally are less than 1 percent efficient: Of the total amount of solar energy available to them, less than 1 percent is incorporated as chemical energy in the molecules that make up plant material (biomass). The remaining available energy is either reflected by the plant back into the atmosphere as light energy or lost as heat energy. On an average, herbivores and carnivores actually incorporate only 10 percent of the energy available into their bodies. The loss of heat energy from respiration accounts for a portion of the remaining 90 percent. The rest is not eaten by the consumers but is, rather, eventually utilized by decomposers that also require energy to function. Decomposers also lose energy as a result of respiration, so all the food energy that enters the biosphere is eventually lost as heat energy (Figure 10.2). Efficiencies vary from 5 to 30 percent depending upon the type of organism and its environment, but values of 1 percent for producers and 10 percent for consumers are reasonable averages.

An important consequence of these low efficiencies is that energy must constantly be added to keep the system from collapsing. Another consequence is that little of the original energy fixed by the producers remains at the upper links of the food chain. As an example, let us examine a clover-beef-man food chain. Using the 10 percent figure, a reasonable estimate is that 100 pounds (45.4 kilograms) of clover will produce 10 pounds of beef that in turn will produce 1 pound of man. Every organism including man requires a minimum amount of food energy in order to survive (a limiting factor). The average adult male's minimum energy demand is 2,400 kilocalories per day. This demand, plus the inefficiencies in transfer, usually limit terrestrial food chains to three or four links and the aquatic chains to five or six links. Longer food chains are, quite simply, insupportable.

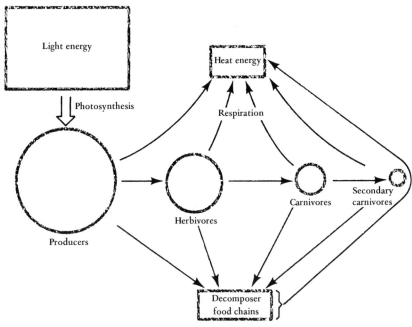

Figure 10.2
Movement of energy through the biotic components of the ecosystem. Notice that the amount of energy present decreases with each link in the chain. In addition, all light energy transformed into chemical energy by photosynthesis is eventually lost as heat energy from respiration.

Although the sun is a tremendous energy source, only a small amount reaches the Earth's surface; as stated, less than 1 percent of the total incoming energy is transformed into food energy by producers. There is, therefore, a finite amount of energy available to producers and consumers in a given area. If this amount of energy available per unit area is divided by the minimum energy demand per organism, the resultant number of organisms per unit area is called the *carrying capacity,* which is expressed as:

$$\frac{\text{energy available/unit area}}{\text{energy demand/individual}} = \frac{\text{number of individuals}}{\text{unit area}}.$$

This value represents the number of organisms that a unit area can feed without destroying the long-term ability of the land to supply the

Concept of Carrying Capacity

food energy (Figure 10.3). For all organisms, including man, this principle means that the Earth can "energize" only so many consumers. Man can change his carrying capacity by moving from carnivore to herbivore level, thereby cutting out one of the inefficient links in the food chain. By the clover-beef-man food chain, man would have 100 pounds of available food if he were a herbivore and only 10 pounds if he were solely a carnivore. Man already has been forced to shorten his food chains in many of the crowded areas of the world. In southeastern Asia, for example, the diet consists almost entirely of rice with an occasional fish for protein supplement. Obviously, Asians cannot afford the 90 percent energy loss that occurs between the herbivores and carnivores.

Man cannot by-pass a link by taking over the activities of producers; as a herbivore he functions as close to the bottom of the food chain as is physically possible. In the United States we can still afford to

Figure 10.3
The carrying capacity of land can vary considerably. *Left:* Well-managed grazing land is able to support herds of cattle. *Right:* Wind erosion due to overgrazing has reduced the carrying capacity of the land. (Left: *Editorial Photocolor Archives.* Right: *Monkmeyer.*).

be partially carnivorous, but if our population continues to increase, we may also approach our ultimate carrying capacity for food energy and only the rich will have the luxury of regularly eating meat.

Carrying capacity can be based upon many environmental factors other than energy. We have seen throughout our discussions that the natural resources of the Earth are limited; its reservoirs contain a finite amount of water, minerals, fossil fuels, and other nonrenewable resources. An individual's space requirements is another way of considering carrying capacity. The dire predictions of people crowded elbow-to-elbow seem unconvincing in view of the fact that the entire population of the United States could indeed stand elbow-to-elbow and yet occupy only half of Manhattan Island. Of more immediate concern are the possible psychological stresses of living in overcrowded conditions. For example, laboratory studies of rats, supplied with enough food and water but overcrowded, have shown such behavioral abnormalities as loss of maternal instinct in the female, cannibalism of the young, and male homosexuality. Although in this case the rats were artificially crowded, they illustrate aspects of study needed on man. The reason that such high densities are not normally found could be that the onset of abnormal behavior prevents the population from reaching high densities.

Food Webs

Natural ecosystems do not consist of a single food chain; rather they are composed of a network of interwoven food chains called *food webs*. As an example, let us take a clover-mouse-weasel food chain, expand it, and then inspect some of the consequences of increased complexity. A variety of species of producers are usually present along with additional species of herbivores and canivores (Figure 10.4). These animals usually have a variety of food sources, so connecting arrows must be drawn. We now begin to see that energy movement through the biosphere follows a complex of interlocking pathways. The diagram is very simplistic. Many more species should be added to appropriate feeding levels in order to represent the actual complexity of food webs found in nature. It is generally accepted that increased complexity leads to increased stability of the ecosystem; examination of our simple food web will show us why this may be true.

Assume that the rabbit population suffers an epidemic that kills off a sizable portion of them. Since rabbits and mice have basically the same food source, the epidemic creates an increased food supply for

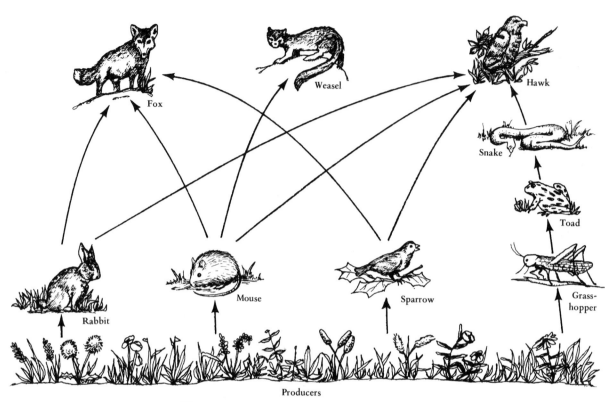

Figure 10.4
A very simplified food web. An actual food web would be much more complex, involving perhaps hundreds of species.

the mice. Soon the mouse population will increase because of decreased *competition* for food. As the population of one herbivore species declines, the population of another increases, ensuring approximately the same percentage of harvest of the producers and thus roughly the same amount of energy available to the carnivores. The fox eats rabbits or mice and therefore would have essentially the same amount of food available. There may be a small time-lag for the system to come into a new balance. During this readjustment period, a few foxes may have to migrate or starve, but the effect is usually small, with little variation in carnivore population. When the rabbit population begins to recover, the mouse population begins to decrease as the competition for food increases.

The above example is simplified, but it does illustrate the types of stabilizing influences present in ecosystems containing complex food webs. We can see similar principles operating in commerce: As companies diversify, conglomerates become common. If one part of the economy becomes sluggish, the conglomerate's other interests take up some of the slack.

Does the concept of food web stability have any significance for man and his food energy sources? We can gain insight by examining the Irish potato famine of the 1840's. Ireland's soil and climate are ill-suited for most crops. From the time of its introduction at the end of the 16th century, the potato was the main source of Ireland's food energy because it grew well and yielded a much higher number of calories per acre than other food crops. As potato production flourished, the population approximately doubled between 1780 and 1845 to a level of 8,500,000. In that year a fungus that caused a plant disease known as potato blight entered Ireland from Europe. The potatoes were susceptible to the fungus and large numbers of potato plants died during the five years that the blight lasted. Because the Irish had no substitute food source, roughly one million of them died from starvation or disease between 1845 and 1850 and another million emigrated. In a period of five years the population declined 25 percent, and the country's economic and social structure was dealt a staggering blow — all largely the result of oversimplifying the food web.

An inspection of modern agricultural practices makes it clear that we have not learned history's lesson. Economic pressures have induced many farmers in the United States to specialize, planting only one or two crops over large areas. In the central Midwest, for example, many farms now grow only corn and soybeans.

The dangers of another sort of simplification — genetic — were well illustrated in 1970 by the southern corn leaf blight. For many years, the fungus that causes the blight was present in the southern United States but had little effect on corn yield (less than 1 percent). The "status quo" was interrupted in 1970 when a new strain of fungus appeared, perhaps by genetic mutation, that was more lethal than the former. Unfortunately, the more lethal fungus did not remain in the

Dangers of Single Crop Agriculture

South but was carried by winds into the corn belt states of Indiana, Illinois, and Iowa. Warm, moist weather allowed the fungus to rapidly infect and reproduce within the corn plants, thereby increasing the number of fungi to be carried elsewhere. The use of pesticides to control the spread of the fungus was uneconomical. Because of the combination of genetic change and atmospheric conditions (all beyond man's control), losses from the blight increased to 12 percent of the estimated corn yield in only one year. And had the weather remained warm and moist throughout the season, losses would have been even greater. It caused a 710 million bushel deficit below the predicted 1970 consumption of corn. The reserve carry-over of corn from 1969 was only one billion bushels. The reserves were not utilized that heavily, however, because as the reserves were tapped, corn prices rose and less expensive corn substitutes were used to make up the deficit.

Another important contributing factor to the large loss in yield involves the resistance of corn to the blight. In 1970, 80 percent of the corn grown was of a single type, one that gives high yield but has a genetic factor that makes the plant highly susceptible to blight.

In 1971 blight was nearly everywhere in the Midwest but damage was slight. Planting weather was excellent, and good weather conditions prevailed through the growing season. A larger percentage of the corn was resistant to the blight. Blight damage in 1970 initiated changes in federal feed grain programs that led to planting of seven million additional acres in corn. The end result was that 1971 was a record year for corn production. It should be pointed out, however, that a major factor in the increased corn yield, the weather, was still beyond man's control.

The above example illustrates the need to be aware of the consequences of trends toward monoculture. Not only are we planting one or two crops over large areas, but the genetic makeup within each crop species is also becoming similar, increasing the potential for crop damage.

CYCLES OF MATTER

As producers, green plants take in from the hydrosphere and lithosphere such substances as nitrates, phosphates, sulfates, iron, and calcium. Carbon and oxygen are the major substances taken in from the atmosphere. All these materials are subsequently incorporated into the molecular architecture of the plant. Thus they are available to be passed from one link in the food chain to the next. When producers and consumers die, decomposers break them down, releasing the constituent parts back into the abiotic spheres for recycling.

We have seen that another member of the biosphere, man, disrupts the rates of transfer between reservoirs. As an example, let us consider the cycling of phosphorus. As a part of the natural erosion cycle, phosphates are removed from the soil surface and washed into rivers. Many are eventually deposited in the ocean or in deep lake sediments where they are effectively out of circulation. Man accelerates the process. In places such as Florida, there are areas where the upper crust is rich in phosphates. Man harvests these deposits; he spreads them over his agricultural lands as fertilizers and incorporates them into his detergents for improved cleaning ability. As a result of runoff from agricultural lands and inefficient removal by municipal treatment plants, large amounts of phosphates make their way into our lakes and rivers.

The problem is that phosphates are being added to our waterways faster than they are being removed by sedimentation and transport to the deeper portions of the oceans. The result is, in effect, a phosphate logjam in the river giving higher than "normal" concentrations of phosphates. We saw in Chapter 9 the disruptive effects of such concentrations on water quality.

LIMITING FACTORS

The principle of limiting factors states that for any environmental factor, an organism has an optimal requirement (Chapter 1). It also has a minimal requirement (tolerance limit) that must be present if the individual is to survive. Just as too little of something can be lethal, too much can have the same result.

Tolerance limits and optimal levels for any organism are ultimately determined by its genetic makeup. Changes in the makeup (mutations) can make the organism less fit to survive in its particular environment, and pollutants such as radioactive wastes can induce mutation.

The young of a species usually have higher optimal levels and reduced tolerance. Also, the components of the environment do not act independently; rather they interact in complex ways. So a species' tolerance to one factor often is influenced by the presence or absence of another factor (e.g., *synergism*). If the environment does not fall within the tolerance limits of the individual, it must either migrate to a more favorable habitat or modify its habitat. If the individual does neither, it dies.

POPULATION GROWTH AND INTERACTION

Anywhere man goes, he places a demand on Earth's fixed resources. Either the resources are present or he must import them. In addition, an individual has a genetically fixed, minimum resource demand necessary for his survival. As the demand aspect of the problem is primarily related to the number of demanding individuals, we shall now consider some principles that govern population growth and interactions.

Population Growth

A species in an optimal environment will reproduce at its inherent maximum rate, which is called its *biotic potential*. Because the world is not overwhelmed by any one species, a second set of interactions must be checking the biotic potential. Checking interactions are collectively known as *environmental resistance*. As a result of the interactions between biotic potential and environmental resistance, the growth of all populations is eventually checked, at least temporarily.

Populations of some species follow a growth curve, as illustrated in Figure 10.5. Initially, there is a slow increase in population, but once the population is established it increases rapidly and approaches its biotic potential. However, at some point in time, environmental resistance becomes limiting and the population levels off. This curve is the generalized Sigmoid (S-shaped) growth curve. In our example, the curve illustrates a stabilized population that has leveled off within the carrying capacity of the habitat.

Many populations, however, tend to overshoot the carrying capacity.

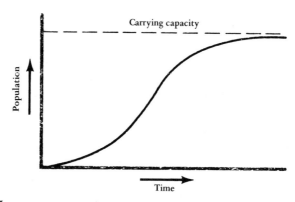

Figure 10.5
A sigmoid population growth curve that illustrates the population leveling off below the carrying capacity.

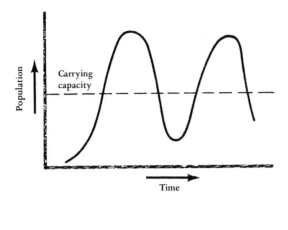

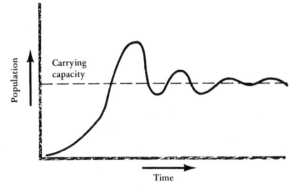

Figure 10.6
Two of the many possible patterns of oscillation of populations around the carrying capacity.

Thus when environmental resistance becomes limiting, instead of leveling off, they come crashing down below the carrying capacity and then may oscillate about it (Figure 10.6). One explanation for the oscillations is that a population on the upswing includes a large number of young individuals who are not yet making full demands upon the environment. When the young mature and require an adult's share of the environment, the population is effectively exceeding the carrying capacity. Then a portion of the population must either migrate or die off in order to get the level within the carrying capacity. The severity of the oscillations depends upon the species and habitat conditions involved.

Environmental
Resistance:
Population
Interactions

PREDATION AND
PARASITISM

Environmental resistance involves many factors, such as population interaction. Let us consider three important population control interactions: predation, parasitism, and competition.

Predation generally is a short-term interaction between two individuals in which the predator kills and eats the prey and then moves on. In contrast, *parasitism* is usually an interaction of longer duration in which a parasite may obtain nourishment from its host for weeks or longer. It is a basic principle of predation and parasitism that if two populations (predator-prey or parasite-host) have a common evolutionary history, a stable interaction tends to evolve that benefits both populations. We use predation to illustrate the principle, but it also applies to parasitism.

Predation is beneficial for the prey population because it tends to hold the number of prey within the carrying capacity. Conversely, a stabilized interaction assures the predator population of a sufficient food source. If the predator killed all of the prey population, it would die off unless alternative food sources were available.

A classic example of the stabilizing influence of predator-prey relations is that of the deer population on the Kaibab Plateau on the north rim of the Grand Canyon in Arizona. When the region was made a federal game refuge in 1906 it had 3,000 deer, along with abundant populations of mountain lions, bobcats, wolves, and coyotes. To allow the deer populations to increase, deer hunting was banned, and war was declared on the animal's predators. By 1923, virtually all large predators had been exterminated. The result was a population explosion of deer (Figure 10.7). By 1925 there were 100,000 deer on the plateau. Man had eliminated a limiting factor — predation. However, another factor — food — soon became limiting.

The carrying capacity for food was soon exceeded. Deer overbrowsed the area destroying favorable habitat conditions. The deer were not able to migrate, and within two years the population decreased to 50,000 as a result of starvation. Further die-offs reduced the herd to 10,000 by 1940. Overbrowsing also degraded the habitat for many other species: Vegetation was killed and exposure of ground increased soil erosion. By the disruption of population interactions, the normal functioning of the entire ecosystem was seriously impaired.

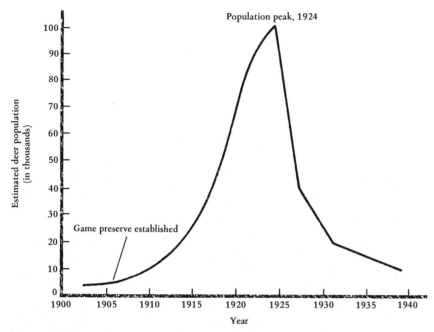

Figure 10.7
The effect of the removal of natural predators on the deer population on the Kaibab Plateau. *(Based on data in D. Irvin Rasmussen, "Biotic Communities on Kaibab Plateau, Arizona,"* Ecological Monographs, *11, p. 236.)*

Predators are not the only component of environmental resistance, but our example demonstrates their significance in population interactions.

Predators are also important because they tend to keep the prey population in a healthy condition by killing off the weak and old members. If a herd is pursued by predators, the sick and old are normally the first to be overtaken. Similarly, in a migrating herd the weaker members tend to lag behind and lose the protection of the herd.

Catastrophic effects often ensue when new predator-prey or parasite-host relations are established. Before the turn of the century, the American chestnut tree was a dominant member of the Appalachian forests. It had its parasites, but conditions were relatively stable. In 1904, Asiatic chestnut trees were brought to New York carrying with them a parasitic fungus to which they were resistant. However, the American chestnuts had no resistance to the new parasite. The fungus quickly spread and by the early 1950s, the American chestnut had been virtually eliminated. In some cases, the roots are alive and continue to send up new shoots, but these are eventually killed back by the fungus. The question remains as to whether the chestnut will become extinct before some stabilizing adaptation occurs. Certainly, the chestnut tree has been removed as an important component of the forest ecosystem. Other examples can be given of the destabilizing effects resulting from the introduction of a new predator or parasite (Figure 10.8).

Figure 10.8
Dutch elm disease is another example of the disruption resulting from new parasite-host interactions. *Top:* Elm-lined Gillet Avenue in Waukegan, Illinois, as it appeared in 1962. *Bottom:* Gillet Avenue in 1969, after the elms were destroyed by Dutch elm disease. *(Elm Research Institute.)*

An important aspect of predator-prey and parasite-host interactions is that as the prey or host population becomes larger, the percentage of predation or parasitism also increases; i.e., predation and parasitism are density-dependent regulators of populations. For example, in the case of parasitism, as the host population increases, so also does the number of contacts among the members. This increases the chances for the parasite population to spread throughout the host population. In addition, the increase in host population may cause it to exceed the carrying capacity, so at least some members of the host population will be weaker and therefore more susceptible to parasitism. Predation and parasitism tend to increase at greater rates than the prey and host populations, thus helping to return the prey or host population to levels within the carrying capacity.

There are two basic types of competition: interspecific and intraspecific. The former occurs between the populations of two different species, the latter among populations of a single species. Two basic conditions must exist before there can be competition. First, both populations must depend upon the same environmental factor or factors, e.g., they need the same food source or nesting sites. Second, the demand of the total populations must exceed the supply, i.e., the carrying capacity.

COMPETITION: INTERSPECIFIC AND INTRASPECIFIC

The consequences of interspecific competition vary considerably. If both populations are approximately equal competitors, there is a decrease in both populations until the combined population is below the carrying capacity for the limiting factor. However, if one species is a much better competitor than the other, one of two things may occur: The less competitive species either becomes extinct or migrates to a new area where conditions are more favorable for it. The results of competition are affected by environmental conditions. If it is optimal for one population but near the tolerance limits for a second, the second species is unable to successfully compete with the first species in that area.

As the population density of one or both species increases, the degree of competition also increases. The more the carrying capacity is exceeded by the combined populations, the more severe the competition. Like predation and parasitism, competition is a density-dependent mechanism for bringing populations within the carrying capacity.

Intraspecific competition may be more severe than interspecific. The reason for this is that all members of the population have approximately the same genetic makeup, so they make the same demands on the environment. As a result of interspecific competition, populations tend to occupy regions of nearly optimal environmental conditions (Figure 10.9). However, as the density of a population becomes greater and intraspecific competition increases, the weaker members are forced into marginal areas where proper food and shelter are inadequate. These already weak individuals become even weaker and more susceptible to predation, parasitism, and stresses of the physical environment.

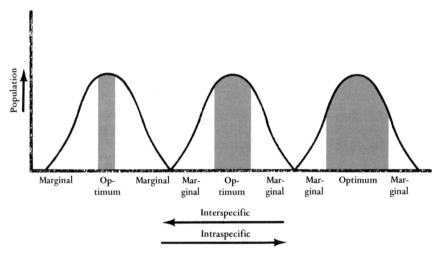

Figure 10.9
The effect of competition on habitat distribution. When interspecific competition is intense, the species tends to be restricted to areas where environmental conditions are near optimum. When intraspecific competition dominates, the species tends to spread out and occupy marginal areas. *(Adapted with permission from Eugene Odum,* Fundamentals of Ecology, *3rd ed.* [Philadelphia: W. B. Saunders Co., 1971], p. 218.)

OVERCROWDING VERSUS
UNDERCROWDING

The above discussion dealt with overpopulation as a limiting factor, but underpopulation can also be limiting. Let us consider a few examples. At night and when not feeding in the daytime, a covey of bobwhite quail forms a compact circle (Figure 10.10). During cold weather they huddle together more tightly, decreasing loss of body heat by exposing a smaller total body surface area to the cold air. Observations show

Figure 10.10
Quail gather in a circle to protect themselves from cold and predators. *(Jack A. Stanford, Missouri Conservation Commission.)*

that members of large coveys survive severe winter temperatures, whereas single birds or small coveys succumb.

It is also interesting to note that the birds face outward from the circle. A covey, in effect, can watch in all directions for the approach of predators. If a predator comes near, a phenomenon known as the confusion effect decreases the chances of a bird being caught. Upon an alarm, the birds suddenly fly in all directions. The predator may become so disoriented by the flurry of activity that he fails to capture any birds. A covey with too few birds to form a circle loses these advantages and the population is likely to be reduced.

Undercrowding can also seriously affect the ability of predators to find and kill their prey. Moose and caribou can repel an attack by one or two wolves, but when the wolves operate as a pack, they can attack a moose on all sides and bring him down. Working together, members of a predator population have a better chance of surviving.

Reproductivity can also be affected by undercrowding. In a small population, the chances of females and males of reproductive age meeting are diminished. With some species, a minimum number must be present to initiate reproductive behavior. A small population also fosters inbreeding, which can reduce the population's vigor and its resistance to predation, parasitism, and climatic extremes.

Environmental
Resistance:
Abiotic Factors

Population interactions are not the only components of environmental resistance. Abiotic factors, particularly climate, can affect population. For example, long, severe winters often kill off wildlife. However, the long-term significance of such control is questionable. Observations indicate that when there is a large winter kill, the resultant decrease in intraspecific competition during the following summer leads to a high reproductive rate. By autumn the population begins to approach previous levels, and if there are no subsequent large winter kills the population may be fully restored within a few years. It appears that unless abiotic factors such as floods, drought, high winds, and temperature extremes decrease populations to levels where the effects of undercrowding are significant, abiotic factors are not important long-term regulators.

KEY WORDS
AND SUMMARY
STATEMENTS

antibiotics	competition	synergism
carrying capacity	biotic potential	predation
food webs	environmental resistance	parasitism

The biosphere is important to man as a source of food energy and nutrients and in maintaining the quality of the air, water, and soil.

As members of food chains, organisms function in the movement of energy through ecosystems. The energy transfer between each link is inefficient, so there must be a continual input of energy into the system.

The maximum population that an area can support indefinitely is known as the carrying capacity. Because the earth's resources are finite, carrying capacity can be considered in terms of food energy, water, space, or any other component of the environment.

A natural ecosystem consists of a complex network of interwoven food chains known as a food web. A high degree of complexity tends to make ecosystems stable.

Modern agriculture tends toward simple ecosystems. The vulnerability of such simplification is illustrated by the Irish potato famine and the recent southern corn leaf blight in the United States.

Organisms also play a role in cycling matter through ecosystems. A common effect of pollution is the disruption of the biosphere by exceeding the tolerance limits of organisms.

As a result of the interactions between the biotic potential of an organism and environmental resistance, many populations follow a characteristic Sigmoid growth curve. Although some populations smoothly level off within the carrying capacity, most populations oscillate about it.

Environmental resistance is composed of such factors as population interactions that include predation, parasitism, and competition.

If predator-prey and parasite-host interactions have a common evolutionary history, a stable interaction tends to evolve that benefits both populations. New interactions, however, tend to be very disruptive.

Competition occurs when the demand exceeds supply. It can take place among members of one population (intraspecific) or between members of two populations (interspecific).

Predation, parasitism, and competition are density-dependent components of environmental resistance; i.e., the interaction becomes more severe as the populations increase.

Environmental resistance also includes abiotic factors such as climate. Unless abiotic factors reduce a population to a level at which the negative effects of undercrowding are significant, they are not important long-term regulators.

1. Opponents of population control point to vast areas of thinly settled land as providing adequate space for expansion of the human population. In light of the concept of carrying capacity and environmental costs, what are the limitations to this idea?

2. Are there indications of psychological stresses in today's societies that might be resulting from overcrowding?

3. For human populations, the restrictions imposed by carrying capacity often become initially evident in terms of increased costs. How is this true of meat prices during recent years? What alternatives are people taking? How do meat prices behave in other countries, such as Japan?

4. As nutrient "pumpers," plants use food energy in taking up nutrients from the soil. How does this process relate to the Second Law of Thermodynamics?

5. Some experts believe that a number of endangered species have been

QUESTIONS AND PROJECTS

reduced to such low populations that even close attention by man will not save them from extinction. How do the problems associated with undercrowding support this opinion?

6. Predator-control programs subsidized by local, state, and federal agencies have been receiving considerable criticism recently. Are there active predator-control programs in your area? What is their purpose? In light of the discussions of predator-prey relationships, can these programs accomplish their purpose? Are they needed?

7. How do the efficiencies of energy transfer of producers and consumers compare with those of automobile engines and electrical power plants? What are the chances of and potential problems associated with increasing the efficiency of organisms?

SELECTED
READINGS

The following give a fundamental introduction to the functioning of the biosphere:

The Biosphere. San Francisco: Freeman, 1970.

Boughey, Arthur S. *Fundamental Ecology.* Scranton, Pa.: Intext Educational Publishers, 1971.

Kormondy, D. J. *Concepts of Ecology.* Englewood Cliffs, N.J.: Prentice-Hall, Inc., 1969.

Odum, E. P. *Ecology.* New York: Holt, Rinehart and Winston, 1966.

11

Human Population Growth and Interactions

In Chapter 10, we considered the major principles of population growth and control mechanisms. Because we are particularly concerned with our welfare, this chapter is devoted to an analysis of how these principles apply to us.

Figure 11.1 shows the human population growth curve. In the beginning there was a long period of slow growth. Within the last 150 years, however, there has been a tremendous increase in human population. In fact, the curve has become almost vertical, and its sharpness is easily illustrated. It took approximately 50,000 years for the human population to reach one billion, which it did around 1850. By 1930, only 80 years later, the population had doubled; by 1960 it stood at 3 billion, and presently it is over 3.7 billion. Not only is population increasing, but it is increasing at an accelerating rate. At the present rate (approximately 70,000,000 per year) it will have taken less than 50 years to go from 2 billion to 4 billion, compared with the 80 it took to go from one to two billion.

The human population growth curve is similar to that of other organisms, except that it has not yet turned. There is no reason to think it will not, however, as the Earth has a carrying capacity for man.

HUMAN
POPULATION
GROWTH

257

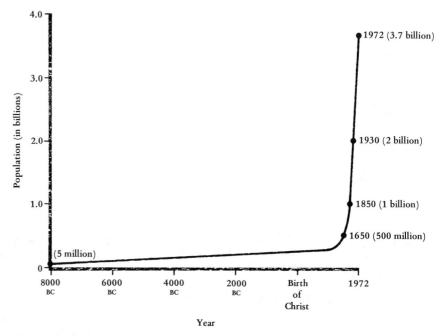

Figure 11.1
The growth of human population.

There is a limited supply of fresh water, agricultural lands, minerals, and fuels. Like the other components of the biosphere, we have genetically fixed minimum demands. At some time a factor such as food, water, or space will become limiting and the growth rate will decline.

Several major questions arise. What is the carrying capacity for man? How will the population level off? Will it level off gradually within the carrying capacity, or will it overshoot and come crashing down? Will there be severe oscillations about the carrying capacity? Have we already overshot the carrying capacity?

To begin to answer these questions, we shall first consider some of the factors comprising environmental resistance that govern human populations. We have seen that predation, parasitism, and competition can be important in controlling population levels of other organisms. Abiotic factors may also be important. Let us examine the role these interactions play in controlling human population.

ENVIRONMENTAL RESISTANCE

Abiotic Factors

We have seen that unless abiotic stresses are very severe, they are not important in the long-term control of populations. The same can be said of human population regulation. The worst disaster in recent years was the typhoon that hit East Pakistan (now Bangladesh) in 1971, in which up to 1 million people lost their lives. Considering that the human population is increasing by approximately 70 million a year, even this loss was made up in only 5 days.

Predation

We can confidently state that predation of man is rare today. In the days of early man predation was perhaps of some importance, but even then his superior brain helped him outwit his predators. As man progressed, he built better shelters and weapons to protect himself, and with the invention of firearms he was able to defend himself against virtually all his predators. And the expansion of civilization has destroyed practically all the habitats of large predators, thereby destroying the predator populations.

Parasitism

Parasitism has been far more important than predation in controlling human members. Epidemics of bubonic plague, for example, often devastated Europe until as recently as the Renaissance (Figure 11.2). Plague is caused by a type of bacteria that is transmitted to man by fleas carried by rats and other rodents. Europe's human population was increasing gradually until 1348, when the first massive epidemic broke out. Within two years Europe's population had decreased by at least 25 percent, and by the end of the century 25 million people had died from the disease. It took almost a century for the population to begin increasing again and another century to return to the 1348 level.

With advances in modern medicine and technology, deaths from disease have decreased dramatically throughout the world. Great strides have been made in sanitation, pharmaceuticals, medicine, and health education. The development of chemicals to kill organisms that transmit parasites to man has also decreased human deaths. The use of DDT to kill the malaria-carrying mosquito is an example.

It should be pointed out that even with our modern-day medicine, the population-controlling potential of disease is still effective, proba-

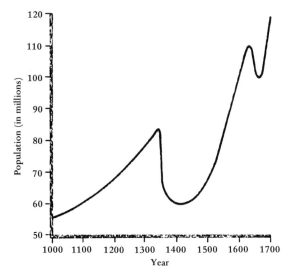

Figure 11.2
Human population levels in Europe, 1000–1700, showing the effects of large epidemics of the Black Plague. *(Redrawn with permission from William E. Langer, "The Black Death,"* Scientific American [*February 1964*], *p. 117. Copyright © 1964 by Scientific American, Inc. All rights reserved.)*

bly more so than in the past. We have seen that one of the basic principles dealing with parasite-host relationships is that as the density of the host population becomes greater, the severity of parasitism also increases. Coupling man's rapidly increasing numbers with the lack of suitable new areas for colonization has resulted in increased population density, made worse by socio-economic pressures that force people to migrate from rural to urban areas. The result is a densely populated metropolitan area where numerous contacts among people create a great potential for the spread of disease. This situation is further aggravated by a worldwide transportation system.

Contrary to popular opinion epidemics occur rather frequently, even in developed nations. Almost every winter, a flu epidemic spreads across the United States: One year it was Asiatic flu, the next year Hong Kong flu. The viruses responsible for these epidemics originated in Asia and were carried abroad. These widespread epidemics have proved fatal mainly to the weaker members of the population — the young, the ill, and the old.

Some people believe that the decrease in deaths from disease is really a double-edged sword. They view the decrease in death rate as a major cause of current problems in emerging countries. Much effort has been expended on improving sanitation and medical conditions to lower the death rate. In the meantime, birth rates have remained high (Table 11.1). Although lives have been prolonged and saved, the problems of overpopulation may in the long run cause greater grief.

Table 11.1
Population statistics for twentieth-century India.

Census year	Total population in millions	Birth rate	Death rate	Percentage rate of natural increase
1901	236	46	44	0.1
1911	249	51	43	0.8
1921	248	49	48	0.1
1931	276	46	36	1.0
1941	313	45	31	1.4
1951	357	39	27	1.3
1961	439	40	21	1.9
1965	490	41	17	2.4
1969	537	43	18	2.5

Source: Reprinted with permission of The Macmillan Company from Arthur S. Boughey, *Man and the Environment,* p. 249. Copyright © by The Macmillan Company, 1963.

Intraspecific Competition

One lethal form of intraspecific competition is war, but it has not been an effective population control mechanism. Total deaths, both civilian and military, from World Wars I and II and the Korean War are estimated at 105,000,000. At the current rate of human population growth (70,000,000 per year), in only 1.5 years world population growth matches the number of these war deaths. In addition, the morality of war as a population control mechanism is the subject of controversy.

There is a human analogy to the intraspecific competition among an animal population that displaces less fit members to marginal habitats. In the competition between the white man and the Indian over the resources of the North American continent, the former emerged as the better competitor. He had greater numbers and better technology, and his competitive ability was so much better that the Indian was displaced to those areas that white man didn't want — areas thought to be very poor in resources. The relationship between white and red men is a classic example of competition between two populations within a species. Even today there is strong competition among the races for jobs, housing, and other social and economic resources.

Interspecific
Competition
for Habitat

Interspecific competition, i.e., that between man and other species, is most severe in terms of man's destruction of natural habitats. Even the most cursory observations indicate that man has vastly changed the biosphere. Complex forest ecosystems have been made into agriculture and tree farms, each with only one or two species. The prairies of the Great Plains once consisted of many species of grasses, herbs, and animals. Now the grasses, corn and wheat, and the animals, hogs and cattle, are dominant members of the ecosystem. Marshes have been filled in to make way for housing tracts, shopping centers, and industrial parks. Stream channelization, strip mining, highway construction, and urban sprawl continue to raise havoc with existing natural habitats. Each year an additional one million acres of land in the United States are intensely developed by man.

ENDANGERED SPECIES

What are the effects of these massive habitat changes? We have seen that each species has genetically determined tolerance limits. When man changes the habitat conditions, he makes it impossible for the former species to survive. As more natural habitat is destroyed, they have fewer places to live and thus become endangered species; i.e., they move toward extinction. An example is the ivory-billed woodpecker, the largest woodpecker in North America (Figure 11.3). It formerly inhabited lowlands and swamp forests throughout the Southeast. Its food source is the wood-boring insects that invade large, dead trees. As the virgin forests were cut and replaced by plantations of uniform age trees, the ivory-bill's food source diminished and likewise the ivory-billed woodpecker. In 1972 the ivory-bill was unofficially sighted for the first time since 1950. This bird requires very specialized habitat conditions, but any species that requires grasslands, virgin forests, or swamps is also endangered.

Habitat destruction is not the only factor threatening the existence of species. Table 11.2 contrasts the characteristics of endangered and safe species. These characteristics are a result of the genetic makeup that renders some species more vulnerable than others to man's activi-

Figure 11.3
The ivory-billed woodpecker is a species of bird that has virtually been eliminated because its specialized habitat requirements have been destroyed by man. This photograph was taken in 1938 in Louisiana. *(James T. Tanner from National Audubon Society.)*

ties. Not listed are those species that have little resistance to pesticides, heavy metals, noxious gases, and other products of man's activities.

A large number of species are today in danger of becoming extinct. The International Union for Conservation of Nature and Natural Resources listed 297 species of mammals and 359 species of birds as being endangered in 1971. In the United States, 101 species of wildlife were listed as endangered in 1971.

Table 11.2
Factors of extinction.

Endangered	Example	Safe	Example
Individuals of large size	Cougar	Individuals of small size	Wildcat
Predator	Hawk	Grazer, scavenger, insectivore, etc.	Vulture
Narrow habitat tolerance	Orangutan	Wide habit tolerance	Chimpanzee
Valuable fur, hide, oil, etc.	Chinchilla	Not a source of natural products and not exploited for research or pet purposes	Gray squirrel
Hunted for the market or hunted for sport where there is no effective game management	Passenger pigeon (extinct)	Commonly hunted for sport in game management areas	Mourning dove
Has a restricted distribution: island, desert watercourse, bog, etc.	Bahamas parrot	Has broad distribution	Yellow-headed parrot
Lives largely in international waters, or migrates across international boundaries	Green sea turtle	Has populations that remain largely within the territory(ies)	Loggerhead sea turtle
Intolerant of the presence of man	Grizzly bear	Tolerant of man	Black bear
Species reproduction in one or two vast aggregates	West Indian flamingo	Reproduction by pairs or in many small or medium sized aggregates	Bitterns
Long gestation period: one or two young per litter, and/or maternal care	Giant panda	Short gestation period: more than two young per litter, and/or young become independent early and mature quickly	Raccoon
Has behavioral idiosyncracies that are nonadaptive today	Red-headed woodpecker: flies in front of cars	Has behavior patterns that are particularly adaptive today	Burrowing owl: highly tolerant of noise and low-flying aircraft; lives near the runways of airports

Let us examine some reasons why it is in our self-interest to preserve species. Each species represents a unique combination of genetic characteristics *(gene pool)* that enables it to adapt to certain environmental conditions. Man never knows when he is going to need these adaptations for his own survival. We have seen that members of the biosphere are important in producing drugs. Fifty years ago nobody would have cared if a soil-dwelling fungus called *Penicillium* became extinct as a result of habitat destruction or some other activity of man. Yet by accident Dr. Alexander Fleming discovered that the fungus produces an antibiotic that kills certain other microorganisms. By introducing this natural bacteria-killing chemical into the human body, the lives of hundreds of thousands of people have been saved.

Drugs such as streptomycin, terramycin, tetracyclines, and many others have been isolated from bacteria and other species of fungi. Some species of higher plants also produce drugs, such as morphine (poppy plant), cocaine (coca tree), quinine (cinchona tree), and marijuana (hemp plant). These chemicals were first isolated and identified from organisms and then mass-produced synthetically. Pharmacognosy, a branch of pharmacy, is exclusively concerned with identifying chemicals in the biosphere that can be used to improve the health of man and his domestic animals. The types of chemical compounds found in nature and their disease-preventing activities remain largely unknown.

Food production also relies heavily upon a vast gene pool. All our crop plants and livestock have been domesticated from native plants and animals, but we cannot now ignore these native species as they are needed to solve present and future problems. For example, the varieties of wheat and rice that have played a major role in temporarily reducing starvation in poor countries resulted from breeding experiments utilizing thousands of varieties of rice and wheat. There are many other problems for which we need to be better prepared. No one knows when a new, perhaps more lethal, disease such as southern corn leaf blight may appear. The increase in salinity of irrigated soils may require the growing of new crop varieties that can tolerate higher levels of salt. If we decrease the gene pool, we decrease our potential for solving the problems that face us.

Thus we need as large a gene pool as possible to provide us with answers to today's and tomorrow's problems. Once a species is gone, it is lost forever. We will never again have access to its particular complex combination of characteristics.

SIGNIFICANCE OF
PRESERVATION OF
SPECIES

Each species also plays a role in the stability of ecosystems. Some are, of course, more important than others. A major reason for the recent concern over the possible extinction of the alligator is that it is a dominant member of ecosystems such as the Florida Everglades. The depressions (gator holes) excavated by the alligator are the last places to dry up during a drought (Figure 11.4). Thus they serve as reservoirs for aquatic life and sources of water and food for birds and mammals until water is plentiful again. If the alligators are eliminated, the gator holes quickly fill in with sediment and aquatic plants, and

Figure 11.4
Alligators maintain depressions, known as "gator holes," which during dry periods serve as reservoirs for aquatic organisms. *(Florida News Bureau, Department of Commerce.)*

wildlife dies off during dry periods. Alligators also affect the Everglades by their feeding habits; they eat large numbers of gar, a major predatory fish. By keeping the gar population low, game fish such as bass and bream are plentifully available to other predators.

Although few species are as important to an ecosystem as the alligator, it is nevertheless true that as more and more species disappear, the system of checks and balances decreases. Stabilizing population interactions such as predation, parasitism, and competition are interrupted and the ecosystem is more subject to disturbance and potential demise.

Some people point out that extinction is a natural process that has occurred since life began and thus merits no special concern. No one will disagree with them that countless species have become extinct as environments have changed. After all, dinosaurs are no longer with us. The point that these people miss is that the natural process of extinction has been greatly accelerated by man. While it can be said that species such as the whooping crane and California condor were already on their way out, the same cannot be applied to many species of wild cats, bears, and birds of prey. These and many other species are becoming extinct not because of weakness or inability to adapt to a slowly changing environment, but because they are endangered as a result of the characteristics listed in Table 11.2, all of which are directly related to man's activities. In addition these critics fail to recognize the practical aspects of maintaining a large gene pool and the stability of ecosystems. The short-term practical aspects of continued human exploitation prevents them from seeing the long-term practical aspects of preservation of representative parts of the world ecosystem.

SIGNIFICANCE OF NATURAL AREAS

Natural areas must be maintained to enable us to study the functioning of natural ecosystems. These baseline studies allow us to more effectively manage our simplified, man-made ecosystems. We have mentioned that the prairie was once a complex ecosystem consisting of many species and that interactions over thousands of years among producers, consumers, decomposers, and the abiotic components made the Midwest prairie soils among the most fertile on Earth. In the past 150 years, man has greatly simplified the prairie ecosystem and has added thousands of tons of fertilizers and pesticides to the soil. And because much of the land was too wet for agriculture, he has drained the wet lowland soils to lower the water table. Before we can adequately evaluate the long-term effects of intensive agriculture management, we first need to understand how the prairie soils became so fertile. Studies of natural prairies enable us to evaluate the role of decomposers, food chains, and abiotic factors (e.g., soil moisture) in nutrient cycles.

Such an approach applies not only to prairie and agricultural ecosystems but to all ecosystems that man attempts to manage: forests, lakes, reservoirs, and *estuaries* (coastal regions where salt and fresh water meet; see Figure 11.5), among others. We must have data that can be used to predict the effects of manipulation before we carry out changes. Too often we manipulate, then worry only after the effects become evident.

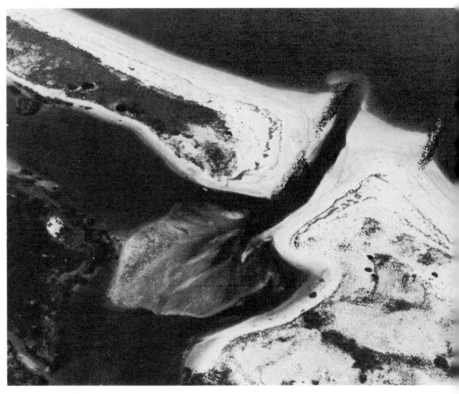

Figure 11.5
Flax Pond estuary is on the North Shore of Long Island. Salt water and fresh water mix in the light area in the center of the photograph. *(Authenticated News International.)*

We should consider other values of natural areas. Wetlands — marshes, swamps, and estuaries — are areas whose values are often as sites for landfill and subsequent development (Figure 11.6). However,

Figure 11.6
Boca Ciega Bay, Florida, in 1949 *(top)* and in 1969 *(bottom)*, after landfill and development. *(Bob Graber, Airflite.)*

wetlands are highly productive; man's most intensive agricultural practices barely match the productivity of estuaries. Estuaries serve as breeding grounds and nurseries for much of the aquatic life in the oceans. As a result, they are responsible for approximately 50 percent of the total food from the sea. Perhaps most important, this kind of production requires little expense on man's part. He only has to harvest the fish. High agricultural production requires much more time and energy expenditure. These expenditures include the planting of two crops a year, heavy fertilizer and pesticide application, and possibly irrigation.

Wetlands everywhere are important as nesting and feeding sites for waterfowl and other aquatic life. In addition, wetlands also serve as natural reservoirs for water. They soak up water, like sponges, and hold it. This phenomenon has two important results. During periods of heavy precipitation wetlands decrease the rate of runoff and lessen flood damage. During drier periods, they slowly release water into drainageways, thereby serving as natural reservoirs.

An example of these effects is the Florida peninsula. Much of the southern portion of the state is (or was) wetlands — Corkscrew Swamp, Big Cypress Swamp, and the Everglades (Figure 11.7). Floridians obtain their water from two sources, the runoff from these swamps and the underground reservoirs that are recharged by the swamps. Although southern Florida receives about 60 inches (152 centimeters) of rain annually, 48 inches is lost by evaporation from water surfaces (lakes, canals, and wetlands) and plants. The remaining 12 inches is barely enough to supply human needs and also assure the preservation of wetlands such as the Everglades National Park. Water conservation districts and an elaborate system of dikes and canals have been established to supply needed water to the megalopolis on Florida's east coast (Figure 11.8). Although southern Florida's water demands are quickly approaching the limits of supply, its population is rapidly increasing. In the meantime, much of the wetlands has been bought by speculators and development is beginning. A proposed airport and its satellite city of 60,000 just north of the Everglades is an extreme example, but it differs only in degree from what is taking place. These wetlands are being drained, filled, and developed, decreasing the natural ability of these areas to function as reservoirs to meet the demands of an increasing population. This situation is further aggravated by salt-water intrusion into ground-water reservoirs.

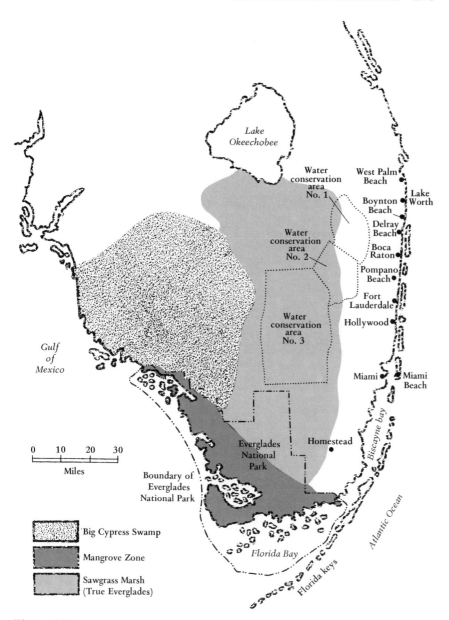

Figure 11.7
Extensive wetlands and water conservation districts are located on the Florida peninsula. Notice that many cities are adjacent to the wetlands. *(Adapted and redrawn with
permission of Holt, Rinehart and Winston, Inc., from John Harte and Robert H. Socolow,*
Patient Earth, *p. 184. Copyright © 1971 by Holt, Rinehart and Winston, Inc.)*

Figure 11.8
One of the many canals used for flood control in Florida. But these canals also drain swamp lands and threaten the existence of these ecosystems. *(Florida State News Bureau.)*

A final significant aspect of natural and seminatural areas is their aesthetic value. Although this value is difficult to assess, its importance is evident in the large masses of people who visit the state and national parks and forests. The camping industry is booming, and private campgrounds are rapidly being built. Hence recreation is becoming an important part of the management of land.

The quality of man's aesthetic environment is receiving considerable attention from psychologists, sociologists, and cultural anthropologists. If man has evolved from a wilderness-type animal, what are the effects of living in the crowded, noisy city? Is there value in the city dweller "returning to nature"? Although campgrounds are often as crowded as the cities, people apparently enjoy the change in surroundings. These experiences contribute to the quality of life and our own well-being.

Tourism is now a multibillion-dollar industry, much of it based on scenic beauty. There is, however, a conflict between expanding tourism and the desire to retain scenic beauty. An example is the Door Peninsula of Wisconsin with the bay of Green Bay on one side and Lake Michigan on the other (Figure 11.9). Much of the peninsula is in a fairly natural state, wooded areas interspersed among small farms and villages. The shorelines have not been extensively developed with hotels, motels. and summer homes, and it has become a favorite vacation spot, particularly for people from the metropolitan areas of Milwaukee and Chicago. Presently, there is increasing effort to develop the area. Commercial campgrounds and new motels are being built.

Figure 11.9
The Door Peninsula in Wisconsin.

Commercial tourist "attractions" and more roadside billboards are appearing. Realtors are subdividing more land for summer homes. Roads are becoming crowded.

Some peninsula residents are concerned that this increased development will destroy the natural beauty of the area. A survey by the chamber of commerce in 1970 found that 80 percent of the tourists visited the area primarily for its scenic beauty. It is apparent that unplanned development and scenic beauty are not compatible. Decisions have to be made. Uncontrolled development irrevocably alters an area.

The morality of man's competition for habitat warrants serious consideration. One concern is the obligation to provide a proper legacy for future generations. Our children should have the opportunity to see an eagle flying overhead and not just a stuffed relic in a museum. They should be able to swim in natural bodies of water rather than only in concrete "swimming holes." Many young adults today are concerned about the kind of world the older generation has left them. What kind of environment will they leave for their children and grandchildren?

Interspecific Competition for Food

A second major example of interspecific competition is that for food. Man continuously competes with rodents and insects for food. Biblical history gives us accounts of locust plagues destroying food crops that resulted in years of famine (Figure 11.10). In such instances, the locust population was a better competitor than man.

PESTICIDE ARSENAL

Since the artificial synthesis of DDT during World War II, competition between man and his food competitors has changed dramatically. DDT was the first weapon of a highly complex arsenal of synthetic chemicals known as pesticides. Most of these are complex compounds of carbon, hydrogen, and at least one other element such as chlorine, arsenic, mercury, sulfur, or phosphorus. Man now uses chemical warfare to aid in his competition for the food energy produced in the world; Table 11.3 gives an idea of the variety of chemicals and the types of target species. We often hear of the chlorinated hydrocarbons such as DDT and dieldrin that are used for insect control, but there are many more types of insecticides. For example, organophosphates such as malathion and parathion represent another large group of chemicals used to kill insects.

Figure 11.10
A dense swarm of locusts obscures the view of an airport terminal building in Hargassa, Somalia. *(Authenticated News International.)*

Fungicides kill fungi. These chemicals usually contain mercury or arsenic compounds. Crop seeds are treated with fungicides to prevent their decomposition while in the ground prior to germination. Use of herbicides is rapidly expanding; prime examples are 2,4-D and 2,4,5-T. The presence of large numbers of weedy plants is a serious problem because the weeds compete with crop plants for nutrients, water, and light energy. The competition is important when any of these factors becomes limiting, so herbicides are used to decrease competition and promote high crop yield. A final type of pesticide is rodenticides, such as strychnine, which are used to kill the rats and mice that damage stored grain.

Table 11.3
A condensed classification of major biocides.

Chemical group or action	Examples
Insecticides and acaricides	
Inorganic	
Arsenicals	Lead arsenate
Copper-bearing	Copper sulfate
Organic, naturally occurring	
Nicotine alkaloids	Nicotine sulfate
Pyrethroids (also synthetic)	Pyrethrum
Rotenoids	Rotenone
Organic, synthetic	
Chlorinated hydrocarbon compounds	Aldrin, dieldrin, lindane, chlordane, DDT, endrin, heptachlor, methoxychlor, toxaphene
Organic phosphorus compounds	Chlorthion, diazinon, malathion, parathion, TEPP
Carbamates	Sevin
Fungicides	
Mercurials	Mercuric chloride
Quinones	Phygon
Dithiocarbamates	Nabam, ziram
Others	Captan, thiram
Herbicides	
Contact toxicity	Sodium arsenite, oils, "dinitro" compounds
Translocated (particularly hormone types)	2,4-D, 2,4,5-T
Soil sterilants	Borates, chlorates
Soil fumigants	Methyl bromide, Vapam
Rodenticides (mammal poisons)	
Anticoagulants	Warfarin, pival
Immediate action	Strychnine, sodium fluoroacetate ("1080"), thallium, endrin
Other vertebrate targets	
Birds	Strychnine, TEPP
Fishes	Rotenone, toxaphene

Source: Adapted with permission from Robert L. Rudd, *Pesticides and the Living Landscape* (Madison: University of Wisconsin Press, 1964), p. 17. © 1967 by the Regents of the University of Wisconsin.

POSITIVE ASPECTS
OF PESTICIDES

It is difficult to evaluate adequately the benefits and costs of biocides to man and the environment. On the positive side, it has been estimated that pesticides are responsible for saving one-third to one-half of the world's annual food harvest that would have been lost to pests. The result is not only more food but lower priced food. We should also remember, however, that advances in fertilizers and plant breeding have also greatly increased food production. As long as the world population continues to increase, there will be mounting pressures to prevent man's competitors from harvesting even greater amounts of agricultural production. As we have seen, moreover, pesticides have been instrumental in decreasing human deaths from diseases such as malaria and yellow fever (Figure 11.11).

Figure 11.11
A helicopter sprays DDT for mosquito control in a residential area of Leopoldville, the Congo. *(United Nations.)*

What are the costs of using pesticides? Before proceeding, a word of caution is necessary. As can be seen from Table 11.3, pesticides include a wide range of chemical compounds. We have learned that different compounds of different molecular structures interact in different ways with compounds found in ecosystems. Thus the following discussion of negative aspects of pesticides should not be construed as applying to all pesticides. Each must be examined individually on the

NEGATIVE ASPECTS
OF PESTICIDES

basis of how its particular molecular structure allows it to interact in the environment.

One negative result of the use of pesticides is the greater number of species that are significant competitors with man for food. We call such species pests. This increase is the product of a lack of specificity of many pesticides (termed *broad-spectrum pesticides*). These pesticides kill not only the target species but other organisms that are present. It is for this reason that pesticides are sometimes referred to as biocides. We have learned that predator-prey and parasite-host relationships are important as population-control mechanisms for some species. If along with its target the broad-spectrum pesticide kills a predator or a parasite of another species, the population of the prey or host species may no longer be held in check. Thus, species whose numbers were once too small to be significant competitors become pests (Figure 11.12).

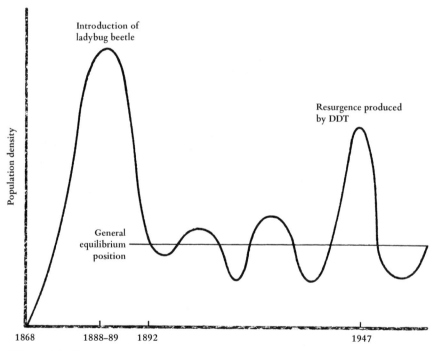

Figure 11.12
When the cottony cushion scale was accidentally introduced into California, it spread rapidly and caused considerable damage to citrus trees. Introduction of ladybugs, a natural predator, reduced the scale population to a level of low economic damage. Later use of DDT in orchards killed the ladybugs, thereby releasing the scale insect. *(After an article by V. M. Stern et al. in* Hilgardia, *29 [1959], p. 93.)*

Furthermore, the pest we are trying to control often becomes an even greater competitor. The same basic principles of population interactions apply. Even a major competitor has its natural predators and parasites. A broad-spectrum pesticide may also kill the predators and parasites of the pest. This usually results in the pest recovering with a higher population and making it a stronger competitor. By using pesticides that lack specificity, we create additional competitors to control.

A second consequence of pesticide application is that over 200 different species, mainly insects, have now become resistant to certain pesticides (Figure 11.13). To explain this, we will first consider the population densities of many insect species. It is common to find thousands of individuals of a single species in an acre of land. Within such a large population, genetic variation can be expected. In fact, some members of the population may already be resistant to the insecticide being applied and are not harmed by it (Figure 11.14). After several applications, the nonresistant members are largely eliminated and a resistant population remains. With the elimination of intraspecific competition between the resistant and the nonresistant members, the resistant population increases rapidly.

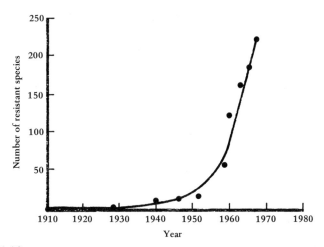

Figure 11.13
The number of species resistant to insecticides has increased rapidly in recent years. There are now over 220 species resistant to at least one insecticide. *(Redrawn with permission from Gordon Conway, "Better Methods of Pest Control," in William W. Murdoch, ed.,* Environment: Resources, Pollution and Society *[Stamford, Conn.: Sinauer Associates, 1971], p. 308.)*

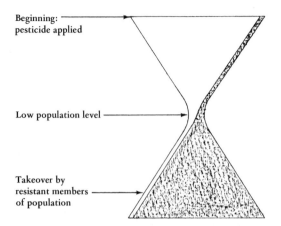

Figure 11.14
A schematic illustration of the selection for a pesticide-resistant population. The shaded area represents pesticide-resistant members of the population; the unshaded area represents pesticide-sensitive members. Time moves toward the bottom.

In effect, man takes "natural selection" into his own hands, but selecting individuals that are most resistant is the opposite of what he hopes to accomplish. Man often has to increase the frequency of application and/or the concentration of the pesticide, or he may be forced to turn to a more toxic chemical. In any case, continuing the process produces increasingly resistant pest populations — "superpests."

An example of this selective process involves the pasture mosquito in California. When DDT was first employed in 1945 the pasture mosquito population appeared to be under control. Within seven years, however, a DDT-resistant population developed, so a new chemical, ethyl parathion, was applied. By 1961, ethyl parathion was no longer effective, so methyl parathion was introduced; but it also became ineffective in 1963 as did flenthion in 1968. Presently there is no insecticide that can be used in safe dosages that will kill the pasture mosquito. Fortunately, the pasture mosquito does not transmit diseases. It is a pest only because it swarms in large numbers and has a painful sting. However, certain populations of malaria-carrying mosquitos have developed a resistance to DDT, and rats that can carry typhus and plague have developed resistance to rodenticides such as Warfarin. We can, therefore, begin to appreciate the potential danger that results from relying upon chemical control alone.

Another source of environmental problems lies in the molecular stability of some pesticides. These chemicals are not readily broken down by either chemical decomposition or by biological action. Most pesticides are synthetic compounds that are foreign to the environment; thus, many organisms lack enzyme systems that can break chemical bonds within the pesticide molecules. There have never been any selective pressures for the pesticide-decomposing enzymes; hence some pesticides tend to persist in living organisms. When dead organisms containing the persistent compound are acted upon by decomposers, the pesticide is released to the abiotic environment where it can be taken up by another organism.

Persistent chemicals may be transported among all of the reservoirs in the ecosystem (Figure 11.15). The ability of pesticides to be transported great distances was dramatically shown when fish, penguins, and other birds in Antarctica were found to contain DDT, dieldrin, and other chlorinated hydrocarbon insecticides. This is startling because no insecticides had been used within a thousand miles of Antarctica.

The chlorinated hydrocarbons (Table 11.4) are a group of compounds whose molecular structure is very stable; they persist for long periods in the environment. The organic phosphate insecticides have a much lower persistence and are essentially broken down in one to twelve weeks. However, we must be aware of the trade-offs involved. Although organophosphates are much less persistent, they are generally five to ten times more toxic than the chlorinated hydrocarbons. Thus they may cause greater environmental problems over their short life spans than the chlorinated hydrocarbons do over their more extended ones. Finally, it should be pointed out that very little is known of the persistence and toxicity of the breakdown products of pesticides. It may be that these products are more toxic and persistent than the original pesticides. Such matters must be considered in evaluating the merits of any pesticide.

The dynamics of food chains result in higher concentrations of persistent pesticides in individuals at the upper levels of the chains. This phenomenon of *food chain accumulation* is also known as biological magnification. To understand how this occurs, let us consider a tidal marsh ecosystem on Long Island, New York. After 20 years of using DDT for mosquito control, analysis of marsh water indicated a DDT concentration of 0.00005 ppm, a small concentration of no apparent significance.

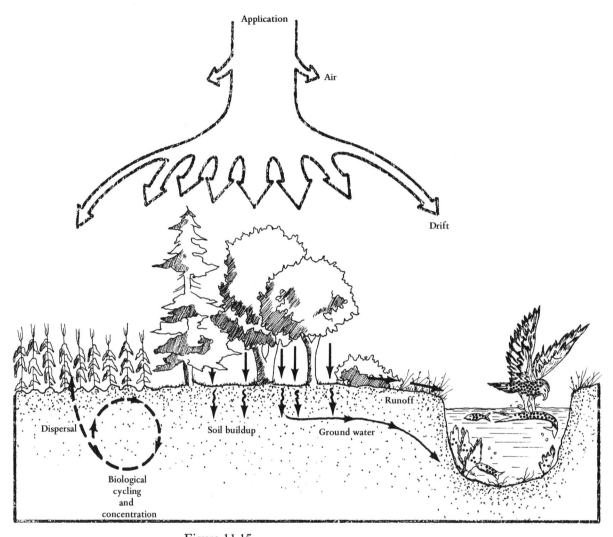

Figure 11.15
Pathways for the movement of pesticides in the environment. In addition to moving among the abiotic components of the environment, pesticides can accumulate within food chains, as shown by the activity in the pond on the right. Black dots show the relative concentration of pesticide within each organism. *(Modified with permission from Robert L. Rudd, "Pesticides," in William W. Murdoch, ed.,* Environment: Resources, Pollution and Society *[Stamford, Conn.: Sinauer Associates, 1971], p. 286.)*

Let us look further, however, and consider the biotic components of the marsh ecosystem (Figure 11.16). Producers (algae) were found

Table 11.4
Maximum longevity of chlorinated
hydrocarbon insecticides in soils.[a]

Pesticide	Percentage remaining 14 years later
Aldrin	40
Chlordane	40
Endrin	41
Heptachlor	16
BHC	10
Toxaphene	45
	15 years later
Aldrin	28
Dieldrin	31
	17 years later
DDT	39

Source: Data from Ralph G. Nash
and Edwin A. Woolson, "Persistence of
Chlorinated Hydrocarbon Insecticides in
Soils," *Science*, 157 (August 25, 1967),
pp. 924-925.

[a] Values are greater than in average
cases because of experimental design.

to contain 800 times more DDT than the water. At the consumer level, herbivores such as clams, snails, and eels contained DDT in concentrations 3,200 times greater than that in water. Concentrations 40,000 times greater were found in carnivorous fish. Finally, fish-eating birds such as herons and cormorants had concentrations of DDT up to 500,000 times greater than the water. Thus food chains can accumulate persistent pesticides in concentrations much higher than the abiotic source of the ecosystem. The consequences of pesticide accumulation in the upper levels of the food chain are related to the organism's resistance, which varies with age. Let us divide the life cycle into three stages — reproduction, young, and adults — and consider the effect of DDT on each. We use DDT as an example because it is the pesticide that has been used and investigated most extensively.

The species whose reproductive capacity has been most severely limited by pesticides are birds that prey upon fish, e.g., the bald eagle, peregrine falcon, osprey, and brown pelican. During the past 15 or 20 years the population levels of some of these birds have fallen tremen-

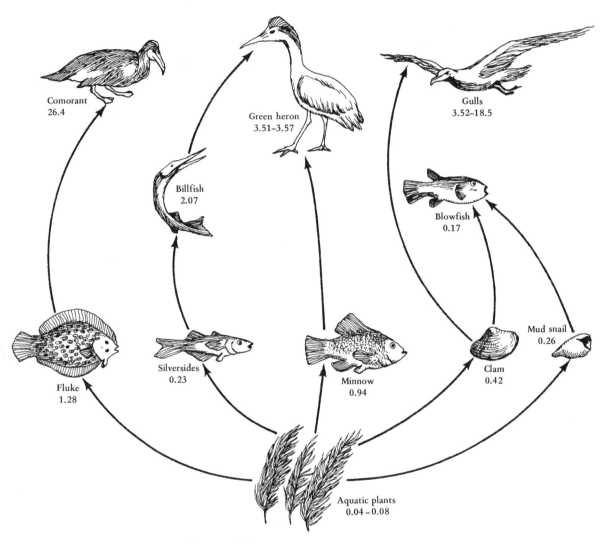

Figure 11.16
A small portion of the food web of a tidal marsh on Long Island, illustrating the accumulation of DDT. The DDT values are given in ppm. *(After George W. Woodwell, "Toxic Substances and Ecological Cycles,"* Scientific American, *216 [March 1967], pp. 26–27.)*

dously. The osprey (fish hawk) population in one coastal area of Connecticut decreased from 154 breeding pairs in 1958 to only ten in 1968 (Figure 11.17). In 1969 brown pelicans failed to reproduce on the coastal islands of California, and in 1970 only one young pelican was found to survive the nesting season. Between 1950 and 1968, the nesting population of peregrine falcons decreased in the eastern United States by 100 percent and in the western United States by 80 to 90 percent. Nesting populations of peregrines in Finland have declined by 95 percent, in West Germany by 77 percent, and in Great Britain by 60 percent. The population decreases are worldwide.

What happened to cause such a drastic decline? Examination of nesting sites revealed that a large number of eggs were broken before they had hatched, suggesting that the eggshells were thinner than they

Figure 11.17
The osprey is a bird of prey that appears to be suffering a population decrease due to accumulations of DDT and other pesticides in its system. *(Michigan Department of Natural Resources.)*

formerly had been. Thus began the tedious task of collecting and measuring broken shells from many nesting sites. Old shells from museums were then measured to provide the needed comparison. Results showed that the present-day shells were significantly thinner than the shells of eggs collected prior to 1945 (Table 11.5). The thinner shells made the eggs more susceptible to breakage during nest activities.

Adult birds were found to contain significant concentrations of DDT. This is not surprising since they are at the top of the food chains. Many people blamed DDT for the decrease in shell thickness, but the problem was to establish the link between the two. Laboratory investigations subsequently showed that DDT decreased the activity of a female hormone known as estrogen. In birds this hormone regulates calcium, which is accumulated in the bones and later incorporated into the eggshell. Decreased estrogen activity results in decreased availability of calcium; thus thinner eggshells.

Table 11.5 illustrates an interesting aspect of food chain dynamics. The predator species that are declining tend to feed on fish, whereas the stabilized species are those that tend to feed upon land animals. Because aquatic food chains are usually two to three links longer than terrestrial chains, there is greater biological concentration and these

Table 11.5

Relation of change in eggshell thickness to population levels of certain birds of prey.[a]

Populations	Weight of eggshell (percentage change)
Declining	
Peregrine falcon, California	−18.8
Osprey, New Jersey	−25.1
Bald eagle, Florida	−19.8
Stationary	
Red-tail hawk, California	+ 2.7
Golden eagle, California	+ 2.9
Great horned owl, California	+ 2.4
Peregrine falcon, British Columbia	− 1.4

Source: Adapted with permission from Joseph Hickey and Daniel Anderson, "Chlorinated Hydrocarbons and Eggshell Changes in Raptorial and Fish-Eating Birds," *Science*, 162 (October 11, 1968), p. 271. Copyright 1968 by the American Association for the Advancement of Science.

[a] Percentage change represents difference between eggs sampled before and after 1945 when DDT usage became common.

birds are exposed to higher pesticide levels. The effects of DDT on eggshell thickness and therefore population levels of birds of prey wasn't suspected until only a few years ago. After all, DDT is only an *insect*icide. The above example demonstrates how little we know about the effects of our synthetic chemicals on the biosphere.

Also vulnerable are the young. In 1968 the Michigan Department of Natural Resources collected coho salmon eggs from Lake Michigan for rearing and future stocking. The newly hatched fry developed normally for a few days, but then turned brown and died. Over 700,000 perished. Apparently, some DDT moved along with nutrients from the adult into the eggs during their formation. As the developing fry used the food stored in the yolk sac, they took up the DDT (Figure 11.18). Although adult coho have been found with DDT levels of 16 ppm with no apparent ill effects, concentrations as low as three ppm are lethal for the small fry. This example not only demonstrates the effects of DDT on young, but also reemphasizes the difference in tolerance between young and adult.

One of the original arguments against DDT was the mass die-off of adult robins following attempts to control Dutch elm disease. Despite rainfall, DDT remains on the elm leaves throughout the summer. After leaf fall, DDT is released into the soil by decomposers. In addition, spraying techniques, excessive applications, and negligence also contributed large amounts of DDT directly to the soil.

Robins provide an example of adult members of a species succumbing to pesticide accumulation. Earthworms are a common food source for robins, but the robins do not, of course, discriminate between

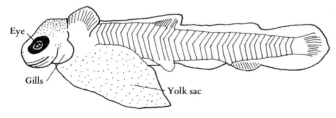

Figure 11.18
The yolk sac of the young salmon fry contains DDT, which is then subsequently used by the developing fry. *(Redrawn with permission from Karl F. Lagler,* Freshwater Fishery Biology, *2nd ed.* [Dubuque, Iowa: William C. Brown, Co., 1956], p. 105.)

contaminated and noncontaminated worms. With continued ingestion of contaminated earthworms the robins accumulated toxic levels of DDT, went into convulsions, and died. In communities where the use of DDT has been discontinued, robin populations have recovered.

We have seen that the effects of pesticides vary with the life stage and with the particular species. It is important to realize that no matter where the life cycle is broken (reproduction, developing young, or adults), the species is doomed to extinction.

Man is also at the top of food chains. Do we then ingest DDT and other pesticides in our diet? Federal Food and Drug Administration studies have shown that chlorinated hydrocarbons such as DDT are commonly found in many foods. Meat, fish, poultry, and dairy products account for more than half the intake, although there is little direct application of biocides to these products. There is, then, accumulation in agricultural food chains as well as in "natural" food chains. U.S. Public Health Service studies show that everybody, from infancy till death, retains DDT in his fatty tissues. The average for U.S. citizens is about 10 to 12 ppm. Worldwide averages vary from 3 ppm in Alaskan Eskimos to 25 ppm in the people of India (Table 11.6). Even in the United States, DDT levels vary with race, socio-economic status, and geographic location (Figure 11.19).

What are the effects of carrying low levels of DDT in our fatty tissues? This question brings forth conflicting answers. Although many deaths result from accidents or improper handling of pesticides (181 in 1969), "officially" no one has died from long-term, low-level exposure to pesticides. Some investigations into the effect of DDT in the diet have resulted in the observation of "no clinical effects." These investigations focused, however, on nervous system disorders (DDT is

Table 11.6

Average human residual loads of DDT and DDE (a toxic breakdown product of DDT), showing the universality of the presence of pesticides in man.

Country	ppm	Country	ppm
India	26	Canada	5
Hungary	12	Germany	4
United States	12	England	3
France	9	Alaska	3

Source: Reprinted with permission of the Editor and the *British Medical Journal* from an article by H. Egan, R. Goulding, J. Roburn, and J. O'G. Patton in *British Medical Journal*, 2 (1965), p. 68.

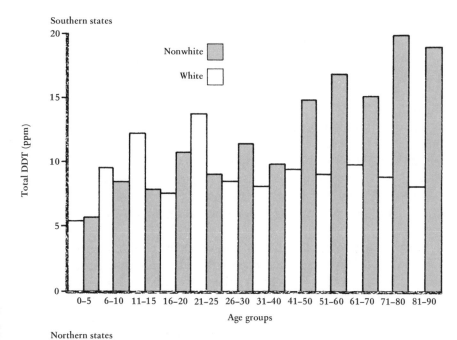

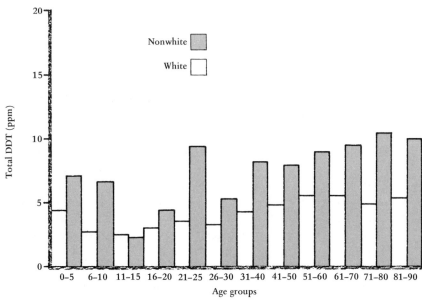

Figure 11.19
Comparison of DDT content in human fatty tissues by age, race, and geographical location. Data are for 1968. *(After Mrak,* Report on Pesticides and Their Relationship to Environmental Health, *U.S. Department of Health, Education and Welfare, 1969.)*

a nerve poison). Hormonal changes such as found in birds were not studied, nor were the effects of low levels of DDT on women and children. Other preliminary investigations indicate that DDT may interfere with enzyme activity of the liver and may also be related to liver cancer. The herbicide 2,4,5-T has been implicated as a cause of birth defects.

Though little is known about the long-term health effects of small amounts of pesticides in the human body, the entire human race continues to undergo life-long exposure. There is little ground for forebodings of disaster but even less for complacency. It is ludicrous to continue this unofficial experiment on the human race, particularly when many alternatives to persistent pesticides are available.

TRENDS IN PEST
CONTROL

Our concern over the effects of pesticides becomes even greater when we consider the projected growth of the industry. Although the production of DDT has declined since 1967, increases in other chlorinated hydrocarbons and organophosphate insecticides have more than compensated for the decrease. The production of synthetic organic pesticides is increasing by about 15 percent a year. By 1975 total sales are expected to be $3 billion annually. Thus it appears that in the absence of official prohibitions, the manufacture and application of synthetic pesticides will continue to increase.

We seem to be in a dilemma. On the one hand, pesticides have been important in combating our food competitors and greatly decreasing the incidence of diseases such as typhus and malaria. Pressure to use pesticides is increasing as the human population expands. On the other hand, use of pesticides is also contaminating sources of food (particularly aquatic), reducing the gene pool, and creating instability in ecosystems.

This dilemma is actually an illusion. There are many real and potential alternatives to the use of broad-spectrum persistent pesticides, but inadequate emphasis has been placed on their development. Let us now consider some advantages and disadvantages of other methods of controling our competitors.

ALTERNATIVES

One alternative is the production of chemicals that are toxic only to target species. These chemicals should also be biodegradable or able to be chemically broken down to nontoxic by-products in a short period. Although narrow-spectrum pesticides have many environmental benefits, they do not have the economic advantages of broad-spectrum pesticides. If a single product can destroy many pest species, it will have wider, hence cheaper, usage than a narrow-spectrum one. In addition, the development costs for the chemical will probably be smaller compared with total sales, insuring greater profits for the manufacturer.

Greater emphasis should also be placed on the use of chemicals occurring naturally in ecosystems. For example, many insect species produce their own unique hormones called *juvenile hormones.* Decreasing concentrations of the hormone allow the insect to pass through its life stages (Figure 11.20). By applying the juvenile hormone in the proper concentration at the right time, we can cause the insect to remain in a particular stage of its life cycle. Continued use of the chemical over a growing season will interrupt the life cycle of the insect. These substances are potentially effective population control agents and have the advantage of being specific to certain insect species.

When we consider the long evolutionary history of most predator-

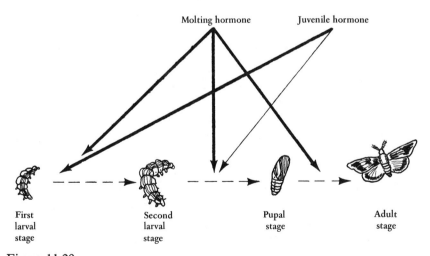

Figure 11.20
The role of juvenile hormone in the development of a moth. When the molting hormone plus large amounts of juvenile hormone are present in the moth, it will remain in the larval stage. But when the juvenile hormone is present in very small amounts, the larval form will change to the pupal stage. When no juvenile hormone is present, the adult develops.

prey and parasite-host relations, it seems reasonable to assume that there are many naturally occurring pesticides tailor-made for control of certain species. For example, pyrethium, which is a component of some "popular" insecticide aerosols, occurs in the flowers of a daisy-like plant. It remains for man to find more of these. The advantage of using natural poisons is that they are usually biodegradable and resistant populations rarely occur.

The use of sex attractants is also becoming a useful tool in controlling certain pest populations. Many insects release chemicals that aid in bringing the sexes together for mating. Insect traps are baited either with live females or with the chemical sex attractant. If large numbers of males are attracted and caught, the breeding population is reduced. Gypsy moths, which have caused considerable damage to trees in the eastern part of the United States, have been partially controlled by this method.

An alternative to the use of chemicals is *biological control,* i.e. using the pest's own predators and parasites to control its population. This method has the advantage of using natural population control mechanisms. There have been notable successes, such as the use of ladybird beetles (ladybugs) to control cottony cushion scale that threatened the citrus industry in California (Figure 11.21). Other examples include the control of rabbits in Australia by the myxoma virus and control of prickly pear cactus (also in Australia) by the Cactoblastis moth. However, there also have been failures. The Indian mongoose was introduced into Jamaica and Puerto Rico to control rats in sugar-cane fields. Although the rat population was greatly reduced, the mongoose became a pest by preying on poultry and species of ground-nesting birds. It also became a carrier of rabies. Effective biological control requires considerable time for careful study of the pest and its predators and parasites before large-scale introductions of control agents are made. In addition to the advantage of relative specificity and lack of toxic residues, the control population needs only to be introduced once. In contrast, adequate control by pesticides requires frequent applications. A major disadvantage of biological control is the time needed for the predator population to become established; most farmers would not want to suffer the economic losses they would incur before the pest was brought under control.

Other alternatives concern our agricultural practices. Crop rotation prevents the buildup of pest populations in soil and crop residue. For

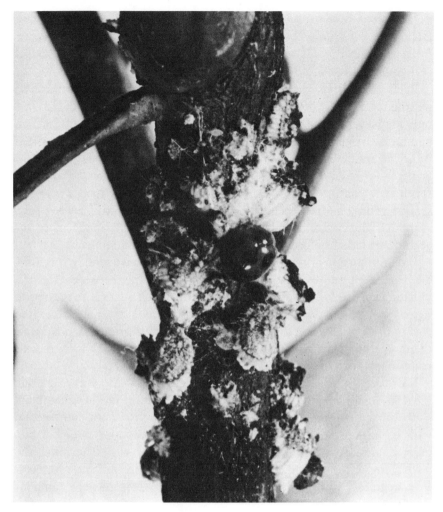

Figure 11.21
An example of biological pest control is the use of ladybugs to control cottony cushion scale on citrus trees. *(Florida Department of Agriculture and Consumer Services.)*

example, by replacing corn (a grass) with soybeans (a legume) it is possible to avoid larger populations of corn rootworm. Crop diversity is also important. The development of disease-resistant crops can be a useful tool in our competition for food. For example, at one time Hessian fly damage to wheat cost several hundred million dollars a year. However, the breeding of resistant wheat varieties has reduced the pest to a minor status. Other pests such as corn borer, aphids, and loopworm have also been controlled by resistant crops. A major difficulty with this alternative is obtaining resistant varieties that also give high yields.

Each alternative has advantages and disadvantages that must be weighed against the benefits and costs of persistent pesticides. We must, however, make use of our knowledge of the principles by which natural ecosystems function. Knowing that populations are controlled by a variety of factors, it is foolish to rely upon only one method of control — pesticides. All the methods listed above must be brought together to control pests on an environmentally sound basis. *Integrated control* programs have been used successfully to control some pests. Although alternative methods are becoming available, much more research is needed before they can be successfully integrated.

Integrated control requires perhaps more time and money for sufficient research and evaluation than does control by pesticides, but the greater expense will eventually be more than offset by the reduction in environmental degradation. Furthermore, it is estimated that the cost of pesticides is less than 2 percent of the retail price of food. Thus, the increased development costs for better pest control are insignificant from many points of view.

We have dwelt on pesticides at great length because they illustrate the wide range of effects that man's activities have on his cohabitants of the biosphere. If our population continues to grow, our competition with other consumer species for the limited food supply will become even more intense. Our methods of competing will determine the well-being of the biosphere. We could possibly win the battle for food with chemical warfare, yet lose the war by making the environment uninhabitable.

KEY WORDS AND SUMMARY STATEMENTS

gene pool
estuaries
broad-spectrum pesticides

food chain accumulation
juvenile hormones

biological control
integrated control

Although there was initially a long period of slow growth, the human population now has a doubling period of approximately 35 years.

The population growth curve for man is similar to that of other organisms except that the growth curve has not yet leveled off.

Predation is of no significance in controlling man's population.

Although parasitism has a large potential for controlling human population, advances in modern medicine have greatly decreased deaths from disease, at least temporarily.

Short of all-out atomic warfare, intraspecific competition is also of little importance in controlling human numbers.

Man is temporarily winning the interspecific competition for habitat by turning complex natural ecosystems into cities, suburbs, farms, and highways.

As a result of habitat destruction and other man-related activities, many species are now on the endangered list. Each species, however, is important to man because each possesses unique adaptive characteristics that man may need some day; also, each species makes a contribution to the stability of ecosystems.

Ecosystems such as grasslands, virgin forests, and swamps are also becoming endangered. Natural areas are important for man as areas for baseline studies, natural reservoirs, aesthetic value, and recreation.

Man is intensely competing with other consumers for the earth's food energy. The use of pesticides to kill such competitors as insects, rodents, fungi, and weeds has increased dramatically in the past two decades.

Pesticides are said to be responsible for saving from one-third to one-half of the world's annual food harvest from the ravages of pests. They have also been instrumental in decreasing human deaths from such diseases as malaria and yellow fever.

The use of broad-spectrum pesticides has brought some species up to a pest status by disrupting the population-controlling interactions of predation and parasitism.

By selecting for resistance, more than 200 species of pests now have populations that are resistant to at least one pesticide.

Because some pesticides are persistent they can be accumulated in food chains, resulting in high concentrations in organisms occupying the upper levels of food chains. Such concentrations are lethal to some species.

Alternatives to broad-spectrum, persistent pesticides include biological control, sex attractants, juvenile hormones, agricultural practices such as crop rotation and the breeding of pest-resistant crop varieties, and synthetic chemicals that are narrow-spectrum and nonpersistent.

A combination of several alternatives selected to best control the particular pest under given environmental conditions is the basis of integrated control.

1. Consider the similarities between man's role in increasing the number of endangered species and disrupting cycles of materials. Are his motives the same?

QUESTIONS AND PROJECTS

2. Can you give recent examples of natural and seminatural areas in your community that have been lost to development?

3. What would be your reply to the person who asks, "What is more important, me or an eagle?"

4. How would you assess the role of botanical gardens, zoos, parks, and the like in preserving the gene pool? What considerations are involved in caging animals in a zoo?

5. What are the possible reasons for the DDT content of humans varying with age, race, and geographical location?

6. Why should we take a second look at claims that certain materials are of no harm to man because the materials are released in only very dilute amounts into the environment?

7. Why do you suppose that the pasture mosquito became resistant to methyl parathion only 2 years after it became resistant to ethyl parathion, whereas it took 9 years to become resistant to ethyl parathion after it had become resistant to DDT?

8. What would be your answer to someone from an underdeveloped African nation who demands that the United Nations use DDT to control disease in his country?

9. Comment on deaths from auto accidents as a form of intraspecific competition.

SELECTED READINGS

Carson, Rachel. *Silent Spring.* Boston: Houghton Mifflin, 1962. A book with strong emotional appeal that brought the problems of pesticides to the public.

Conway, Gordon R. "Better Methods of Pest Control." In *Environment: Resources, Pollution, and Society,* edited by W. W. Murdoch. Stamford, Conn.: Sinauer, 1971. A comprehensive review of the alternatives available for pest control.

Ehrenfeld, David W. *Biological Conservation.* New York: Holt, Rinehart and Winston, 1970. Interesting discussion of factors contributing to endangered species and natural ecosystems and also means of preservation.

Ehrlich, Paul R., and Ehrlich, Anne H. *Population, Resources, Environment: Issues in Human Ecology,* 2nd ed. San Francisco: Freeman, 1972. An account of the history and present trends of human population growth. Also examines possible solutions to population growth and exploitation and degradation of the environment.

Hardin, Garrett, ed. *Population, Evolution, and Birth Control: A Collage of Controversial Ideas,* 2nd ed. San Francisco: Freeman, 1969. A series of short readings on a wide range of controversial topics dealing with the problems of human population growth.

Rudd, Robert. "Pesticides." In *Environment: Resources, Pollution, and Society,* edited by W. W. Murdoch. Stamford, Conn.: Sinauer, 1971. An account of the problems associated with current pesticide usage practices.

chapter

12

Human Carrying Capacity: Food Energy

We have seen that population interactions are not currently significant limiting factors on the growth of human numbers. We now turn our attention to an examination of the Earth's carrying capacity for food energy.

Meeting man's food requirements involves many interacting factors; there is more to it than sowing, fertilizing, cultivating, and harvesting. We must also be concerned with preservation and storage, distribution, economics, politics, and customs. Our chief concern here, though, will be the basic agricultural aspects.

It is estimated that over half of the world's population is either *undernourished* or *malnourished*. Undernourishment is the lack of the required minimum number of calories (food energy) in a diet, whereas malnourishment is the lack of the proper types of food. A malnourished person may be consuming sufficient calories and still be deficient in certain essential proteins or vitamins. For example, some children take in enough carbohydrate to supply the minimum energy requirements, yet they suffer from protein deficiency diseases such as kwashiorkor (Figure 12.1). Tragically, protein deficiencies may result in mental retardation, thereby greatly depreciating a human resource. Large investments in remedial education cannot correct the damage.

There is considerable debate over the amount of food available

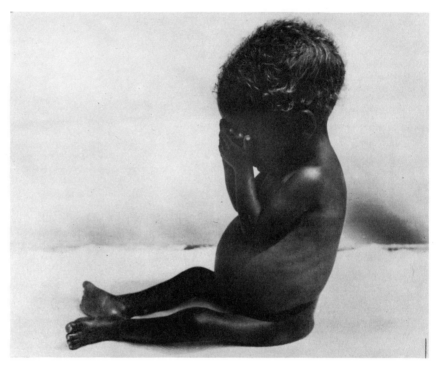

Figure 12.1
An African child suffering from kwashiorkor has the distended belly and thin legs that are common symptoms of this protein deficiency disease. *(FAO photograph.)*

today. Some say that if distribution and economic problems were solved, there would be enough food for everyone. Others believe that there simply isn't enough food to go around. Regardless of which position is valid, the yearly increase of 70,000,000 people necessitates continual efforts to increase food production. There are several means whereby these additional needs may be met.

PRODUCTION FROM NEW LANDS

One method of increasing the carrying capacity for food energy is for man to expand cultivation into new areas. However, the United States is the only country with a readily available reserve of good cropland. There is little potential for the expansion of croplands in other temperate regions such as Europe and Asia. The greatest potential for expansion of cropland lies in two types of regions: semiarid and tropical. Let us examine the potential of each.

The Amazon basin and the sub-Saharan region of Africa are the only remaining large regions of potentially arable land with sufficient rainfall for intensive agriculture. The heavy vegetation of tropical ecosystems such as rain forests would seem to indicate high fertility and hence a large capacity for growing food crops. These areas would be particularly useful agriculturally since they also contain a large portion of the world's hungry people (Figure 12.2). Rain forest soils are, however, poor in nutrients. High temperatures and heavy precipitation accelerate rates of decomposer activity. Dead plants and animals are rapidly broken down and the nutrients are released into the soil. Some of these nutrients are taken up by the plants, but the heavy rainfall speeds the loss of remaining nutrients either in runoff or seepage into the ground-water reservoir. Most of the nutrients present in tropical ecosystems are thus found in the vegetation and not in the soil.

The ramifications of this distribution of nutrients in tropical ecosystems have long been known to local inhabitants, who practice "slash and burn" agriculture. They move into an area and select a small plot, which they cut and burn (Figure 12.3). The remaining ash contains

Figure 12.2
Shaded areas are the regions of the world in which human diets are deficient in calories and/or protein. (After Economic Research Service, The World Food Budget, 1970, Foreign Agricultural Economic Report 19, USDA, 1965.)

Figure 12.3
Using slash and burn agriculture, workers in Borneo plant rice on a burned patch of forest. *(De Wys, Inc.)*

some of the nutrients that were present in the vegetation and can be used as fertilizer. Within three to five years, harvesting of the crops with their incorporated nutrients and the continual high precipitation results in the depletion of soil nutrients. The natives then move on to another area and begin anew. Within 20 to 25 years the first plots are once more overgrown with vegetation, so the people can return, and start the cycle again. Slash and burn agriculture is the best method devised thus far for these tropical soils.

Although some tropical soils are low in most nutrients, they are high in iron and aluminum. When the vegetation is removed and these soils are exposed to the tropical sun, they bake to an iron-hard brick-like material called *laterite* (Figure 12.4). If the cleared area contains only a few acres (1 acre = 4,047 square meters), such as is normally used for slash and burn agriculture, it will become revegetated. However, if it is much larger than this, a vast rock pavement results that will support little vegetation. A few years ago, the Brazilian government set up an agricultural colony in the heart of the Amazon basin. Although the soil appeared to be rich the nutrients were depleted after only two plantings, and the exposed soil began to bake. In less than five years, the cleared fields became virtually a rock surface unsuitable for agriculture.

It is difficult to evaluate the potential of lateritic soils for increasing the world's food supply. There is growing evidence that these soils do not present a permanent limitation to agricultural development in the tropics. However, much more must be learned about the management of tropical soils once the protective vegetation has been removed before substantial gains can be made in increasing food production from these new lands.

Figure 12.4
A house constructed of lateritic bricks in South America. *(Organization of American States.)*

Expansion in Semiarid Regions

NEED FOR IRRIGATION

Other major areas of potential expansion are semiarid and arid regions, such as the Southwest of the United States, North Africa, and the Middle East. In many of these areas, the soils are fertile because low precipitation has resulted in little runoff and leeching. By irrigation, over 450 million acres of such land is now being farmed, more than 33 million acres of it in the United States. For example, the Imperial Valley of California was once a desert. Since 1940, when a canal 200 feet (61 meters) wide began bringing water from the Colorado River, the valley has been producing lettuce, tomatoes, watermelons, onions, sugar beets, asparagus, oranges, and dates.

SHORTCOMINGS OF IRRIGATION

Irrigation is not, however, without its problems. Only one out of every four gallons drawn for irrigation is actually taken up by the plants (Figure 12.5). Part of the remainder is lost by seepage from the

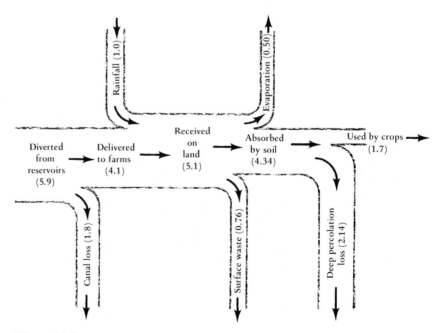

Figure 12.5
Balance sheet showing sources and losses of water in irrigation operations. Values are given in acre-feet. (An acre-foot is the amount of water that would cover one acre of land to a depth of one foot.) *(Redrawn with permission of The Macmillan Company from Georg Borgstrom,* Too Many, *p. 185. Copyright © 1969, 1971 by Georg Borgstrom.)*

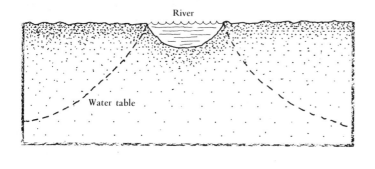

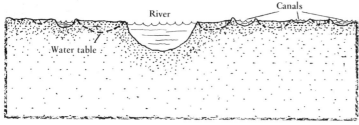

Figure 12.6
Seepage from irrigation canals results in a rise in the water table. *(Redrawn with permission from Roger Revelle, "Water," Scientific American [September 1963], p. 100. Copyright © 1963 by Scientific American, Inc. All rights reserved.)*

canal into the soil, which can have serious consequences in flat areas such as flood plains and deltas where subsurface drainage is inadequate. The seepage may raise the water table high enough to drown plant roots (Figure 12.6). Close to 10 million acres in Pakistan were converted into marshlands as a result of this kind of seepage. In the early 1960s, a team of scientists from the United States studied the problem and recommended that wells be constructed to lower the water table. The ground water could then be used to supplement river water for irrigation. This procedure has been successful, and the marshland has now been returned to agriculture. Canals can be waterproofed by using plastic liners (Figure 12.7) or asphalt, but the costs are high.

Another major loss of irrigation water is by evaporation from the canals and soil surface. All water carries dissolved salts, and when it evaporates before it can seep into the soil, salt deposits accumulate on the soil surface (Figure 12.8). In some instances the ground water, which also contains dissolved salts, moves upward toward the soil sur-

Figure 12.7
Lining irrigation canals with plastic helps to prevent seepage from the canals. *(U.S. Department of the Interior, Bureau of Reclamation.)*

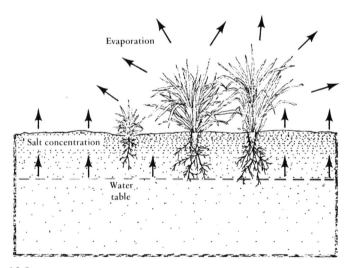

Figure 12.8
Salt accumulates in upper soil as a result of evaporation. Some irrigation water is evaporated before it moves into the soil. Water may also rise from the water table to the soil surface, where it evaporates. *(Redrawn with permission from Roger Revelle, "Water," Scientific American [September 1963], p. 100. Copyright © 1963 by Scientific American, Inc. All rights reserved.)*

face where it evaporates and leaves a salt deposit. As salt concentrations continue to increase, plant growth is retarded and eventually eliminated when tolerance limits are exceeded. It is estimated that millions of acres in Pakistan, Egypt, Greece, and South America have become salt deserts as a result of salt accumulation in soils *(salinization)*. This effect is also causing an abandonment of farms in the Imperial Valley (Figure 12.9) and in parts of the Southwest.

Figure 12.9
Although irrigation can be used to make deserts bloom, improper usage can make the land unusable for food production. These photographs show the Imperial Valley, California, desert before irrigation was begun *(left);* during irrigation, when crops such as barley were grown *(middle);* and after irrigation had caused salinization of the land *(right).* (Left: *U.S. Department of the Interior, Bureau of Reclamation.* Middle and right: *USDA–Soil Conservation Service.*)

Flushing fields with large amounts of water will wash the salt off into surface ditches, but the practice only causes more problems. Flushing requires large amounts of water — water in limited supply. In addition, this usage of water does not contribute directly to increased food production. Finally, the salt-laden water is often drained into a river, thereby increasing its salinity. For example, irrigation over the past 20 years has increased the salinity of the lower Colorado River by 30 percent. By the time the water gets to Mexico it is too saline for many purposes, including human consumption.

Irrigation has been criticized because it is a consumptive use of water. In the United States, approximately 95 percent of the water used by municipalities and industries can be used again (nonconsumptive). However, over 60 percent of irrigation water is lost from the agricultural system. In addition, irrigation accounts for approximately 40 percent of our per capita water usage (Table 12.1). Some people believe that irrigation-based food production is not needed to meet the United States food requirements. They think that this water could raise the standard of living for more people by using it for municipal and industrial purposes. Irrigated lands do, however, supply much of our fruits and vegetables (Table 12.2). The conflict between agricultural and urban-industrial uses will most likely become more intense as future demands for the fixed water supply increase (Table 12.1).

Table 12.1
Water requirements in the United States.

Type of use	Millions of gallons per day (1 gal. = 3.8 liters)			
	1965	Estimate 1980	Estimate 2000	Estimate 2020
Rural domestic	2,351	2,474	2,852	3,334
Municipal	23,745	33,596	50,724	74,256
Industrial	46,405	75,026	127,365	210,767
Steam electric	84,538	193,303	470,448	914,093
Agriculture				
Irrigation	110,825	135,852	149,824	160,978
Livestock	1,726	2,375	3,397	4,660
Total	269,617	442,626	804,610	1,368,088

Source: Reprinted with permission from H. Bowman Hawkes, "Irrigation in the United States," in *Conservation of Natural Resources*, 4th ed., edited by Guy-Harold Smith (New York: Wiley, 1971), p. 286.

Table 12.2
Acreages harvested from irrigated lands for some fruit and truck crops.

Crop	Acres harvested from irrigated land	Percentage
Truck crops		
Alfalfa	5,210,000	18.5
Cotton	3,769,000	27.1
Sorghum	3,378,000	22.6
All corn	2,428,000	3.8
Land in orchards	2,203,000	51.8
All wheat	1,964,000	4.1
Rice	1,815,000	100.0
Barley	1,504,000	15.3
Sugar beets	1,099,000	79.9
Irish potatoes	609,000	51.9
Dry beans	601,000	44.9
Soybeans	427,000	1.4
Oats	300,000	1.6
Fruits and vegetables		
Tomatoes	252,000	64.8
Lettuce	202,000	96.1
Cantaloupe	93,800	75.5
Carrots	72,000	90.1
Watermelon	46,000	18.8
Lima beans	33,500	37.5
Celery	30,800	97.0
Radishes	23,200	76.7
Artichokes	8,800	99.1
Brussels sprouts	6,000	91.8
Parsley	2,400	87.8

Source: 1964 data from United States Bureau of the Census, *Census of Agriculture, 1964,* vol. II, chap. 9, "Irrigation, Land Improvement Practices, and Use of Agricultural Chemicals" (Washington, D.C., 1968), p. 921.

Water for irrigation requires large reservoirs that are often so far from the lands to be irrigated that canals, pipelines, and pumping stations are also needed. These all have an impact upon the environment. We consider in Chapter 14 the varied effects of a large project constructed to provide irrigation waters — the Aswan Dam.

There are many costs associated with expanding agriculture into arid regions. There will probably not be any substantial expansion until rainfall patterns can be altered to increase precipitation over desert areas. However, we have already seen that the possible environmental impact of such changes demands that we proceed very slowly with climate modification. It may be possible to expand into arid regions near oceans if the costs of desalinization can be lowered enough to make sea water economically feasible for irrigation.

It is evident that most of the arable land of the world is already being farmed. Expansion into new lands will be costly and must await new technology. Thus if we are to increase the earth's food carrying capacity for man in the immediate future, we must turn our attention to increasing production on lands already under cultivation.

INCREASED PRODUCTION FROM PRESENT LANDS

Green Revolution

Since 1950 well over 70 percent of the increase in the world's production of grain has been the result of increasing yields on land already in production. Much of this increase has resulted from the development of higher-yielding crop varieties. Improved varieties have let Mexico change from an importer to an exporter of wheat. The Philippines, which formerly imported a million tons of rice a year, may soon be exporting it. To varying degrees, this *green revolution* has also increased yields in many countries in South America, Asia, and North Africa (Figures 12.10, 12.11). The increase has in most cases been greater than the demands of the increasing population, so these countries now have a greater per capita availability of food (Table 12.3).

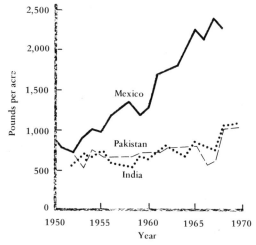

Figure 12.10
Trends in production of wheat in three countries where improved varieties have been introduced. *(Redrawn with permission from Lester Brown, Seeds of Change: The Green Revolution and Development in the 1970's [New York: Praeger Publishers, 1970], p. 39.)*

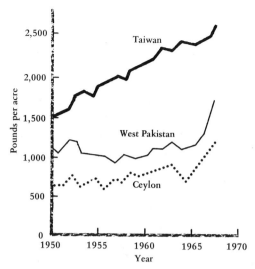

Figure 12.11
Trends in production of rice in three countries where improved varieties have been introduced. *(Redrawn with permission from Lester Brown,* Seeds of Change: The Green Revolution and Development in the 1970's *[New York: Praeger Publishers, 1970], p. 37.)*

Table 12.3
Increase in per capita production of cereal resulting from the use of new seeds (in pounds per capita).

	India: wheat	Pakistan: wheat	Ceylon: rice	Mexico: all cereals
1960	53	87	201	495
1961	55	83	196	496
1962	59	87	213	525
1963	51	86	218	546
1964	46	83	213	611
1965	56	90	150	639
1966	46	71	188	649
1967	49	80	216	655
1968	76	116	247	680
1969	80	121	—	—

Source: Reprinted with permission from Lester Brown, *Seeds of Change: The Green Revolution and Development in the 1970's* (New York: Praeger Publishers, 1970), p. 140.

Limitations on
Green Revolution

WATER MANAGEMENT

The green revolution is not, however, a universal phenomenon. It has been limited largely to rice and wheat crops and to countries that practice sound water management. The new varieties of wheat require high moisture, so to obtain the high yields they must be grown in areas of high rainfall or adequate irrigation. The new rice varieties do not yield well where they are submerged for some time, so natural flooding must be controlled. Effective water management is, therefore, essential for the success of the green revolution.

FERTILIZERS

Water management is not the only factor necessary to achieve the potentially high yields. Potential yield cannot be met without increasing soil nutrient content. It is interesting to note the difference in response to fertilizers by the new and old varieties of rice and wheat (Figure 12.12). The old varieties are not responsive to heavy applications of fertilizers, and overuse causes the grain heads to become too heavy for their tall, spindly shoots. The plants subsequently fall over, making them difficult to harvest and increasing losses to spoilage and pests. The new varieties have been genetically engineered; they are shorter, with thicker stems that can support the heavier heads of grain, and are sometimes referred to as dwarf varieties.

It has been estimated that if food demands are to be met, the use of fertilizers will triple by the end of the century. How will this increased fertilizer need be met? Fertilizers contain three major nutrients – nitrogen, phosphorus, and potassium. Technology has been developed to take nitrogen gas out of the air and to convert it to forms that plants can use (ammonium salts and nitrates). Because 80 percent of the atmosphere is nitrogen, there is a tremendous abundance of this resource. Phosphorus and potassium are extracted from lithospheric deposits. Although there are presently sufficient resources of these two nutrients, future costs are likely to increase as supplies, particularly of phosphorus, are depleted. The costs of extracting and processing lower-grade deposits will also rise.

A more immediate problem is the unequal world distribution of fertilizer deposits. The United States has large reserves, but some countries such as India are seriously deficient. In addition, many countries that do not have the reserves also lack the financial resources to

Figure 12.12
The shorter IR rice on the right can actually produce more grain per acre because these dwarf varieties can support heavier grain heads and are more efficient in fertilizer utilization than the longer variety on the left. *(The International Rice Research Institute.)*

obtain them. Difficult problems of national and international trade and politics must be solved.

A third requirement for success of the green revolution is the use of pesticides, which have been discussed in Chapter 11.

PESTICIDES

There are other problems that must be solved if the green revolution is to meet its potential of decreasing hunger, problems that are not directly related to the environment but are worthy of at least brief discussion.

ECONOMICS

Increased food production does not necessarily mean that the food is reaching hungry people. This is well illustrated even here at home. Although the United States has a more than ample food supply and a per capita income of $1,321 (1968), the McGovern Senate Select

Committee on Nutrition and Human Needs found in 1969 that millions of people in this country were hungry. If poor Americans cannot afford proper food, how will they get it? Food-stamp programs and efforts to help the poor to be self-sufficient have met with limited success. The situation is much worse in developing countries where the average annual income per person is approximately $100 and the government cannot support the masses. Thus, increased production in the field does not ensure that a corresponding number of people will be fed.

There is also a potential problem regarding world markets. Mexico now competes with Canada and the United States in the world wheat market. If the economic status of poor countries does not improve and there is no market for these excess grains, the wheat farmer will not receive as high a price for his crops. If farmers lose incentive and production decreases, even more people will be numbered among the hungry.

INCREASED PRODUCTION BY INNOVATION

One technique for increasing the Earth's food carrying capacity for man is that of growing unicellular organisms such as yeast on certain petroleum by-products. There are now a few experimental plants producing high protein yeasts (approximately 50 percent protein) that are then fed to cattle. It is hoped that the yeast can be eaten by humans, but such technology requires further development.

Perhaps the most successful innovations are in the area of substituting vegetable products for animal products. This places man lower on the food chain, thereby increasing the carrying capacity. The use of oleomargarine is an example. Oleomargarine, which is converted from vegetable oils, has largely replaced butter. In 1940, an average of 14 pounds (6.4 kilograms) of butter and only 2 pounds (0.91 kilograms) of oleomargarine were consumed by Americans. By 1970 the reverse was true, an average of 10 pounds of oleomargarine for every 6 pounds of butter.

A recent innovation is the substitution of vegetable protein for animal protein; technology is now available to make "vegetableburgers." Via new techniques, vegetable proteins can be spun into fibers that can be pressed together, flavored, and colored to simulate various meats. These are now produced only in small quantities, but if they become economically competitive and tastier, man will have taken a big link out of the food chain.

INCREASED PRODUCTION FROM THE SEAS

Potential-Improved Technology

Thus far, our attention has been focused upon terrestrial food production; let us now consider the oceans as food resources. There has been much speculation that farming the sea will solve many of the world's food problems, but most projections indicate that the most we can expect is to double the current harvest from the sea.

Improved production will be a result of advancements on several fronts. One aspect will be improved methods of detection and harvesting of fish. Echo sounders (sonar) and spotter planes are now used to find schools of fish. Other advances include the use of lights and electrodes to attract fish and improved pumps and nets to land them. Some fishing fleets now include mother ships, spotters, catchers, and floating factories to process the fish quickly (Figure 12.13). In fish farms already being developed in the Far East, part of a lake or a bay is blocked off with an earthen dam. These artificial ponds are stocked with fish, and nutrients are added to hasten growth rates. Research is now directed toward the development of faster-growing varieties of fish that are better adapted to fish farm conditions.

Figure 12.13
This Portuguese fishing vessel off the coast of Greenland has facilities on board for processing the catch. *(Pickerell from Black Star.)*

Limitations on Food from Oceans

FOOD CHAIN INEFFICIENCIES

Increased production from the seas will be significant only in terms of protein, not caloric value. It has been estimated that if food production from the sea is doubled by the year 2000 and if the population growth rate remains stable, the sea could supply 30 percent of the world's minimum protein requirements. However, under the same conditions, the sea could only supply 3 percent of the projected caloric needs. The small supply of calories is another result of food chain dynamics. Aquatic food chains often contain four to six links, compared with two to three links in terrestrial food chains. Because of the 80 to 90 percent inefficiency in energy transfer, only a very small amount of the initially fixed energy remains at the end of a six-link food chain. It would thus seem logical to go to the lower levels of the food chains as we now do with terrestrial systems. However, these organisms are too small and dilute for effective harvesting with present technology; more energy would be lost in labor to harvest the lower organisms than the catch itself would contain.

There is another problem involving food chain inefficiencies. The total world fish catch for the oceans in 1968 was 57 million metric tons (63 million tons) (Figure 12.14). Of this total, 34 million metric tons were consumed directly by man. The remaining 23 million metric tons were made up of the less desirable trash fish, e.g., skates and dogfish, which were processed into fish meal. This process resulted in only five million metric tons of fish meal that was fed to domestic animals, particularly chickens and hogs. As a result of food chain dynamics, most of the energy was lost and we ended up with only one million metric tons of livestock from the five million metric tons of fish meal. Thus a total of 35 million metric tons was available to man from the sea. A large portion of the projected doubling in production will come from increased harvests of trash fish. We may double the harvest, but unless man starts to eat these rough fish directly, much of this "doubling" will not be available to man because of energy lost in processing the rough fish through agricultural food chains.

OVERFISHING

If man expects to maintain this potential level of harvesting, he must be careful to leave sufficient numbers for reproduction, thereby helping to assure a sustained maximum catch. Even today, overfishing is resulting in the decline of takes of East Asian sardine, California sardine,

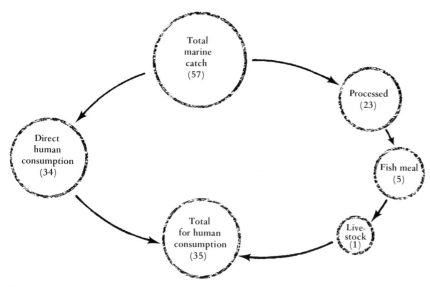

Figure 12.14
Two routes whereby man obtains food from the oceans. Notice the large loss when the catch is passed through agricultural food chains. Values are in millions of metric tons.

Northwest Pacific salmon, Atlantic salmon, Atlantic herring, and the Antarctic blue and fin whales. In addition, the annual harvesting of such species as tuna, cod, perch, and flounder is not increasing despite increased effort. Problems of overfishing will continue without rigorously enforced international agreements on fishery management.

The most productive areas of the oceans are adjacent to the continents: estuaries, reefs, and regions of upwelling (Table 12.4). *Upwelling regions* are areas where nutrient-rich bottom waters come to the surface. The remaining vast expanses of the oceans are essentially biological deserts. The explanation for this is that the requirements of marine producers are the same as those of terrestrial producers: light energy and nutrients. Little light energy penetrates the water to depths beyond 400 feet and the nutrients are more concentrated in the bottom waters. In deeper waters these two essential factors are not present together in sufficient amounts, so producers are almost wholly absent. In contrast, both requirements are available in shallow estuaries (Figure 12.15) and upwellings. High producer populations

PRODUCTIVE AREAS
AND POLLUTION

Table 12.4
Distribution of the estimated productivity of the sea.

Area	Percentage of ocean	Area (sq. miles)	Average no. of feeding levels (approx.)	Annual fish production (metric tons fresh weight)[a]
Open ocean	90	123,000,000	5	1,440,000
Coastal zone	9.9	13,700,000	3	98,000,000
Coastal upwelling areas	0.1	137,000	1.5	98,000,000

Source: Adapted with permission from two tables in John Ryther, "Photosynthesis and Fish Production in the Sea," *Science,* 166 (October 3, 1969), pp. 73 and 74. Copyright 1969 by the American Academy for the Advancement of Science.
[a] 1 metric ton = 1.1 tons.

support high consumer populations, thereby providing larger fish catches for man.

Continental shelf waters are particularly nutrient-rich because they are the terminals for land drainage. We have discussed erosion cycles and the movement of materials to the oceans via rivers and ground water. This is a natural process that has resulted in high productivity near many coastlines.

Unfortunately, the rivers are now transporting, besides increased loads of nutrients from the soil, pesticides and industrial and municipal wastes. When these pollutants reach the ocean, their greatest con-

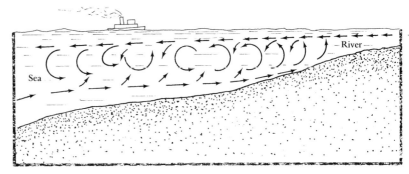

Figure 12.15
Circulation in an estuary illustrating the mixing of lighter fresh water with denser sea water to produce a nutrient trap. *(Redrawn with permission from Eugene Odum, Fundamentals of Ecology, 3rd ed. [Philadelphia: W. B. Saunders Co., 1971], p. 354.)*

centration is near the mouths of the rivers. The same process that once enriched the estuaries is now degrading them. It is ironic that the pesticides and fertilizers used to increase food production on land are now decreasing the quantity and quality of the food supply in the waters.

As man's demand for industrial energy increases, continental shelf areas are being exploited more intensively. The Santa Barbara oil spill and the oil-rig fires in the Gulf of Mexico dramatically demonstrate the potential problems of increased offshore oil drilling. Some shelf areas are also rich in certain mineral deposits, e.g., manganese. Technologies must be developed that will allow offshore exploitation without endangering oceanic ecosystems.

CONCLUSIONS

What conclusions can we make regarding the Earth's carrying capacity for food production? It is always risky to predict the future. In the early 1960s there was considerable fear that famine would be widespread in undeveloped countries by the mid-1970s, but the green revolution has temporarily alleviated the threat.

Projections of carrying capacities vary considerably. A report by the National Academy of Sciences entitled "Resources and Man" estimates that food production could be increased to 10 times the present level. This forecast is based upon the assumption that the problems that we have discussed in this chapter will be solved – a tenuous assumption. Even if this increase were possible, world population, if growth continues at current rates, would match it in only 100 years. There would be nearly 30 billion people, almost all of them on the brink of starvation.

Most investigators suggest that food productivity can be realistically increased to meet the demands of only one more doubling of world population. Dr. Norman Borlaug, who won the Nobel Peace Prize in 1970 for his work on improving wheat varieties, has stated that the green revolution has bought us only 30 years of time, within which the increase in demand must be greatly reduced; i.e., population growth must be brought under control.

There is an increasing belief that our immediate concern ought not to be focused on providing enough food but rather on reducing the environmental degradation that results from attempts to increase yields. Pesticides, fertilizers, and water management are required to increase food production, but we have seen the numerous negative environmental consequences attaching to their use. In addition, these three inputs greatly increase our energy consumption because of energy needed for their construction, extraction, production, transportation, and application. It appears that we are rapidly approaching the point where our attempts to increase food production may well result in a catastrophic deterioration of the Earth's ecosystems.

KEY WORDS
AND SUMMARY
STATEMENTS

| undernourished | laterite | green revolution |
| malnourished | salinization | upwelling regions |

It has been estimated that over half of the world's population is either undernourished or malnourished. Regardless of whether there is enough food to go around today, the yearly increase of 70 million people necessitates a continual effort to increase food production.

There is a potential for expanding agriculture into the tropical and semiarid regions of the world. However, many tropical soils are presently limiting factors to this expansion because of their low fertility and tendency to bake into iron-hard laterite. Expansion into semiarid regions is limited by the availability of water for irrigation and problems of seepage and salinization.

With the development of dwarf varieties of rice and wheat, the green revolution has largely eliminated the immediate threat of mass starvation. In a number of countries, food production is increasing at a greater rate than the population.

Limitations on the green revolution involve factors of availability of resources and technology: water management, fertilizers, pesticides, and economics.

Carrying capacity for food energy may be increased by innovations that allow man to function lower down on the food chain. Such innovations include using vegetable oils (oleomargarine) in place of butter and processing vegetable proteins into meat substitutes.

Harvesting of food from the oceans can be increased by improving methods of detection and harvesting of fish, using fish farms, and developing faster-growing varieties of fish.

Limitations on production from the sea include inefficiencies in energy transfer along food chains, overfishing, and pollution of productive estuaries and reefs.

Although estimates of the potential carrying capacity of the earth for man's food energy vary widely, most estimates suggest that food productivity can be only doubled.

There is increasing concern that the environmental degradation resulting from attempts to increase the food supply will become more limiting than the food supply itself.

QUESTIONS AND
PROJECTS

1. It could be postulated that children whose mental and physical abilities are impaired by protein or vitamin deficient diets are parasites on society. Comment on the validity of this statement. Is this a population-controlling mechanism?

2. Comment on the similarities between man's attempts to farm marginal lands and the consequences of intense intraspecific competition.

3. Although the tropics receive more solar energy than the temperate regions, most of the hungry people live in the tropics. Comment on this apparent paradox.

4. A large percentage of the fruits and vegetables produced in the United States are grown on irrigated lands. In view of the fact that irrigation is a consumptive use of water, what value has this produce? Can we get along without it and use the water for other purposes?

5. Man is now taking more than 40 million tons of nitrogen out of the air and adding it to the soil annually. What effects might this new transfer have on the environment?

6. Because of illiteracy and adherence to tradition, it was once thought that it would be difficult to convince farmers in the undeveloped countries to grow the new dwarf varieties. However, once they saw the economic gains made by farmers who did plant the new seeds, they too adopted these varieties. How does this example show the need for incentives to solve our environmental problems?

7. Estuaries cannot serve both as food sources and as landfill sites for development. What criteria would you use to evaluate the more important usage?

8. It has been estimated that the fish protein now harvested from the sea would supply the world's minimum protein requirements. Instead, the fish are fed to chickens, hogs, and cats in developed countries. What problems must be solved to use fish protein to eliminate long-term protein deficiencies?

SELECTED
READINGS

Borgstrom, G. *Too Many.* New York: Macmillan, 1969. An interesting look at many factors necessary for increasing food production.

Brown, Lester R. *Seeds of Change: The Green Revolution and Development in the 1970's.* New York: Praeger, 1970. An examination of the past, present, and future of the green revolution.

Brown, Lester R., and Finsterbusch, Gail W. *Man and His Environment: Food.*
New York: Harper and Row, 1972. An examination of the varied social and
economic as well as environmental aspects of man's attempts to feed his
growing numbers.

Holt, S. J. "The Food Resources of the Ocean." *Scientific American,* vol. 221,
no. 3 (September 1969), pp. 178-194. The potential and limitations of
man's harvest of the oceans.

National Academy of Science–National Resource Council. *Resources and Man.*
San Francisco: Freeman, 1969. Chapters 1, 4, and 5 discuss many aspects
of the earth's carrying capacity for food energy.

chapter

13

Human Carrying Capacity: Industrial Energy

Having considered the Earth's carrying capacity of food energy, let us now consider an aspect of carrying capacity that is unique to man. We have seen that carrying capacity may be determined by the amount of resources that each individual requires from the environment. For all species except man, this consumptive level per individual remains constant for each environmental requirement. However, the demands of an industrial society make us unique members of the biosphere. Our per capita level of consumption of resources such as metals, minerals, and fossil fuels has not remained constant but has been increasing rapidly with our rising standard of living. The reserves of these non-renewable resources are rapidly being depleted, so the Earth's carrying capacity for these resources is therefore decreasing.

A good example of this phenomenon is man's demand for power to run industry, commerce, farms, and residences. Primitive man's energy demands were largely limited to food energy and amounted to approximately 8.6×10^5 kilocalories (1,000 kilowatt hours) per year. Today, in the United States, an average 7.3×10^7 kilocalories (85,000) kilowatt hours) per year is required to meet our individual demands (Table 13.1). Although our per capita energy consumption has increased far more quickly than the world average, Figure 13.1 indicates that increased energy consumption is becoming common to more countries as economic development progresses.

INCREASED
PER CAPITA
CONSUMPTION

325

Table 13.1
Breakdown of fuel consumption in the United States (in percentages).

Consuming sector	1947	1955	1965
Household and commercial	20.4	21.6	21.9
Industrial	38.2	34.7	32.6
Transportation	26.5	24.6	23.6
Electrical utilities	13.3	16.7	20.7
Other	1.6	2.4	1.2
Total energy in calories per year	0.84×10^{19}	1.01×10^{19}	1.35×10^{19}

Source: Adapted with permission from *U.S. Energy Policies—An Agenda for Research.* © 1968 by Resources for the Future, Inc. Distributed by The Johns Hopkins Press.

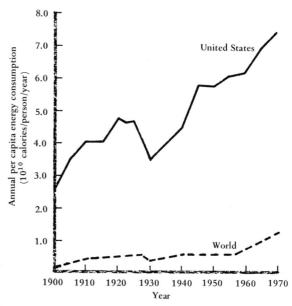

Figure 13.1
Per capita annual energy consumption for the world and the United States. *(Adapted and redrawn with permission of Holt, Rinehart and Winston, Inc., from John Harte and Robert H. Socolow,* Patient Earth, *p. 286. Copyright © 1971 by Holt, Rinehart and Winston, Inc.)*

We get a better idea of the magnitude of increased power consumption by considering the use of electrical power in the United States

(Figure 13.2). In 1950 per capita consumption was 2,000 kilowatt hours, and by 1968 it was 6,500 kilowatt hours — an increase of 320 percent. Electric utilities' predictions that power demands will double every 10 years would, by the year 2000, increase per capita consumption to approximately 25,000 kilowatt hours — 12 times that in 1950 (Table 13.2). Meanwhile, the population of the United States will "only double." Electrical power consumption is thus a dramatic example of man's unique characteristic of increased demand per individual.

Figure 13.2
Lines and towers for the transmission of electrical energy frequently create unsightly and even eerie views. (© *Pierre Berger 1971 from Photo Researchers, Inc.*)

Table 13.2
United States electrical power consumption.

	1950	1968	Estimate 1980	Estimate 2000
Population (millions)	152	202	235	320
Total power capacity (millions of kw[a])	85	290	600	1,352
kw capacity/person	0.6	1.4	2.5	4.25
Power consumed per person per year (kw-hr)	2,000	6,500	11,500	25,000
Total consumption (kw-hr)	325 billion	1.3 trillion	2.7 trillion	8 trillion

Source: Adapted with permission from Dean E. Abrahamson, *The Environmental Cost of Electrical Power*, Scientists Institute for Public Information (1970), p. 4.
[a] kw = kilowatt = 8.6×10^5 kilocalories.

CARRYING CAPACITY FOR INDUSTRIAL ENERGY

We hear much today about the great expectations of undeveloped countries for increasing their standard of living. Predicted power demands of the United States indicate that the energy demands of other developed countries will also increase. What, then, is the Earth's carrying capacity for supplying man's future energy demands? Are there enough energy reserves to continually increase the world's standard of living?

Fossil Fuels

Fossil fuels today meet about 95 percent of our total energy demand. Although the amount of coal used continues to increase, there has been a shift lately toward the use of oil and natural gas (Figure 13.3). A major reason for this is their lower sulfur content.

However, all three types of fossil fuels are nonrenewable. Thus they will be available for only a limited time. Just how long is a difficult question. Estimates vary widely, but it is generally agreed that within 60 to 70 years, the world will not have the reserves of petroleum and natural gas to maintain the predicted level of consumption at that time. This is not to say that we will run out of gas and oil at that time, but rather that supplies will no longer be able to keep up with demand and costs will be high. Other estimates indicate that the United States has about a 30–35 year supply of petroleum and a 20 year supply of natural gas. Coal reserves are considerably larger. Coal will remain a

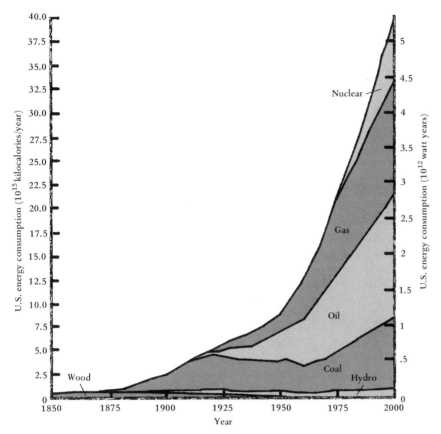

Figure 13.3
Past and projected United States energy consumption, illustrating the contribution of the various energy sources. *(Redrawn with permission from Chauncey Starr, "Energy and Power,"* Scientific American *[September 1971], p. 39. Copyright © by Scientific American, Inc. All rights reserved.)*

major energy source for two or three more centuries and could take up much of the slack as reserves of petroleum and natural gas are depleted. Table 13.3 indicates the possibility for changes in international relations as fossil fuels become limiting.

There are drawbacks to increased use of coal. We have seen that it is "dirty" fuel, and as we continue to consume reserves, coal of a higher sulfur content will probably be mined, thereby increasing the problems of air pollution. Further exploitation will also mean greater environmental deterioration as a result of extraction methods and acid

Table 13.3
The world's reserves of fossil fuels.

Coal (in 10^{18} metric tons)	
Asia (excluding U.S.S.R.)	681
U.S.S.R. (including European part)	4,310
United States	1,486
North America (excluding U.S.)	601
Western Europe	377
South and Central America	14
Oceania (including Australia)	59
Africa	109
Petroleum (in 10^9 barrels)	
Europe	20
Africa	250
Middle East	600
Far East	200
Latin America	225
Canada	95
United States	200
U.S.S.R. and China	500

Source: Data from the Committee on Resources and Man of the Division of Earth Sciences, National Academy of Sciences-National Research Council, *Resources and Man* [1969], pp. 194 (petroleum) and 203 (coal).

mine wastes. Coal is a long-range energy source, but many problems must be solved so that expanded usage does not result in further environmental deterioration.

Hydroelectric Dams

Another potential source of energy that man is already tapping is the hydroelectric dam. Dams harness part of the energy in the hydrologic cycle by converting the kinetic energy of moving water to electrical energy. Total potential water power capacity is about four times that of today's total installed electric power production, but the world uses only 8 percent of this potential. Even the industrialized North American continent has developed only 19 percent of its potential. Why aren't we building more dams? One reason is that dams are expensive to construct. They may also be far removed from the areas they will serve, which will increase costs for transmission lines. There are also many environmental costs to consider. The land beneath a proposed reservoir may be important as a wildlife habitat or for its aesthetic value. Rich agricultural lands are often inundated by reservoirs. In the case of salmon in the Columbia River we have seen that dams can seriously disrupt the biotic component of rivers. Finally, dams do not have as much potential magnitude for power generation as other sources such as nuclear or solar power. Thus less emphasis is being placed on development of hydroelectric sources of energy.

Two other potential sources are oceanic *tidal energy* and *geothermal energy*. Tidal power may be gained by harnessing energy involved in the daily tidal oscillations. The Earth's interior is a source of heat that is concentrated in certain localities in the form of geysers and hot springs. The thermal energy contained in these hot waters can be tapped. Although both can be of significance locally, they can supply only a small part of the world's power needs.

Tidal and Geothermal Energy

The sun appears to be a logical source of energy to meet our future energy requirements. It certainly can be considered as a renewable energy resource because it will be around for several billion more years. It is also the largest source of energy available to man: The amount of solar energy intercepted by the Earth is about 100,000 times greater than the entire world's presently installed electrical power generating capacity. Less than 1 percent of the sun's energy that strikes the Earth's surface runs the entire biosphere (i.e., the solar energy fixed by photosynthesis). But there are problems in harnessing solar energy in sufficient quantities to meet our potential requirements. Two physical limitations must be considered. The efficiency of transforming solar to electrical energy is only about 10 percent. Secondly, the sun's energy is spread over a large area, so a large collecting grid is needed. As a consequence, if we want to match by solar means the power produced by a nuclear plant (500 megawatts), a grid network of about 8 square miles would be required (on a clear day and at mid-latitudes). There is also the need for large batteries to store energy for use at night and during cloudy weather. The technology may become available, but the cost in land and nonrenewable materials to make a sufficient number of grids and storage sites is likely to be prohibitive.

Solar Energy

There is a possibility of using large space-stations to capture solar energy, which could then be beamed down to the earth. However, the technology is not now available, and only speculative estimates can now be made concerning the environmental consequences of such devices.

Nuclear Energy

ADVANTAGES OF
NUCLEAR
ENERGY

Another source of energy lies in the nucleus of the atom. We have seen that the nucleus contains vast amounts of energy. If this source could be managed properly, enough energy would be available to supply man's energy needs for thousands of years. It is partly for this reason that less emphasis is placed on developing the potential of the energy sources presented above. Nuclear power has some additional advantages; pollutants such as sulfur dioxide, nitrogen oxides, and particulates, and coal piles and accompanying dust are absent. However, there are problems with which we must contend.

RESERVES OF
FISSIONABLE ISOTOPES

Nuclear power plants in use or presently under construction employ nuclear fission reactions to release the energy within the nuclei of atoms. These reactions involve the splitting of a nucleus into 2 parts, which releases huge amounts of energy. These nuclear reactions take place within fuel cells that make up part of the reactor core (Figure 13.4). The fuel cells contain the two uranium isotopes, U-235 and U-238. Of these two, only the U-235 nucleus can capture a slow-moving neutron and fission, thereby sustaining a chain reaction (Figure 13.5). However, naturally occurring uranium is made up of only 0.7

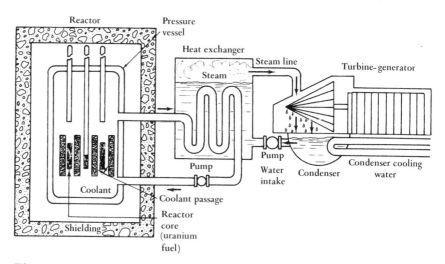

Figure 13.4
A schematic diagram of a nuclear fission power reactor used to generate electricity.

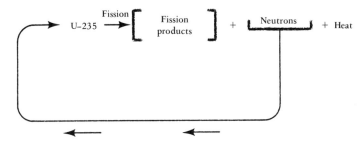

Figure 13.5
Schematic representation of a nuclear power reactor for the fissioning of Uranium-235. When an atom of U-235 captures a neutron, the resulting unstable atom splits, producing two different atoms (fission products) plus additional neutrons that can be captured by other atoms of U-235. *(Redrawn with permission from M. King Hubbert, "Nuclear Energy and the Fossil Fuels," American Petroleum Institute, Drilling and Production Practice [1956], p. 20.)*

percent of U-235, the remainder (99.3 percent) being U-238. Current low-cost reserves of U-235 will last only 20 to 30 years, beyond which fission by U-235 may no longer be possible.

An alternative to the small supply of fissionable U-235 is the *breeder reactor.* Under proper conditions, these currently experimental reactors can convert the isotopes U-238 and thorium-232 to plutonium-239 and uranium-233 respectively, both of which are fissionable. In a breeder reactor, the fuel cells contain either U-238 or Th-232. When a nuclear chain reaction is sustained in the presence of these isotopes (U-238 and Th-232) they capture some of the neutrons and are converted to fissionable isotopes (Figure 13.6). The reactions of U-238 are:

$$\text{Step 1:}\quad {}^{238}_{92}\text{U} \;+\; {}^{1}_{0}n \;\rightarrow\; {}^{239}_{92}\text{U}.$$

$$\text{Step 2:}\quad {}^{239}_{92}\text{U} \;\rightarrow\; {}^{239}_{93}\text{Np} \;+\; {}^{0}_{-1}e.$$

$$\text{Step 3:}\quad {}^{239}_{93}\text{Np} \;\rightarrow\; {}^{239}_{94}\text{Pu} \;+\; {}^{0}_{-1}e.$$
$$\text{(fission-}$$
$$\text{able)}$$

Thus as the reactor operates, more fissionable material is produced. In fact, these reactors actually breed more fissionable material than is used up in the chain reactions. An additional advantage of these reac-

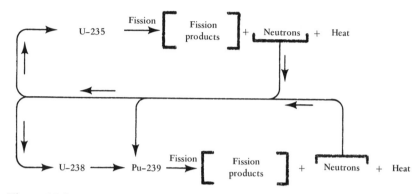

Figure 13.6
Schematic representation of a breeder reactor for Uranium-238. *(Redrawn with permission from M. King Hubbert, "Nuclear Energy and the Fossil Fuels," American Petroleum Institute, Drilling and Production Practice [1956], p. 20.)*

tors is that they can use the more abundant isotopes to produce energy, but U-235 is still needed to begin the chain reaction.

It is important, however, to remember that these reactors are still in the research stage of development and will probably not be commercially available until the 1980s. In fact, it was not until 1971 that the United States government decided to appropriate funds for hastening the development of breeder technology. If present nuclear power plants and those under construction are to function as breeder reactors or use the new fissionable products (Pu-239 or U-233), they may well require extensive modification.

EFFECTS OF
RADIOACTIVE WASTES
ON ORGANISMS

In addition to the energy produced in the fission reactor, over 200 different isotopes are also formed. Most of these are radioactive, and small amounts of them are normally released into the environment from nuclear power plants. Other man-made sources of radioactive wastes include weapons testing and hospital and research laboratories that make use of radioactive isotopes.

Radioactive wastes are of concern because of their effects on organisms. The energy present in the particles released by these wastes can be sufficient to disrupt the molecular architecture of an organism. Cancer of the blood (leukemia) and skin cancer can be caused by exposure to high radiation levels. Radioactive rays are also known to break chromosome molecules, which can produce molecular rearrangements (mutations). Chromosome damage in the sex cells, for example, may lead to various physical deformities and mental retardation of offspring.

The biological effects of dilute radioactive wastes have been the subject of considerable controversy. We are exposed daily to natural background radiation from cosmic rays and naturally occurring radio-active isotopes in the Earth's crust such as U-238, thorium-232, and potassium-40 (Table 13.4). Because the levels of background radiation are greater than the levels of man-induced radiation, some people play down the latter. They neglect, however, the fact that exposure to radiation has an additive, or cumulative, effect. Man's radioactive wastes are added to the natural background, thus exposing him to a greater total amount of radiation. Furthermore, some scientists believe that there is no threshold value for radiation damage. They state that the variation in the tolerance ranges of individuals in the human population is such that increasing the radiation by just a small amount will be injurious to more members of the population. Other experts state that there is a definite threshold value and that as long as exposure levels are below the threshold, there will be no harmful effects from

DILUTE EMISSIONS
AND FOOD CHAIN
ACCUMULATION

Table 13.4
Sources of radiation to persons in the United States.

Source	Dose per year (millirads)[a]
Man-made	
Diagnostic X-ray (1964)	55
Therapeutic X-ray (1964)	10
Radioactive fallout (1964)	9
Nuclear industry (1970)	1
Subtotal	75
Natural	
Terrestrial radiation, external to body	60
Cosmic rays	30
Radioisotopes, internal to body	25
Subtotal	115
Total	190

Source: Reprinted with permission of Holt, Rinehart and Winston, Inc., from John Harte and Robert H. Socolow, *Patient Earth*, p. 309. Copyright © 1971 by Holt, Rinehart and Winston, Inc.
[a] 1 millirad = 0.24×10^{-8} calories per gram of absorbing material.

radioactive wastes. Resolution of the controversy awaits further research.

Some of the more troublesome radioactive wastes of fission are iodine-131, strontium-90, and cesium-137, all beta emitters. Although beta particles have relatively low penetrating power, they can cause serious localized damage if they are taken into the body. In addition, their persistence (half-lives of 28 years for Sr-90 and 33 years for Cs-137) allows them to accumulate in food chains before complete decay.

Food chain accumulation of radioisotopes has been well documented. The complicated movement of radioisotopes in ecosystems is illustrated by the lichen-caribou-Eskimo food chain. The Alaskan tundra ecosystem was contaminated by atmospheric fallout from nuclear weapons testing. Researchers found a doubling of Cs-137 concentration at each successive link in the chain (Figure 13.7). However, Sr-90 concentration only doubled in the caribou, and little was present in the Eskimos. Because Cs-137 substitutes for potassium (both are in the same column of the periodic table), it is concentrated in muscle tissue of the caribou, whereas Sr-90 substitutes for calcium (also in the same column of the periodic table) and is concentrated in bones. The Eskimos eat the caribou meat but not the bones; hence, they accumulate Cs-137 but little Sr-90.

The uptake of these radioactive wastes by plants also presents complications. If calcium is present in the soil, it will be taken up preferentially over the Sr-90 even if larger amounts of Sr-90 are present. Arctic tundra soils, however, are poor in nutrients, so Sr-90 does enter the lichens. Cesium-137, on the other hand, is not taken into the plants, but strongly adheres to the lichens. In either case, the radioisotopes are taken in by the caribou when it eats the lichens.

Another complicating factor is *biological half-time*, i.e., the period required for half of an ingested material to be excreted from the body. Although Cs-137 has a long radioactive half-life, its biological half-time in the caribou is only three to five weeks. But since the caribou eat more often than once every three to five weeks, they will accumulate greater amounts of Cs-137 if they continue to feed on contaminated lichens. The biological half-time of Cs-137 in the Eskimos is double that of the caribou. For lichens the biological half-time is 13 years. Thus the lichens will remain a contaminated food source for a long time.

Figure 13.7
The pattern of accumulation of two radioisotopes in an arctic tundra ecosystem. Cesium-137 *(figure A)* accumulates in lichens from atmospheric fallout. When caribou eat the lichens, increased concentrations of Cs-137 accumulate in their muscles. Eskimos, who eat caribou meat, acquire still greater concentrations of Cs-137 in their muscles. Strontium-90 *(figure B)* also accumulates in lichens, but because increased concentrations of it appear in the caribou bones, which Eskimos do not eat, it does not accumulate in the Eskimos. (Black dots indicate concentration of radioisotopes.)

The Eskimo case history demonstrates that the movement of isotopes through food chains depends upon the chemical properties of the isotope, the characteristics of the members of the food chain, and conditions in the abiotic spheres. As expected, many interrelated environmental factors affect the movement of radioisotopes, just as they affect the movement of any element in the ecosystem. It should come as no surprise that synthetically produced radioactive wastes are cycled through ecosystems and accumulate in food chains.

Although radioactive wastes can accumulate in food chains, the very dilute wastes released into the environment by nuclear power plants are probably not as yet a significant problem. In view of the controversy over the threshold for radiation damage, however, power plants should be required to reduce waste emissions to the lowest technologically feasible levels.

CONCENTRATED WASTES

Of perhaps much greater potential danger than dilute wastes are the concentrated wastes stored underground. After one to two years of operation the fuel cells become depleted of fissionable U-235 and contaminated with radioactive fission products. A reactor must be shut down and the fuel cells reprocessed. The remaining U-235 is separated from the wastes and repacked into new fuel cells. Presently, the concentrated wastes are stored in huge underground concrete silos at four locations in the United States (Figure 13.8). These wastes have to be

Figure 13.8
Huge tanks such as these being constructed at the Atomic Energy Commission's Hanford facility near Richland, Washington, are used to store radioactive wastes. *(Battelle-Northwest, U.S. Atomic Energy Commission.)*

constantly mixed to prevent "hot spots" from forming; cold water continually flows around the waste containers within the silos to provide further cooling. Unfortunately, there is evidence that some of the silos at the Hanford, Washington, plant are leaking and that the seepage is being carried toward the Columbia River by the ground-water flow.

It is estimated that the Hanford Plant, which was the first installed by the Atomic Energy Commission, already contains more radioactive wastes in its silos than would be released in an all-out nuclear war. As of 1969, 80 million gallons of concentrated nuclear fuel wastes were stored in 200 underground tanks at the four storage sites. With some 90 more nuclear power plants to be operating within the coming decade, safe storage of this waste represents the most serious potential environmental hazard of the nuclear power industry. To avoid problems associated with silos, the Atomic Energy Commission is studying the use of salt mines and deep rock strata as safer places for storage. Because of the long half-lives of many of these wastes, future generations will have to watch over these wastes for at least 600 years. Implicit is the assumption that our society will remain stable throughout this period — an unlikely event in view of past history. This is a unique legacy that we leave for our children.

With the trend toward more and larger nuclear power plants, there is growing concern over what to do with excess heat energy produced by the power plants. Present-day nuclear power plants transform only about 32 percent of the potential energy into electrical energy, fossil-fuel plants about 40 percent.

THERMAL POLLUTION

It is estimated that by 1980, power plants will require a volume of water for cooling equal to one-sixth of the annual runoff in the United States. We know from observation that runoff is seasonal; rivers may overflow their banks in spring, but the flow is usually low in the late summer. During periods of low flow, power plants could heat the entire flow of a river by 10–20°F (5–10°C). All the nuclear power plants are situated next to oceans or large lakes and rivers (Figure 13.9). With the trend toward larger power plants, smaller aquatic ecosystems cannot handle the larger heat discharge. There remains considerable controversy today over the effects of thermal discharge on the larger bodies of water; some of its known effects on aquatic organisms (and the alternatives to such discharge) are discussed in Chapter 9.

Legend

Operable	■	(23)
Being built	▲	(54)
Planned(reactors ordered)	●	(52)

Figure 13.9
Location of nuclear power plants in the United States. To provide sufficient water for cooling, they are situated adjacent to large rivers, lakes, or the oceans. *(From Annual Report to Congress of the Atomic Energy Commission [January 1972], p. 33.)*

CONCLUSIONS

The impact of increasing and expanding energy exploitation can be divided into three phases: production, processing, and utilization. In production (or extraction), land is disrupted by coal, oil, and uranium mining. Acid mine wastes degrade surface and ground waters. Solar grids covering large tracts of land would make them unusable for agriculture. Hydroelectric installations induce filling of river channels. Oil spills are a continual hazard of offshore drilling and transport. In processing, disposal of waste products is the major problem. Depending upon the physical and chemical properties of these effluents, they exert environmental consequences of varying significance and extent, sometimes very extreme. In utilization, pollutants are emitted into the atmosphere by the combustion of fossil fuels. Power plants raise the temperature of surface waters. Thermal energy is concentrated in cities, bringing about local air circulation patterns that concentrate smoke and grime.

Man's multiphase utilization of energy is thus exerting a two-fold effect upon the environment: an alteration of the composition of the four spheres and an acceleration in the rates of energy exchange among the spheres. In most instances these changes in energy have disrupted the spheres. It now appears that the environment contains sufficient energy to meet our future demands, but as with our quest for food energy the environmental degradation associated with production, processing, and utilization may be our limiting factor.

tidal energy   breeder reactor   biological half-time
geothermal energy

KEY WORDS AND SUMMARY STATEMENTS

Man's demand for energy is increasing rapidly as all countries strive to raise their standard of living.

Fossil fuels currently meet about 95 percent of man's energy demands, but they are nonrenewable. It is estimated that within 60–70 years the supply of petroleum and natural gas will no longer be able to keep up with demand. However, coal will remain a major energy source for two to three more centuries.

Although man has only tapped about 8 percent of the potential energy from flowing water, fewer dams are being constructed because of high costs, environmental degradation, and the fact that solar and nuclear energy have much greater potential energy outputs.

Tidal and geothermal energy are only of local significance.

The sun is an enormous source of energy and can be considered as a renewable energy source. Problems associated with a low efficiency of conversion from solar to electrical energy, dispersal of the sun's energy over the earth's surface, and batteries to store the energy remain to be overcome.

Nuclear energy has the potential for supplying man's needs for thousands of years. One limitation, however, is that the current nuclear power plants require the use of uranium-235, which is in short supply. An answer may be breeder reactors, but their commercial operation is at least a decade away.

The radioactive breakdown products of fission reactors can cause cancer and even death. Although the levels of background radiation to which we are exposed are greater than those of man-induced radiation, exposure to all sources of radiation has an additive, or cumulative, effect.

There is considerable controversy over the presence or lack of a known exposure threshold for radiation damage.

Some radioactive isotopes can be accumulated in food chains.

After reprocessing fuel cells, concentrated radioactive wastes are currently stored in underground silos where they are continually mixed and cooled. They will remain a potential hazard for generations to come.

Because of large thermal discharges, nuclear power plants must be situated near large bodies of water. Additional means of dissipating the excess heat may also be required.

It appears that we have sufficient energy sources available, but as with our quest for food energy, the environmental degradation resulting from the consumption of energy resources may be man's limiting factor.

QUESTIONS AND PROJECTS

1. In view of recent shortages of electrical power in the United States, comment on the price structure of electric power, i.e., the system of decreasing costs for increasing consumption.

2. Continual exploitation of energy sources creates conflicts with the management of other resources. Find examples in your locale and give possible alternatives to such conflicts.

3. Carrying capacity is determined by the resource demand per individual. Does there exist an optimal demand for power?

4. Is it possible for the United States to fulfill its projected energy demands without conflicts of interest with other countries?

5. There is evidence that even natural background radiation is harmful to some people. What is the importance of such evidence in light of the higher levels of radiation from man-made sources?

6. How would you reduce power consumption? Can it be done without lowering our standard of living?

7. Radioactive wastes have been called our chief pollutants because of their very long half-lives. Would you agree with this?

8. How would you assess the benefits of the atom (electricity, treatment of diseases, preservation of food) against the costs of human health and environmental degradation? What are the alternatives?

SELECTED READINGS

Cook, Earl. "Ionizing Radiation." In *Environment: Resources, Pollution, and Society,* edited by W. W. Murdoch. Stamford, Conn.: Sinauer, 1971. A look at the sources of radiation and the resultant environmental degradation. Examines the "no threshold" controversy.

"Energy and Power." *Scientific American*, vol. 224, no. 3 (September 1971). A series of articles dealing with energy resources, uses, and future decisions on the production of power.

Harte, John, and Socolow, Robert H. *Patient Earth*. New York: Holt, Rinehart and Winston, 1971. Chapters 17 and 18 consider the many aspects of our energy consumption and the sources and biological effects of radiation.

Novick, S. *The Careless Atom*. Boston: Houghton Mifflin, 1969. Examination of the problems associated with nuclear reactors.

chapter

14

The Shortcomings of Technology

We have illustrated in the previous chapters that many of our environmental problems can be at least partially solved by technology; we should realize, though, that it has negative as well as beneficial aspects. The most underrated factor in the traditional analysis of population versus resources is the environmental impact of the technology that is used in attempting to bring about a balance. As Georg Borgstrom put it, technology "has grossly underrated the magnitude of the actual needs and its true tasks. On the whole, we can say that technology is an indispensable prerequisite for man's existence and progress. But it has bitten off more than it can chew."*

One of the classic examples of the negative aspects of technology is the Aswan Dam on the Nile River in Egypt (Figure 14.1). The $1.5 billion dam, built over a period of 10 years, was intended to solve some of Egypt's many complex problems. When an irrigation system is completed in 1975, the water behind the dam will put some 1.3 million additional acres into needed agricultural production to feed Egypt's swelling numbers. The dam also provides hydroelectric power to stimulate industrialization. This in turn is expected to provide jobs and

NEGATIVE TECHNOLOGY: THE ASWAN DAM

---

* Georg Borgstrom, *The Hungry Planet* (New York: Macmillan, 1965), p. 431.

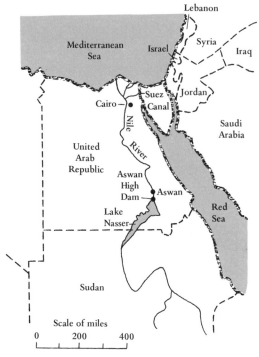

Figure 14.1
Location of the Aswan Dam and Lake Nasser in Egypt.

raise the country's standard of living. There are, however, costs that are only now being recognized. Figure 14.2 shows some of the cultural destruction. The following discussion relates some of the changes that have occurred within ecosystems associated with Nile waters.

Damming the river has interrupted the natural cycling process of many nutrients. Instead of being carried to the oceans, the nutrients are deposited behind the dam. This change in rate of nutrient transfer from land to ocean results in many alterations of the Nile's dependent ecosystems. Before being dammed the Nile flooded yearly, depositing silt and associated nutrients in the Nile Valley and Delta – a process that took place for thousands of years. Because these nutrients are no longer added naturally, fertile soils are becoming nutrient-deficient and need fertilizing to maintain high crop yields. Egypt has resources available to provide the needed fertilizer, but this represents additional costs to the Egyptian farmer for food production.

Figure 14.2
Many of Egypt's remarkable ancient monuments were flooded by the
Aswan Dam project. *Top:* Remains of the village of Semna, Egypt's
southern frontier in 2000 B.C. *Above:* This temple, dedicated to the
goddess Isis, is now permanently half-submerged. *Right:* This Nubian
monument was preserved by cutting and moving blocks weighing up to
thirty tons. (Top and above: *Authenticated News International.* Right:
Nenadovic, UNESCO.)

The sardine industry has been virtually destroyed off the Nile Delta. The catch has decreased from a yearly harvest of 18,000 tons to 500 tons (a $7 million annual loss). This is related to a combination of two events, both resulting from the construction of the dam. The nutrient content of the Nile waters is now considered the limiting factor controlling the producer populations that are subsequently eaten by the sardines. Secondly, the decrease in the flow of the Nile below the dam has increased the salt concentration of the delta waters, perhaps yet another important limiting factor. It is of little significance which effect is more important; both are results of decreased flow caused by the dam.

Some of the sardine losses are offset by fishing deeper waters, which was made possible by Soviet loans of special fishing boats. However, this does not negate the fact that another food-producing area has been lost. Some of these fishing losses may be regained by fishing Lake Nasser behind the dam, but this necessitates the considerable expense of relocating the people and facilities in the fishing industry.

The decreased flow of the Nile has yet another consequence. A river delta is the result of two opposing forces — expansion of the delta by sedimentation of the river and erosion of the delta by ocean or sea waves. With decreased sediment load sea waves are now cutting back the delta lands. The resultant land submergence is dislocating people and decreasing cultivatable lands. Salt-water intrusion into the ground water is also becoming a major problem.

One benefit of the dam is to extend the previously seasonal irrigation to a year-round operation. This allows the cultivation of additional crops. Although continual irrigation greatly benefits Egyptian agriculture, the constantly filled irrigation ditches also pose health problems for the Egyptians. These canals are breeding sites for species of snails that serve as hosts for schistosomes (blood flukes) (Figure 14.3). This parasite causes schistosomiasis (snail fever) in man. Although the disease is essentially unknown in the United States, it is now the most common human disease and affects one out of every 14 people in the world. The symptoms can take several forms depending upon the species of fluke, but all are very painful and result in general debilitation. Infected individuals become nonproductive members of society.

The blood fluke requires the presence of the snail to complete its life cycle (Figure 14.4). With the continual presence of water the snails are always present, increasing the number of people infected and rein-

Figure 14.3
A male schistosome *(Schistosoma haematobium),* a species of blood fluke that causes schistosomiasis in man. *(Science Software Systems, Inc.)*

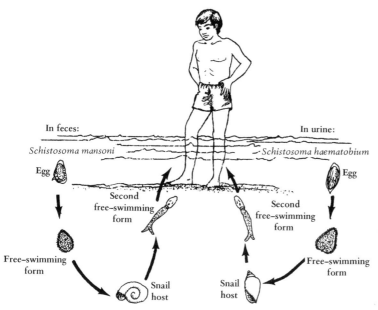

In feces: In urine:

Schistosoma mansoni   *Schistosoma hæmatobium*

Egg   Egg

Second
free-swimming
form

Second
free-swimming
form

Free-swimming
form

Free-swimming
form

Snail
host

Snail
host

Figure 14.4
The life cycles of two species of blood flukes. Upon contact with water, eggs hatch and the free-swimming form of each species infects its species of snail host. The emerging second free-swimming form penetrates directly into human skin. People can be infected while swimming, bathing, washing clothes, or engaging in any activity that involves contact with water containing the blood flukes. *(Modified with permission from Peter Jordan and Gerald Webb,* Human Schistosomiasis *[London: William Heinemann Medical Books, Ltd., 1969], p. 7.)*

fected. This effect has been well documented in Sudan and Rhodesia, where the advent of year-round irrigation has resulted in the increased incidence of schistosomiasis from a few percent to well over half of the population.

This situation is aggravated in that the continuously filled ditches promote another species of snail that harbors a blood fluke *(S. mansoni)* more harmful than the one that inhabits seasonally filled canals. Thus not only has continuous irrigation fostered conditions for more infections and reinfections, but a more virulent blood fluke is now common.

It is too early to adequately weigh the benefits and costs of the Aswan Dam, but some general trends are emerging. The huge project will provide power and stimulate industry, creating more jobs. However, it will also cause much misery from schistosomiasis and the dislocation of people caused by filling the reservoir and the loss of the delta area. As often is the case, the people who receive the benefits of technology are not the ones who must bear most of the burden of its costs.

It also now seems likely that the dam alone will not solve Egypt's food problems. Its population will increase by more than 9 million between the 1960 start of the dam and 1975, target date for the completion of the irrigation system. Even with the new acreage to be irrigated (1.3 million acres), the land flooded by the reservoir and that lost in the delta must be subtracted from the total acreage under cultivation. There will be, therefore, much less cultivated land per capita than before. It seems clear that Egypt would have been better off if at least some of the money for the dam had been spent on population control. At present, her population is doubling every 25 years and the people are more poorly fed than before the dam, and there is no project of sufficient magnitude to significantly increase food production. Even if population growth is controlled in the future, it appears that Egypt's problems are greater now than they were before the dam was built.

TECHNOLOGICAL DILEMMAS

The Aswan Dam is an example of man's underrating the environmental consequences of large, localized projects. We have previously seen the effects of other advances in technology such as pesticides, fertilizers, nuclear power generation, and the use of fossil fuels in industry and transportation. Yet the enormous impact of these "advances" is generally not included in the cost of trying to win the race between growing population and demand on resources.

Man finds himself faced with a technological dilemma: Emerging countries need energy and materials to raise their standards of living to those of developed countries. But these latter nations must sustain at least their present rate of production of energy and products to maintain their standards of living. Even if we wanted to, it is not possible to reverse the tide and regress to the life style of pioneer days. We have a fixed demand that must be supplied, and regardless of the technology we implement to supply it, there are problems.

For example, it is reasonable to assume that mass transportation systems will greatly improve and expand in the future. However, it also appears that the private automobile will not only remain but that it will be present in even greater numbers simply because of population increases. There is much talk today of a low-pollution car. But do we retain the internal combustion auto and reduce its pollutant emissions, or do we develop a replacement such as a battery-operated car? In either case, energy must be supplied to perform the work of moving the vehicle, and this creates waste products. To eliminate carbon monoxide and hydrocarbons from automobile emissions, catalytic afterburners will be required on all new cars by 1975. However, the high temperatures needed to convert carbon monoxide and hydrocarbons to carbon dioxide and water will result in more favorable conditions for the reaction between nitrogen and oxygen, thus producing greater amounts of nitrogen oxides. Despite the anticipated per vehicle decrease in carbon monoxide and hydrocarbon emissions, air pollution levels will again increase by 1985 as a result of more vehicles (Figure 14.5).

Those who believe battery-operated cars will greatly alleviate air

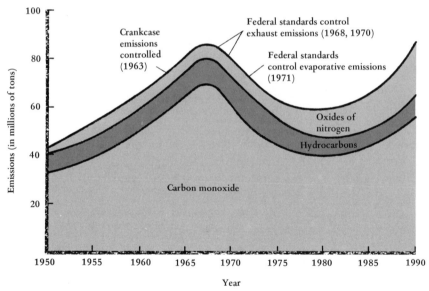

Figure 14.5
Emissions from automobiles are decreasing as a result of federal controls. However, without additional emission control, pollution from automobiles will again increase as a result of a greater number of automobiles. *(Data from a report submitted by the U.S. Department of Health, Education and Welfare to U.S. Senate hearings, chaired by Edmund Muskie, held March 16–18, 1970, pp. 373–374, pt. 1.)*

pollution problems overlook the fact that the energy used to recharge the batteries has to come from a fossil fuel or nuclear power plant. We would merely be shifting the origin and types of pollutants. If nuclear fuel is used, we aggravate the problems discussed in Chapter 13. In any event, we must contend with the law of conservation of matter that dictates that all processes produce by-products (wastes). Difficult decisions must be made concerning alternatives that will minimize the environmental impact.

TECHNOLOGY AND HUMAN ATTITUDES

Although technology may be available, it is not always implemented. Financing and trained manpower are needed to install, operate, and maintain improved facilities for maintaining a quality environment. For example, sewage treatment facilities are often not built or upgraded because of the defeat of bond issues by a poorly informed citizenry. In addition, qualified sewage treatment operators are in short supply. The technology available to limit family size may be unused, often because of overriding moral convictions. Science and technology can provide alternatives to our environmental problems, but social scientists must also play a role in educating and motivating people to consider these alternatives and promote them after an effective course of action has been charted.

Let us examine some of our basic assumptions regarding technology. One examination of attitude can be summarized as knowledge versus wisdom; i.e., "Can we? If so, should we?" Although we have the knowledge (technology) to do it, have we the wisdom to decide whether or not to do it? The fact that we can do something has often been used to justify doing it. One argument used by SST (supersonic transport) proponents was that we have the capability to construct an SST, so we should construct it. We have been able to build a highly complex industrial society and also to increase agricultural production by the use of fertilizers, pesticides, irrigation, and highly mechanized farm equipment. Even with all this knowledge, however, we have lacked the wisdom to question the impact of our technology on the environment and society. This lack of wisdom or moral foresight has caused science and technology to fall into disfavor with many people, particularly so with regard to military technology.

Yet, many people are convinced that technology will solve all of our problems: "Don't worry, the know-how is available or soon will be." Faith in technology, however, does not ensure that technology is available to solve even today's problems, much less those of tomorrow. Though we cannot definitely say that the technology will not be found, we should not count on it until it is available — even then, we must be wary of its limitations.

Our discussion of the Aswan Dam illustrated some of the limitations of technology in its attempt to keep pace with the demands of a growing population. We have seen numerous examples of technological dilemmas where all alternative solutions to a problem result in environmental pollution and degradation. Many other examples could be given to demonstrate the shortcomings of future technology. For example, even if a technique were developed that allowed us to use lower-grade minerals, it would be successful only by using greater amounts of power and producing increased amounts of wastes. Thus the application of advanced technology (if it is available) to increase exploitation of resources will very likely result in greater environmental degradation. Absolute faith in the knowledge of technology is not a part of the wisdom that insures our long-term survival.

Another attitude that requires reevaluation is the "bigger the better" syndrome, the matter of quality versus quantity. Almost all of us are brought up on "bigger." We want bigger paychecks to live in bigger houses, to drive bigger and faster cars — just to obtain "more." Cities and states try to attract more and bigger industries. The larger the gross national product, the higher the supposed status of the country. However, we often lack the insight to assess the effects of this attitude on the quality of the environment. Bigger also means greater exploitation and subsequent greater deterioration and pollution. A burgeoning Los Angeles with its spectacular auto pollution has confined its children to their classrooms at recess time. The largest dam of its kind has also produced the greatest problems. As things get bigger and more complex, our ability to understand and cope with them seems to diminish.

Perhaps the most strongly entrenched attitude is that any change, particularly if it results in growth, is progress. There is little questioning of the effects of change. The Aswan Dam is used the world over to illustrate the progress that man has made in harnessing nature to serve him. Unfortunately, people accept as progress the big changes resulting from the application of technology, but seldom do the awful upheavals caused by progress get the attention they deserve. Because attention is drawn away from the basic causes of our dilemmas, little or no real progress is made.

Technology is often used to justify change. Another reason to justify building the SST was that it would be a logical extension of our technology. Again, there is no question of the effects of this attitude. Another common statement is, "You can't stop progress." Why can't we? All we need is enough people to say no.

Many advances in technology are really just trade-offs. Pesticides and fertilizers increase food production on land but also pollute estuaries. The apparent progress in increasing food production turns out to be merely a measure of compensation for the loss of aquatic food production and scenic beauty.

Improved technology will aid in the solving of some of the problems, but it has serious shortcomings. It can and must alleviate some stresses and buy us some time, but it cannot solve the basic problem of too many people for the Earth's ecosystem to sustain.

QUESTIONS AND
PROJECTS

1. Compare the sources and types of pollution associated with gasoline and battery-powered vehicles. Which source would be easier to control and have the lesser environmental impact?

2. Prepare an environmental impact statement for a development project in your region.

3. Comment on the environmental significance of the statement, "It's not nice to fool Mother Nature."

SELECTED
READINGS

The following books provide further illustrations of the influences of technology on society.

Mesthene, E. *Technological Change: Its Impact on Man and Society.* New York: New American Library, 1970.

Calder, Nigel. *Technopolis: Social Control of the Uses of Science.* New York: Simon and Schuster, 1970.

Epilogue

Our analysis of the environment has been in terms of ecosystems and the four interdependent spheres. Alternatively, we may divide the environment into three closely linked systems: urban-industrial, rural-agricultural, and wilderness-seminatural (Figure E.1). Most of us live in the urban-industrial system, the center of manufacturing, trade, and commerce. The rural-agricultural system provides the food for the survival of not only its own inhabitants but also those of the urban-industrial system. Wilderness and seminatural areas serve man for recreation, as sources of food, and as gene pool reservoirs. The stable coexistence of all three systems is vital to our well-being.

A WHOLISTIC APPROACH

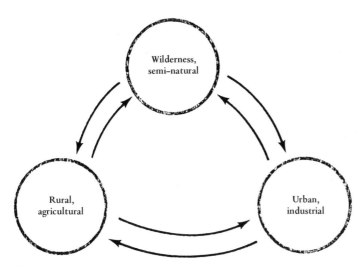

Figure E.1
Interacting systems.

357

From the wilderness system, man created first the rural-agricultural system and then the urban-industrial system. During this time man's activities produced increasingly negative interactions among the three systems. In Chapter 7 we saw that air pollution — mainly from the urban-industrial system — results in annual agricultural losses in the United States in excess of $500 million. Much of this damage is to vegetables and citrus fruits. The loss not only reduces the food supply but also adversely affects the local economy, reducing the grower's income and adding to unemployment. The effects of air pollution are also evident in the wilderness-seminatural system. Recall, for example, the severe effect of Los Angeles smog upon ponderosa pine in the San Bernardino Mountains. We have also seen that nutrients such as nitrates and phosphates from both urban-industrial (sewage) and rural-agricultural (fertilizers) sources result in eutrophication of rivers, lakes, and estuaries (wilderness-seminatural).

We sometimes plan and go about our activities oblivious of the intricate interrelation of the three systems and the essential requirement of retaining the integrity of each. There are many examples of man's treatment of the wilderness areas as separate and dispensable. We have previously noted the problems of southern Florida. Many people assume that it is a question of survival of either man or the wetlands; they exclude the possibility of coexistence.

This elitist viewpoint is also present in confrontations concerning the control of pollution. Too often, perhaps, the environmentalist is caught up in the goal of establishing a quality environment "at any cost." However, the cost may include the loss of jobs — jobs essential to provide livelihoods and promote social tranquility. Few of us become concerned about environmental quality until we possess the means of providing for our basic needs. Conversely, some pressure groups use the "loss of job" specter as an excuse for inaction in upgrading environmental quality. The end result of confrontation is loss in time with little gain for anyone.

If we are to survive in an environment in which life is worth living, we must take a wholistic view. Proper evaluation of any problem is not possible when only a few of the factors involved are considered. If the wholistic approach is to be successful, contributions must be sought from many and varied points of view. We must call upon people who are familiar with the rudiments of the "whole" and are able to identify the contributions that others can make to solving our problems.

Although most of us will develop specialties, we should be able to communicate in spite of our different backgrounds. Only in this way can we effectively contribute to the making of wholistic decisions that will help to solve the problems of the "total" environment.

When the environment is viewed wholistically, several conclusions can be drawn. When we consider the limitations of the Earth's ecosystems in supplying our demands and absorbing our wastes, it appears that the breaking point is being approached. A team of M.I.T. scientists recently reported the results of their analysis of current worldwide trends in critical environmental parameters. They project to the year 2100 present-day statistics and policies on world population growth, food production, industrial production, resource depletion, and pollution (Figure E.2). The analysis indicates a dramatic decline in world population within 130 years following a sharp depletion of the per capita supply of food and resources. The report concludes that the survival of humanity is possible only if the five environmental parameters are stabilized. One projection in the report requires a stabilization of world population by 1975 and a 75 percent decrease in pollution and resource consumption from their 1970 values (Figure E.3).

CARRYING CAPACITY REVISITED

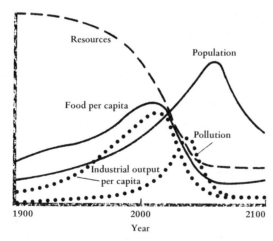

Figure E.2
M.I.T. projections of present trends in critical environmental parameters to the year 2100. *(Redrawn with permission from D. H. Meadows, D. L. Meadows, J. Randers, and W. W. Behrens, III,* The Limits to Growth. *A Potomac Associates book published by Universe Books, Publishers, Inc., 1972. Published in London by Earth Island Limited.)*

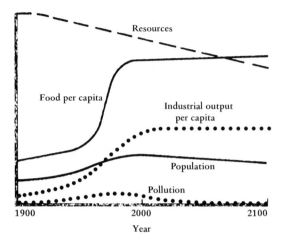

Figure E.3
M.I.T. projection of trends in critical environmental parameters if world population is stabilized by 1975 and pollution and resource consumption are reduced 75 percent from their 1970 values. *(Redrawn with permission from D. H. Meadows, D. L. Meadows, J. Randers, and W. W. Behrens, III,* The Limits to Growth. *A Potomac Associates book published by Universe Books, Publishers, Inc., 1972. Published in London by Earth Island Limited.)*

Yet it is difficult for many in the United States to believe that we have a resource-population problem. One reason for this lack of belief is illustrated by contrasting our way of life with that of the other human inhabitants of the globe:

If all the people in the world could be reduced proportionately into a theoretical town of 1,000 people, the picture would look something like this: In this town there would be 60 Americans, with the remainder of the world represented by 940 persons. This is the proportion of the population of the United States to the population of the world, 60 to 940. The 60 Americans would have half the income of the entire town with the other 940 dividing the other half. About 350 of these would be practicing Communists, and 370 others would be under Communistic domination. White people would total 303, with 697 being non-white. The 60 Americans would have 15 times as many possessions per person as all the rest of the world. The Americans would produce 16% of the town's food supply although they eat 72% above the maximum food requirements. They would either eat most of what they grow or store it for their own future use at an enormous cost. Since most of the 940 non-Americans in the town would be hungry most of the time, it would create ill feelings toward the 60 Americans, who would appear to be enormously rich and fed to the point of sheer disbelief by the great majority of the townspeople. The Americans would also have a disproportionate share of the electric power, fuel, steel, and general equipment. Of the 940 non-Americans, 200 would have malaria, cholera, typhus, and malnutrition. None of the 60 Americans would get these diseases or probably ever be worried about them.*

For the vast majority of us living in the United States, not only are our basic needs satisfied but we are also heavily endowed with luxuries. It is difficult for us to appreciate the resource-population problems of underdeveloped and emerging countries. However, upon examination the problems of overpopulation appear all about us. Indeed, because our society is one of the more "advanced" on Earth, these problems have unique forms. As our numbers increase, agricultural and industrial wastes close in on us. Classrooms and campgrounds are overcrowded. Treatment plants are overloaded with sewage. Our new interstate highways are already jammed with cars and trucks. Many of our demands are met by importing resources. The impact of the demands of a large and mounting population are everywhere.

Our high standard of living has a significant impact upon the world's resources and hence global environmental quality, so the responsibility rests heavily with the United States to take the initial steps for improvement. These measures should not only involve a cleanup at home, but the United States must play a major role in controlling international pollution. Regardless of source, the potential of long-range cycling of pollutants in the environment is not limited by political boundaries. We have seen that water that becomes saline in the United States by irrigation is carried into Mexico by the Colorado River.

Waterways contaminated by inadequately treated wastes feed into international ocean waters. Hence, while pollution must be controlled at its source (e.g., smoke stacks, drainage basins), the effort must be international in scope if a quality environment is to be achieved for all.

In our consideration of the Earth's carrying capacity, we have been speaking in terms of maxima. More appropriately, we should be thinking in terms of an optimal human population level that will permit ecosystems both to sustain us and to maintain a quality environment. To specify this level is difficult. Some people have estimated it to be

* Data from Dr. Henry Leiper.

one billion people for the world and 150 million for the United States — both figures well below present levels. Each of us must examine the role he is to play in governing the growth of human numbers — preferably with a wholistic viewpoint. Stabilization of population is not sufficient to solve all of our environmental problems, but it is a necessary precondition.

CLOSING THOUGHTS

Each of the Earth's ecosystems evolved within a narrow range of environmental conditions. The result was the establishment of a stable interdependence of the components of one biotic and three abiotic spheres. Man's activities, however, have begun to significantly alter this stability. He redistributes materials and energy among the spheres and changes the transfer rates of substances and energy among reservoirs. As a result, streams that were formerly clear have become turbid with silt and polluted with nitrates and metals. Skies formerly blue have turned murky with dust and acid mists.

There is thus a man-induced tendency toward the establishment of new interrelations among components of ecosystems. As our activities continually expand, no identifiable equilibrium is achieved. Alterations in the original stable ecosystem are hostile to many organisms. Some species have become extinct and many more are endangered. Ironically, many pests adapt and thrive in the modified environment while many valuable organisms perish. Because man evolved within stable ecosystems, it is not surprising that the new conditions are also becoming hostile to him. Perhaps our endangered national bird is telling us where all the flowers have gone.

SELECTED READINGS

Commoner, B. *The Closing Circle.* New York: Knopf, 1971. An overview of the social causes of environmental problems.

Meadows, D. H., Meadows, D. L., Randers, J., and Behrens, W. W., III. *The Limits to Growth.* New York: Universe Books, 1972. The report of an M.I.T. study team concerning the basic factors that limit growth on Earth and prospects for the future.

Appendixes

I

The Geologic Time Scale

Era	Years before present	Period	Animal life	Plant life	Major geologic events
Cenozoic	1×10^6	Quaternary	Rise of civilizations	Increase in number of herbs and grasses	Continental glaciation
	65×10^6	Tertiary	First men; dominance of land by mammals, birds, and insects	Dominance of land by flowering plants	
Mesozoic	135×10^6	Cretaceous	Age of dinosaurs	Conifers dominant on land; first flowering plants appear	Building of Rocky Mountains
	180×10^6	Jurassic			
	225×10^6	Triassic			
Paleozoic	275×10^6	Permian	Expansion of reptiles		Building of Appalachian Mountains
	350×10^6	Carboniferous	Age of amphibians	Great coal forests	
	413×10^6	Devonian	Age of fishes		
	430×10^6	Silurian	Invasion of land by invertebrates	Invasion of land by primitive plants	
	500×10^6	Ordovician	First vertebrates	Abundant marine algae	
	600×10^6	Cambrian	Abundant marine invertebrates	Primitive marine algae	
Precambrian			Primitive marine life		

363

II

Expressing Numbers as Powers of Ten

Very large or very small numbers often enter into scientific discussion. Rather than writing a number with a string of zeros following or preceeding it, it is more convenient to express the number in scientific notation. For example, 4,000,000 is obtained by multiplying 4 by 10 six times ($4 \times 10 \times 10 \times 10 \times 10 \times 10 \times 10$). In scientific notation, the number is written as 4×10^6. A smaller number such as 0.00004 is obtained by dividing 4 by 10 five times. In scientific notation it is written as 4×10^{-5}. A part of the system is shown below:

$$
\begin{aligned}
1{,}000{,}000 &= 10 \times 10 \times 10 \times 10 \times 10 \times 10 &&= 10^6 \\
100{,}000 &= 10 \times 10 \times 10 \times 10 \times 10 &&= 10^5 \\
10{,}000 &= 10 \times 10 \times 10 \times 10 &&= 10^4 \\
1{,}000 &= 10 \times 10 \times 10 &&= 10^3 \\
100 &= 10 \times 10 &&= 10^2 \\
10 &= 10 &&= 10^1 \\
1 &= 1 &&= 10^0 \\
0.1 &= 1/10 &&= 10^{-1} \\
0.01 &= 1/100 &&= 10^{-2} \\
0.001 &= 1/1{,}000 &&= 10^{-3} \\
0.0001 &= 1/10{,}000 &&= 10^{-4} \\
0.00001 &= 1/100{,}000 &&= 10^{-5}
\end{aligned}
$$

III

The Periodic Table of the Elements

The elements are arranged in order of increasing atomic number so that elements of similar electron configuration fall into one column. The number below an element's symbol refers to its average atomic mass. The table allows one to remember trends rather than specific bits of chemical information. For example, elements in the column on the extreme right are considered chemically nonreactive whereas elements in the column on the extreme left are highly reactive. In addition, two neighboring elements or their ions in a particular column tend to display similar chemical properties. For example, calcium (atomic number 20) ions can replace strontium (atomic number 38) ions.

An alphabetical list of the elements, their symbols, and their atomic numbers follows the periodic table.

1 H 1.008	2																2 He 4.00
3 Li 6.94	4 Be 9.01											5 B 10.8	6 C 12.0	7 N 14.0	8 O 16.0	9 F 19.0	10 Ne 20.2
11 Na 23.0	12 Mg 24.3											13 Al 27.0	14 Si 28.1	15 P 31.0	16 S 32.1	17 Cl 35.5	18 Ar 39.9
19 K 39.1	20 Ca 4.01	21 Sc 45.0	22 Ti 47.9	23 V 50.9	24 Cr 52.0	25 Mn 54.9	26 Fe 55.6	27 Co 58.9	28 Ni 58.7	29 Cu 63.5	30 Zn 65.4	31 Ga 69.7	32 Ge 72.6	33 As 74.9	34 Se 79.0	35 Br 79.9	36 Kr 83.8
37 Rb 85.5	38 Sr 87.6	39 Y 88.9	40 Zr 91.2	41 Nb 92.9	42 Mo 95.9	43 Tc (99)	44 Ru 101.1	45 Rh 102.9	46 Pd 106.4	47 Ag 107.9	48 Cd 112.4	49 In 114.8	50 Sn 118.7	51 Sb 121.8	52 Te 127.6	53 I 126.9	54 Xe 131.3
55 Cs 132.9	56 Ba 137.3	see below 57–71	72 Hf 178.5	73 Ta 180.9	74 W 183.9	75 Re 186.2	76 Os 190.2	77 Ir 192.2	78 Pt 195.1	79 Au 197.0	80 Hg 200.6	81 Tl 204.4	82 Pb 207.2	83 Bi 209.0	84 Po 210	85 At (210)	86 Rn (222)
87 Fr (223)	88 Ra (226)	see below 89–103	104 (260)	105 (260)													

57 La 138.9	58 Ce 140.1	59 Pr 140.9	60 Nd 144.2	61 Pm (147)	62 Sm 150.4	63 Eu 152.0	64 Gd 157.3	65 Tb 158.9	66 Dy 162.5	67 Ho 164.9	68 Er 167.3	69 Tm 168.9	70 Yb 173.0	71 Lu 175.0
89 Ac (227)	90 Th 232.0	91 Pa (231)	92 U 238.0	93 Np (237)	94 Pu (242)	95 Am (243)	96 Cm (247)	97 Bk (245)	98 Cf (251)	99 Es (254)	100 Fm (253)	101 Md (256)	102 No (254)	103 Lw (257)

Note: Values in parentheses denote the mass number of the most stable or most familiar isotope.

Element	Symbol	Atomic number	Element	Symbol	Atomic number	Element	Symbol	Atomic Number
Actinium	Ac	89	Hafnium	Hf	72	Praseodymium	Pr	59
Aluminum	Al	13	Helium	He	2	Promethium	Pm	61
Americium	Am	95	Holmium	Ho	67	Protactinium	Pa	91
Antimony	Sb	51	Hydrogen	H	1	Radium	Ra	88
Argon	Ar	18	Indium	In	49	Radon	Rn	86
Arsenic	As	33	Iodine	I	53	Rhenium	Re	75
Astatine	At	85	Iridium	Ir	77	Rhodium	Rh	45
Barium	Ba	56	Iron	Fe	26	Rubidium	Rb	37
Berkelium	Bk	97	Krypton	Kr	36	Ruthenium	Ru	44
Beryllium	Be	4	Lanthanum	La	57	Samarium	Sm	62
Bismuth	Bi	83	Lawrencium	Lw	103	Scandium	Sc	21
Boron	B	5	Lead	Pb	82	Selenium	Se	34
Bromine	Br	35	Lithium	Li	3	Silicon	Si	14
Cadmium	Cd	48	Lutetium	Lu	71	Silver	Ag	47
Calcium	Ca	20	Magnesium	Mg	12	Sodium	Na	11
Californium	Cf	98	Manganese	Mn	25	Strontium	Sr	38
Carbon	C	6	Mendelevium	Md	101	Sulfur	S	16
Cerium	Ce	58	Mercury	Hg	80	Tantalum	Ta	73
Cesium	Cs	55	Molybdenum	Mo	42	Technetium	Tc	43
Chlorine	Cl	17	Neodymium	Nd	60	Tellurium	Te	52
Chromium	Cr	24	Neon	Ne	10	Terbium	Tb	65
Cobalt	Co	27	Neptunium	Np	93	Thallium	Tl	81
Copper	Cu	29	Nickel	Ni	28	Thorium	Th	90
Curium	Cm	96	Niobium	Nb	41	Thulium	Tm	69
Dysprosium	Dy	66	Nitrogen	N	7	Tin	Sn	50
Einsteinium	Es	99	Nobelium	No	102	Titanium	Ti	22
Erbium	Er	68	Osmium	Os	76	Tungsten	W	74
Europium	Eu	63	Oxygen	O	8	Uranium	U	92
Fermium	Fm	100	Palladium	Pd	46	Vanadium	V	23
Fluorine	F	9	Phosphorus	P	15	Xenon	Xe	54
Francium	Fr	87	Platinum	Pt	78	Ytterbium	Yb	70
Gadolinium	Gd	64	Plutonium	Pu	94	Yttrium	Y	39
Gallium	Ga	31	Polonium	Po	84	Zinc	Zn	30
Germanium	Ge	32	Potassium	K	19	Zirconium	Zr	40
Gold	Au	79						

Glossary

abiotic. Refers to the nonliving components of the environment.

absolute zero. The theoretical temperature at which all motion ceases.

acid. A substance that when added to water increases the hydronium ion concentration.

actual mixing ratio (Wa). The actual water content of an air parcel.

aerobic decomposition. The decomposition of organic material by microorganisms that require oxygen. The major products of decomposition are carbon dioxide and water.

air pollution. The accelerated transfer of natural and synthetic substances into the atmospheric reservoir, usually as a consequence of man's activities.

albedo. The fraction of incident radiation that is reflected by a surface.

algae. Primitive green plants; many are microscopic.

algae bloom. A population explosion of tiny green plants in surface waters.

alpha particle. A high-speed particle made up of two protons and two neutrons ejected from some unstable nuclei.

anaerobic decomposition. The decomposition of organic material by bacteria in the absence of oxygen. The major product of decomposition is methane.

antibiotics. Chemicals produced by microorganisms that are capable of killing other microorganisms.

aquifer. A layer of rock or soil that is permeable.

artesian well. A well from which water flows freely from an aquifer that is sandwiched between impermeable lithospheric layers.

atmospheric pressure. The weight of the Earth's atmosphere over a unit area of the Earth's surface.

atmospheric turbidity. A decrease in atmospheric visibility resulting from suspended pollutants.

367

atom. The smallest existing unit in nature that loses its properties upon further division.

atomic mass. The approximate sum of the number of neutrons and protons in the nucleus of an atom.

atomic number. The number of protons in the nucleus of an atom. It identifies an element.

basalt. A fine-grained igneous rock that is the prime constituent of the portion of the Earth's crust that lies beneath the oceans. It also forms a relatively thin substratum at the base of the granitic crustal plates.

base. A substance that when added to water increases the hydroxide ion concentration.

Bergeron-Findeisen Theory. A theory of precipitation formation that applies to clouds that are made up of a mixture of ice crystals and supercooled water droplets.

beta particle. A high-speed electron ejected from the nucleus of an unstable atom.

biological control. The use of a pest's own predators and parasites to control its population.

biological half-time. The period required for half of an ingested material to be excreted from the body.

biological oxygen demand (BOD). The amount of oxygen required to decompose the organic material in a given volume of water.

biotic. Refers to the living components of the environment.

biotic potential. The inherent maximum population growth rate that occurs under optimum conditions.

blue-green algae. A type of tiny green plant that often causes surface waters to appear like pea soup.

breeder reactor. A type of nuclear reactor that produces slightly more fissionable material than it consumes.

broad spectrum pesticide. A chemical that kills more than the target species.

buoyant. Upward forces exerted by the fluid (air or water) in which a body is immersed.

calorie. The amount of energy required to raise the temperature of one gram of water one Celsius degree.

carnivore. An animal that uses other animals as a food source.

carrying capacity. The maximum population that a given ecosystem can support indefinitely.

chemical change. The process whereby the arrangement of atoms in molecules (reactants) is changed to form different molecules (products).

chemical energy. Energy derived from the combination or recombination of atoms.

chromosomes. Genetic material containing the information that ultimately determines the optima and tolerance limits of an organism for environmental factors.

coalescence process. A theory of precipitation formation that applies to a cloud that is composed exclusively of water droplets.

coliform bacteria. Bacteria normally found in the human intestine whose presence in water in sufficient numbers is used to indicate the possibility of contamination by inadequately treated sewage.

combined sewer. Sewer system where both storm water and sanitary wastes are carried by one large pipe to a treatment plant.

competition. An interaction between members of the same population or two populations resulting from a greater demand than supply for a mutually required resource.

compost. A fertilizer composed of the organic fraction of refuse.

compound. A substance with fixed composition that contains more than one element.

concentration. The amount of a component in a given weight or volume of material.

condensation. A change from the vapor state to the liquid state.

condensation nuclei. Tiny solid or liquid particles upon which deposition or condensation occurs.

conduction. The transfer of thermal energy from one particle to another through direct contact.

consumers. Organisms that use other organisms as a food source.

contour plowing. Furrows plowed parallel to land height contours.

convection. Thermal energy transfer through the movement of heated substances, e.g., hot air.

cooling tower. A device used to transfer thermal energy from water to the atmosphere.

core. The subdivision of the lithosphere that is below the mantle and forms the center of the Earth.

covalent bond. The force that holds two atoms together, resulting from the sharing of electrons.

crust. The uppermost subdivision of the lithosphere.

cultural eutrophication. The result of activities of man that increase the amount of plant nutrients entering surface waters, hence increasing algae and other aquatic plant populations.

cyclone collector. A device that removes particulates from an effluent air stream by gravitational settling.

decibel. A unit measure of sound energy intensity.

decomposers. Microconsumers, e.g., bacteria and fungi.

deep-well injection. The disposal of liquid wastes by pumping under pressure into subsurface cavities and pore spaces.

deposition. A direct change from the vapor state to the solid state.

drainage basin. The region drained by a river or stream.

dust. Tiny particulate material that is the product primarily of wind erosion of soil.

dust dome. A dome-shaped accumulation of particulates over urban-industrial complexes.

dust plume. A dust dome elongated downwind from a city.

earthquake. A movement of the ground resulting from the fracture of rocks beneath the Earth's surface.

ecosystem. A functional unit of the environment that includes all the living organisms and physical features in a given area.

electromagnetic energy. Energy that can move through a vacuum in the form of waves, e.g., visible light.

electromagnetic spectrum. The span of wavelengths that includes all forms of electromagnetic energy from the highly energetic gamma waves to the least energetic radio waves.

electron. A fundamental particle possessing one unit of negative charge but having little mass.

electrostatic precipitator. A device that removes particulates from an effluent air stream by inducing an electric charge.

element. A collection of atoms all having the same atomic number, i.e., same number of protons.

energy. The ability to perform work.

environmental resistance. The sum total of all factors in the environment that limit population growth.

epilimnion. The warm, less dense top layer in a stratified lake.

erosion. The removal and transport of weathered lithospheric materials by wind, running water, or glaciation.

estuary. Coastal ecosystems where fresh water and salt water meet.

eutrophication. A natural process whereby lakes gradually become more productive. If the process is man-accelerated, the term "cultural eutrophication" is used.

eutrophic lake. A lake that has high biological productivity because of high rates of nutrient cycling.

evaporation. A change from the liquid state to the vapor state.

faulting. The fracturing and displacement of rock masses.

First Law of Thermodynamics. A law stating that although energy can be transformed from one form to another, it cannot be created or destroyed; also expressed as the conservation of energy.

fissionable isotope. An isotope capable of capturing a neutron, splitting, and releasing more neutrons, thereby sustaining a chain reaction.

fog. A ground-level cloud.

food chain. A sequence of organisms, including producers, herbivores, and carnivores, through which energy and materials move within an ecosystem.

food chain accumulation. The increase in concentration of certain chemicals in food chains.

food web. A complex of interlocking food chains.

fossil fuels. The remains of once-living plants and animals that are burned to release energy. Examples are coal, oil, and natural gas.

frequency. The number of up and down oscillations a wave makes in one second.

fungus. Primitive plants that function as consumers. Most act as decomposers (e.g., mushrooms), although some are significant parasites (e.g., rusts and blights).

gamma rays. High energy electromagnetic radiation originating in the nucleus of an atom.

gene pool. The sum total of characteristics possessed by a species.

geothermal energy. Heat energy conducted from the Earth's interior.

global-scale circulation. The largest scale of atmospheric motion; includes the wind systems that circle the globe.

granite. A coarse-grained igneous rock that is the prime constituent of the continental portions of the Earth's crust.

greenhouse effect. The absorption and reradiation of terrestrial longwave energy by atmospheric water vapor, carbon dioxide, and ozone.

ground water. Water that is contained in subsurface rock and soil layers.

half-life. The amount of time required for one-half of the radioactive nuclei of an isotope to decay.

heat of fusion. The amount of heat required to change one gram of a substance from the solid state to the liquid state.

heat of vaporization. The amount of heat required to change one gram of a substance from the liquid state to the vapor state at its boiling point.

herbivore. An animal that uses plants as a food source.

hydrogen bonding. An attractive force between neighboring water molecules resulting from unequal charge distribution on the molecules.

hydrologic cycle. A ceaseless circulation of water among terrestrial, oceanic, and atmospheric reservoirs.

hygroscopic. Having a special affinity or attraction for water molecules.

hypolimnion. The colder, denser bottom layer in a stratified lake.

igneous rock. A rock formed by the solidification of magma (or lava), either within the crust or on the Earth's surface.

infiltration component. The portion of precipitation on land that seeps into surface layers of soil and rock.

integrated control. A combination of different pest control methods that is best suited for the particular pest and environmental conditions.

ion. A positively or negatively charged unit composed of one or several atoms.

ionic bond. An attractive force that holds oppositely charged ions together.

isotope. Atoms of the same element that have different atomic masses.

jetty. A structure perpendicular to the shoreline and extending offshore.

juvenile hormone. A chemical that controls the ability of an insect to pass through its life stages.

kinetic energy. Energy an object possesses because of its motion.

latent heat transfer. The transport of energy as the result of changes in the phases of water.

laterite. A leached tropical soil high in iron and aluminum.

laterization. A weathering process that occurs in a warm, moist climate and results in a high rate of soil leaching.

LD_{50}. The single-dose quantity of a substance that will kill 50 percent of a population.

leaching. The dissolving and transport of soil materials by water seeping downward.

limiting factor. Any component of the environment that limits the well-being of an organism.

lithification. The process by which sediment is converted into rock.

longshore current. The component of water motion parallel to the shoreline.

magma. The molten rock material within the Earth.

malnourished. A condition in which an individual's diet is lacking in one or more essential nutrients.

mantle. The subdivision of the lithosphere that is situated between the crust and the core.

mechanical energy. Energy required to put an object in motion or to change the speed of an object already in motion.

meso-scale air motion. Air motion that is confined to local areas.

mesosphere. The subdivision of the atmosphere that is situated between the stratosphere and an altitude of about 50 miles (80 kilometers).

metamorphic rock. A rock formed when a pre-existing rock is subjected to the high temperatures, confining pressures, and chemically active fluids deep within the crust.

micro-scale air motion. The smallest scale of atmospheric motion; includes circulation patterns within inches of surfaces such as the ground and vegetation.

mineral. A solid that is characterized by an orderly internal arrangement of atoms and a fixed chemical composition.

mixing ratio (W). The ratio of the weight of water vapor contained in an air parcel to the weight of dry air in the air parcel.

molecule. Two or more atoms bonded together to form a unit that has its own characteristic properties.

mutation. A change in the information contained in the chromosomes.

neutral air layer. An air layer in which introduced air parcels are not displaced upward or downward.

neutralization reaction. A reaction between an acid and a base that forms water and dissolved ions.

neutron. A neutral fundamental particle possessing one unit of atomic mass.

nuclear change. A change in the nucleus of an atom that releases energy.

nuclear energy. Energy originating within the nucleus of an atom because of changes in nuclear structure.

nuclear fission. The fragmenting of a nucleus resulting in the release of neutrons and the formation of two new nuclei.

nuclear fusion. An extremely high-temperature process whereby two or more nuclei are fused into one.

oligotrophic lake. A lake with low biological productivity; usually has clear water and aesthetic appeal.

omnivore. An animal that can use both plants and other animals as food sources.

orographic rainfall. Rainfall resulting from air flow up the side of a mountain or highland.

oxygen sag curve. A characteristic pattern showing the decrease in dissolved oxygen resulting from the input of organic wastes into a river.

parasitism. A population interaction in which one organism (the parasite) obtains needed energy and nutrients by living within or upon another organism (the host).

part per million (ppm). A means of expressing concentration of a component. A one ppm concentration of copper is one part of copper and 999,999 parts of other material.

pathogenic organisms. Organisms that cause disease.

permeability. The capability of a lithospheric material to transmit a fluid.

pH. A measure of the acidity or alkalinity of a solution.

photosynthesis. The process by which light energy is converted by green plants to chemical energy (food energy).

physical change. The rearrangement of molecules within a substance without alteration of the arrangement of atoms that make up the molecules of that substance.

polar molecule. A molecule with an unequal distribution of electrons causing negatively and positively charged sites on the molecule.

pollution. A change from the normal transfer rate of materials or energy between any two reservoirs.

potential energy. Stored energy that may be converted to kinetic energy.

potential mixing ratio (Wp). The maximum amount of water that an air parcel could contain in the vapor state.

power. The rate at which work can be performed; expressed as energy output per unit time.

predation. A population interaction in which one organism (predator) kills and eats another organism (prey).

primary air pollutants. Substances introduced into the atmosphere that, unaltered, may pose a serious hazard to environmental quality.

primary treatment. Physical processes used in removing suspended materials from waste water.

producers. Organisms capable of carrying out photosynthesis.

proton. A fundamental particle possessing one unit of atomic mass and one unit of positive charge.

radiation. The term used to describe the transfer of electromagnetic energy from place to place.

radiation inversion. A temperature inversion that results from the rapid loss of terrestrial radiation from ground surfaces.

recycling. The recovery and reuse of resources.

relative humidity. The ratio of actual mixing ratio (Wa) to potential mixing ratio (Wp) multiplied by 100 percent.

respiration. The liberation of energy from food within an organism.

rock. A solid composed of one or more minerals.

rock cycle. The transformation of one rock to another rock as a consequence of change in the rock's environment.

runoff. The component of running water situated on land surfaces, i.e., rivers and streams.

salinization. The accumulation of salts in soils or in bodies of water.

salt-water intrusion. The contamination of ground water by landward displacement of oceanic ground water.

sanitary landfill. A landfill consisting of layers of solid waste sealed between layers of clean earth.

sanitary sewer. The system of pipes that transports domestic wastes to a sewage treatment plant.

saturated solution. A solution that has reached its capacity for dissolving a substance.

saturation. The condition in which an air parcel contains its maximum amount of water vapor; expressed as actual mixing ratio (Wa) equals potential mixing ratio (Wp).

scrubbing. The removal by water sprays of water-soluble pollutants from an effluent air stream.

secondary air pollutants. Products of reactions among primary air pollutants.

secondary treatment. A biological process used mainly to remove dissolved organic materials from waste waters.

Second Law of Thermodynamics. A law stating that all energy transformations are less than 100 percent efficient.

sedimentary rock. A rock formed by the compaction and cementation of particles (sediments) of abiotic or biotic origin.

sensible heat transfer. The transport of heat energy as a result of conduction and convection.

separated sewer system. A sewer system in which two pipes are used — one transports surface runoff and the other transports sanitary wastes.

shielding layer. A surface air layer maintained by friction.

smog. A mixture of gaseous, solid, and liquid air pollutants that restricts visibility; a blend of smoke and fog.

soil. A living, dynamic system composed of weathered rock, organic matter, air, and water that provides moisture and essential nutrients for plant growth.

soil horizons. Layers within a soil profile that are differentiated on the basis of kinds and arrangements of constituents and type and degree of weathering.

soot. Tiny, solid particles of carbon emitted during the combustion of fossil fuels.

sound energy. Energy transmitted as vibrations through air or other substances.

specific heat. The amount of thermal energy, measured relative to water, required to heat a unit mass of a substance one Celsius degree.

stable air layer. An air layer that inhibits the dispersal of air parcels that are introduced into it.

storm sewer. A system of large pipes that transports runoff in an urban area.

stratosphere. The subdivision of the atmosphere that lies between the troposphere and an altitude of about 30 miles (50 kilometers).

stream channelization. The straightening of meandering streams in order to transport water more rapidly downstream.

strip mining. A surface mining method that covers a wide geographical area and is usually used for the removal of near-surface coal.

sublimation. A direct change from the solid state to the vapor state.

subsidence inversion. A temperature inversion that develops above the shielding layer and results from descending air currents.

supercooled water. Water in the liquid state at a temperature below 32°F (0°C).

synergism. An interaction of two factors in which the total effect is greater than the sum of the effects of the two factors evaluated independently.

synoptic-scale air motion. Atmospheric motion that spans continents.

tertiary treatment. An advanced waste-water treatment process used to remove more efficiently chemicals such as phosphates and nitrates.

thermal energy. Energy caused by the motion of the minute particles making up a substance.

thermal inversion. The temperature profile of an air layer characterized by an increase of temperature with height.

thermocline. The transition zone in a stratified lake where a rapid temperature decrease occurs with increasing depth.

thermosphere. The uppermost subdivision of the atmosphere; characterized by a continuous increase of temperature with height.

troposphere. The lowest subdivision of the atmosphere; the site of most weather events.

turbidity. A decrease in visibility resulting from the scattering of light by suspended particles.

undernourished. A condition in which an individual's diet does not contain enough calories.

unstable air layer. An air layer in which rising air parcels continue to rise, resulting in mixing within the layer.

upwelling region. An area adjacent to a continent where bottom waters rich in nutrients are brought to the surface.

urban heat island. A region of relatively warm air centered over an urban-industrial area.

water table. The surface forming the upper boundary of the ground-water reservoir.

wavelength. The distance between successive crests or troughs of a wave.

weathering. The chemical decomposition and mechanical disintegration of rock.

Wien's Law. A law stating that the higher the temperature of a radiating body, the shorter is its wavelength of maximum radiational energy emission.

work. A measure of the amount of energy required to perform a task.

zone of aeration. A layer of soil or rock material whose pore spaces are partially filled with air and partially filled with water.

zone of saturation. A layer of soil or rock material whose pore spaces are completely filled with water; i.e., the ground-water reservoir.

Index

Italicized numbers indicate illustrations.

379

DATE DUE

5.16.'85	
MAY 10 '8	

BRODART, INC.   Cat. No. 23-221

CONVERSION TABLES

Length

English
Mile = 1,760 yards = 5,280 feet = 63,360 inches

Metric
Kilometer (km) = 1,000 meters

Meter (m) = 100 centimeters (cm) = 1,000 millimeters (mm) = 10,000 microns

English to metric
Mile = 1.609 kilometers = 1,609 meters

Yard = .914 meters = 91.4 centimeters

Foot = 30.48 centimeters

Inch = 2.54 centimeters

Metric to English
Kilometer = .62 miles = 1,091 yards = 3,273 feet

Meter = 39.37 inches

Centimeter = .39 inches

Millimeter = .04 inches

Area

English
Square mile = 640 acres

Acre = 4,840 square yards = 43,560 square feet

Metric
Square kilometer (km^2) = 100 hectares (ha) = 1,000,000 square meters (m^2)

Hectare = 10,000 square meters

Square meter = 10,000 square centimeters (cm^2)

English to metric
Square mile = 2.59 square kilometers = 259 hectares

Acre = .405 hectares = 4,047 square meters

Square yard = .836 square meters

Metric to English
Square kilometer = .3861 square miles

Hectare = 2.47 acres = 11,955 square yards

Square meter = 1.196 square yards

Volume and capacity

U.S. liquid measures
Gallon = 4 quarts = 231 cubic inches

Cubic foot = 7.48 gallons

Metric
Liter = 1,000 milliliters = 1,000 cubic centimeters